Running Dog

Maintenance

Penny Taylor

ISBN 978-0-9567029-0-6

All images, photos etc are copyright of the author, Penny Taylor, unless otherwise stated.

Published by Skycat Publications, a subsidiary of Magdalene Technology.
www.skycatpublications.com

Designed and edited by Ian Kossick, Skycat Publications.

Printed by Lavenham Press Ltd, Arbons House, 47 Water Street,
Lavenham, Suffolk CO10 9RN
Telephone: +44 (0)1787 247436
Fax: +44 (0)1787 248267

Disclaimer
Whilst many injuries and problems can be successfully treated by the experienced owner it is advised that professional advice be sought at all times. All products and equipment referred to in this book are current at the time of publication. Please note that any photographs and information are intended only as a guide and are not intended as complete instructions for any medical procedures. The author and publisher cannot be held responsible for any loss or mishap arising from any individual's failure to seek proper veterinary advice where necessary. Readers should note that it is illegal to treat any animals other than their own, and that failure to ensure the proper and correct protocol when treating injuries or illness in their animals could result in prosecution if it is found that they have caused any unnecessary suffering. Any reference made to the hunting of game other than rats or rabbits is for historical and reference purposes only.

Cover photo: Penny Taylor.
Back cover photo: Craig McCann, www.wildlife-through-the-lens.co.uk

Acknowledgements

During the writing of this book I realised that this was not solely the work of one person, for without the input of many people over many years, I should never have gained the knowledge needed to get 'it' all down in writing.

So I wish to thank everyone who has knowingly, or unknowingly, contributed to the finished effort; from those unseen friends on the internet with whom I've had such valuable communication over the past few years, to the many professionals who have supported my endeavour allowing me to pick their brains from time to time, and to my long suffering real life friends who have had to put up with me during the long and tedious months it has taken to bring this work to the finishing line.

I would also like to thank the following people who have kindly allowed me to use their photos, for without them this manual would have been poorer by far: Matty Jones, Samuel Coleman, Robert Wilkins, Yvonne Tilbury, Phil Jones, Gavin Evans, Paul Nightingale, Mike Bridle, Mark McBride, Andrew Quarrell, Barry Leavesley, Donovan Glyn, Ray Cross, Steve Taylor, Roly Boughton, Karen Marr, Steve Brown, Jackie Drakeford and Lurcherlink. I sincerely hope that I've credited your photos correctly, and my abject apologies if I've failed in that task.

Also, a special thank you to Mark Harvey (*www.mark-harvey.com*), Craig McCann (*www.wildlife-through-the-lens.co.uk*) and Chris Doyle (*www.lampypics.co.uk*) for being so generous as to allow me access to their galleries and portfolios.

A massive thank you to Jackie Drakeford for her help and support in the final stages. I thank David and Denise who have made this all possible, and Debbie who has kicked me up the rear on several occasions when I appeared to be faltering, and who provided much needed support when the going got tough!

Finally, my sincere thanks to Ian, beleagured editor, a man with the patience of a saint!

Dedication

I dedicate this work to Andy and our dogs: Andy for his unstinting support in my quest for greater understanding of the dogs with which we share our lives (and put up with my unbearable questing as well) and of course to the dogs themselves, who have given unquestioning loyalty over the years. Without my canine workmates there would have been no book in the first place and I would never have known the primitive joys of the running dog in its role of both companion and game provider; a creature of speed, power and beauty and a way of life which no one shall deny. Keep the faith.

Useful addresses

Dorwest Herbs
The leading manufacturers of licensed herbal medicines and supplements for dogs since 1948.
Dorwest Herbs Ltd, Shipton Gorge, Bridport DT6 4LP. Tel 01308 897272.
www.dorwest.com

The Greyhound Superstore
Unit 7, Homestall, Buckingham Industrial Estate, Buckingham MK18 1XJ.
Tel 01280 824974
Email: *info@greyhoundsuperstore.co.uk*
www.greyhoundsuperstore.co.uk

Greyhound Megastore.com
Friendly phone order service, many useful supplements, bedding, coats, book etc.
Tel 0208 652 7444. *www.greyhoundmegastore.com*

Further reading

Veterinary Advice for Greyhound Owners by John Kohnke
Publisher: Ringpress Books Ltd 1993. ISBN 0 948955 23 6
Comprehensive question and answer book containing advice on a variety of problems.

Essential Care in the Field by Jackie Drakeford and Mark Elliott
Publisher: Swan Hill Press 2007. ISBN 978 1 84689 014 7
Very useful book containing first aid procedures, bandaging techniques, general dog care and much more.

Homeopathic Remedies for Dogs by Geoffrey Llewellyn
Kingdom Books GB046
Basic introduction to Homeopathy with user friendly symptom and treatment format.

Contents

Diseases of Dogs and their Cure -
Facsimile of a Miniature in the Manuscript of Gaston Phoebus (Fourteenth Century).

Introduction

When I first started keeping sighthounds many years ago there was little or no information on how to best look after these dogs. My first sighthound was hardly what we'd nowadays term a 'running dog' as she was an Irish Wolfhound, but despite her size and bulk this dog could and did catch rabbits on a regular basis. She was in part responsible for my later interest in lurchers, an interest that developed into a passion and way of life which continues to this day.

Sighthounds are amongst the oldest types of canine on the planet and I suspect that many people who do not use their dogs for hunting are touched by a romantic, nostalgic image of the hound which can catch you your dinner.

Many running dog owners still benefit from their hound's prowess in the field and lurchers in particular are enjoying a rise in popularity quite different to the shadowy images of the past. Nowadays, many lurchers form part of an indispensable pest control team, in conjunction with humans and ferrets. They've come a long way from the poacher's slinking companion of yesteryear.

From my earliest childhood rabbit featured regularly as part of the menu in our home (if only I could recreate the delicious rabbit pie my mother made!) either shot by my father or lamped with a blue Greyhound called Bingo who belonged to our neighbouring farmer in the wilds of the Cornish moors.

Care of running dogs, those animals that are fast enough to catch their prey by speed seemed, in the old days, to be shrouded in mystery; an art and a science kept secret by those in the know. Medieval records speak of a 'dog boy' who lived in the castle kennels with the hounds, (hunting dogs were the preserve of the rich and titled in those days) attending to their needs and caring for them when injured. Good dogs would have been as highly valued in those far off days as they are now, though of course today we seldom depend entirely on our dogs as bringers of meat to the table. Today many people keep lurchers and sighthounds because they appreciate the nature, beauty and charisma of these dogs, and of course their speed.

I never tire of watching a running dog in action; the fleetness of foot, the supple arching back that bends and bows with each long stride of the gallop, and the pure joy in the animal's eyes as it revels in its ability to leap, twist and turn at speeds which we mere humans could never attain. However, such speed brings risk of injury, and this is the reason I've written this book. If, when I started out with lurchers, I had been able to look up the various injuries which beset my dogs from time to time, I would have known better how to care for those niggling problems, known when to rest a dog, known when to see that saviour of running dogs, the canine chiropractor and when to call the vet. As it was, I learned little by little that running dogs are prone to all sorts of problems seldom seen by the average pet dog vet.

Soft tissue damage is something that is usually treated with painkillers, anti-inflammatories and rest; but these alone are often not enough to treat a damaged muscle or tendon. Those people who have suffered injury to soft tissue themselves will know all too well that alternative treatment in the form of remedial massage and other therapies to be found within the pages of this manual are often the only way to achieve a full return to proper function of the injured area.

Yes, most such injuries will heal by themselves to allow a return to partial movement or function, but if we want our running dogs to be able to fulfil their function as athletes, then we need to address this type of soft tissue injury in a way that few GPs or small animal vets would do. Specialist athletes need specialist treatment if they are to continue performing free from pain and discomfort, and whilst I could never do without my general practitioner vet for major traumas I have learned that the services of a canine chiropractor or specialist greyhound vet are needed on a more regular basis than those of the GP.

I would be lying if I said that I know everything there is to know about running dogs. I doubt I'll ever stop learning, that's the wonderful thing about living creatures, they are always capable of teaching us something new. If I have managed, in this book, to help one or two people to avoid some of the pitfalls that my dogs and I fell into through ignorance, then I've succeeded.

Some of the injury photos are necessarily gory, but they have been included to show the remarkable healing powers of the canine body when fed and cared for correctly. Owners who are new to some of the more dramatic injuries sustained by their fast dogs are apt to go faint with horror when their beloved hound first injures itself, often on the dreaded barbed wire, so hopefully this book will give you some idea of what and how to do it when the inevitable accident does occur.

I have tried to restrict myself to running dog problems, but some of the injuries and problems that beset fast dogs are also likely to affect slower dogs, especially those working hard in the field. Treatment for most injuries is the same whether the dog is a terrier, a gundog or a sighthound. Take what you need from the book and apply it to your own dog regardless of its breeding.

I have included a list of recommended reading at the back of the book for those of scientific bent or those who wish to broaden their knowledge of alternative therapies and treatments.

There is no substitute for experience, and whilst I have learned many procedures over the years there are still some which I would never attempt myself. If you value your dog then its care and health must come before any ideas of how clever you might think you are at certain home treatments.

Finally, I am indebted to everyone who has contributed their photos to this book, for I would never have achieved such a comprehensive selection all by myself, even with my dogs' best efforts to provide me with alarming injuries.

CHAPTER ONE

Exercise and conditioning

There is to my mind nothing more beautiful to behold than a superbly fit running dog, an animal up on its toes, bursting with life and ready to run like the wind, taking all obstacles in its path as though it has wings.

Maybe this is a bit of a fanciful image, but I hope you'll forgive me when I use that vision to illustrate what a running dog should 'feel' and look like.

Exercise, conditioning, fitness training, call it what you will, is quite simply the most important aspect of owning a canine athlete. Without proper conditioning (from now on I'll refer to fitness training as conditioning) no running dog will be able to run at its best, whether that is in the hunting field, racing against other dogs or simply belting round the local park in fun.

WHAT MUSCLES DO
Let's start with the muscles, for without them no animal could move at all: in fact it would be merely a floppy skeleton covered in skin. The muscles are attached to the bones and in order for the bones to move the body the muscles need to contract and stretch, which in turn moves the bones to which they are attached.

Sorry to start with obvious basics, but it is important to know exactly what muscles are and how they work in order to properly maintain a good working condition of the whole body.

Muscles, strong, stretchy bundles of tissue, are attached to the bones by even stronger sinewy ropes of tissue called tendons, and when the animal wants to move, a message is sent from the brain

There is nothing more beautiful to behold.
Opposite: part of The Hunt in the Forest, by Paolo Uccello c.1470

telling the muscles to start contracting and stretching, thus moving the bones.

The whole thing is like a system of levers and pulleys, the muscles being the pulleys which enable the levers, the bones, to move.

Anyone who has ever eaten meat (think of a chicken leg) will know that what you are eating is the muscle, and you will have seen that the meat is fibrous, with the fibres all running in one direction.

The tough, rubbery bits of tissue, at each end of a muscle, a bit like a thick elastic band, are the tendons which attach the meat to the bone, and they are very tough indeed, not just to eat, but in their capacity to withstand injury.

When you are eating a steak you are eating a cross section of a muscle, and it doesn't take much imagination to realise that once those fibres have been cut or broken across their length they must take far longer to heal than if they had been cut along the length of those fibres.

Muscles vary in type and appearance throughout the canine species; dogs which have evolved for long periods of sustained effort, such as Collies, Huskies and Salukis have muscles which are very different in shape and size to those of a sprinter such as a Greyhound or a Whippet. The reason for this is that a sprinter's muscles contract much faster than those of a marathon runner and they are called 'fast twitch' muscles. The electrical impulses needed to contract and stretch the muscle fire more rapidly in a fast twitch muscle than those of slow twitch muscles which are better suited to long distance runners, be they canine or human. Just as Linford Christie would never win a marathon, no more could Paula Radcliffe win a 100 metre sprint: they are at the opposite ends of the scale when it comes to muscle fibres, with the sprinter's muscles being an excellent example of how the fast twitch muscles influence the overall shape of the body.

One could also compare Paula Radcliffe to a Saluki in type! (And I say this with the greatest respect for one of Britain's most successful marathon runners.) Notice how her overall appearance, tall with long lean muscles, is in fact very similar to that of the Saluki, whose fat-free and slender muscled limbs are the canine equivalent of the human marathon runner.

Slow twitch muscles are a darker red in colour than fast twitch muscles, as they contain a rich blood supply which can absorb oxygen from the blood in order to continue functioning over a long period of time.

Now compare the muscles of a rabbit and a hare: the rabbit, with paler 'white meat' muscles, is designed for fast bursts of speed over short distances whilst the hare has the ability to run for many minutes at a time at top speed, using the oxygen supply from its blood to power those darker coloured muscles.

Fast twitch muscles produce a limited amount of energy very quickly (eg rabbit or Greyhound) and slow twitch muscles produce a lot of energy more slowly (eg Hare, Saluki, Collie).

A hare's heart is also correspondingly larger in proportion to its body mass when compared to that of a rabbit, which allows the hare to pump oxygen round the body over an extended period of time in order to keep those muscles working efficiently. Animals which have evolved or been trained

A good example of a first cross Collie Greyhound. Photo: Ray Cross.

for stamina events have correspondingly larger hearts than those which are short runners.

All animals have a mixture of fast and slow twitch muscles, but those dogs that have been bred with a particular purpose in mind may have more of one type than the other, and once again, I'll use the Collie as an example of a dog which is capable of working at medium to fast speed all day rounding up sheep.

A Collie wouldn't win a race against a Greyhound, which is the most obvious example of a dog which is bred to run flat out at great speed for relatively short periods of time. Conversely, the Greyhound would find it exhausting to run all day in the manner of a Collie. However, it is these very differences between them which allow both breeds to be used successfully to produce lurchers.

Collie lurchers are tough and tireless.

When breeding an all round lurcher, one which may be used on a variety of game over varied terrain, we aim to produce a dog which is capable of short bursts of speed, as well as having the capacity to work all day with maybe some longer runs as well. Hence the typical crossing of those two breeds which in theory (and usually in practice as well) gives us some of the speed of the Greyhound at the same time as retaining the stamina of the Collie.

People who want more speed in a lurcher will generally add more Greyhound to the mixture, giving three-quarters of the Greyhound speed to only one quarter Collie. It would be true to say that these lurchers won't have as much stamina as a first cross Collie Greyhound and this has as much to do with those fast twitch muscle fibres as anything else.

I've used these two breeds as an example of two very different types of dog but it goes without saying that when you set out on that long and rocky road to finding

the right dog for your requirements, there are an almost infinite number of breeds and their crosses to choose from. It just so happens that Collie cross Greyhound is an old and trusted hybrid, one which people for many years have found to be of great use in the field.

You could also compare the Whippet and Saluki to see the contrast between muscle types, and although Whippets possess much more stamina than Greyhounds, they just aren't in the same league when compared with one of the greatest marathon runners in the dog world: the Saluki.

The Saluki (I use this name as a generic term to encompass all the 'saluki' types found across the world) has evolved over thousands of years to run down prey which can travel several miles at great speed. Whilst Salukis don't possess the explosive burst at take-off we associate with Greyhounds or Whippets, they are able to run for distances which would kill almost any other type of sighthound.

Whilst certain Saluki types in more mountainous regions of the world are thicker set and more powerfully muscled than their desert dwelling cousins, none of them bulge with muscle like a Greyhound: endurance is what matters to Salukis, not just pure speed.

CONDITIONING THE MUSCLES
No matter how well a dog is bred, its muscles won't be of any use if the animal is not fit enough for the work the owner asks of it.

No dog can perform at its best if its body has not received the correct type and amount of conditioning. Exercise also needs fuel, and only the right kind of fuel will enable the physical body to remain at a good level of fitness over a long period of time.

Feed rubbish food and don't exercise a dog correctly and you end up with a soft-muscled animal with no stamina and poor strength and speed; in other words, a below standard performer which is just waiting to succumb to an injury.

Repeated use of a muscle conditions it to grow stronger, and better able to do the work which is required of it but you HAVE to start off gently when conditioning muscles. A flat out gallop twice a week will NOT get your dog fit: in fact it's more likely to damage muscles, tearing the fibres and tendons as they over-extend to an unaccustomed level.

If you have reared your dog yourself from a wee pup, then hopefully you'll have given the youngster the right kind of exercise from an early age (see section on Puppies and Growth in this chapter).

However, let's suppose that you are starting a conditioning programme from scratch with an adult running dog which has had very little exercise previously, either because you have only just acquired the animal from an environment where it was not exercised, or because your dog has had a long lay off from running, maybe because of injury or is a bitch which has given birth to a litter of pups a couple of months previously. Whichever the scenario, let's assume that the dog is unfit for hard work, by which I mean running, be that for working, racing or any other activity which needs physical fitness.

The muscles will be soft and flabby to

Above: trotting, note how the legs move in diagonal pairs.

Right: large heavy dogs often pace to save energy. Note how both legs on one side are moving in unison, unlike true trotting where diagonal legs move in unison.

the touch, a far cry from the firm, springy tissue you want to see on a 'fit as a fiddle' animal, but there are also muscles deep within the body which you are unable to see; these are as important as the ones you can see, and include the heart, which is one of the strongest muscles in any mammal body.

The heart needs regular and steady exercise in order to work at its most efficient, just like any other muscle and although the heart is not a muscle which operates voluntarily like those of the legs, for example, it can still be conditioned to operate more efficiently.

CONDITIONING FOR RUNNING

The first step is to walk the dog, which might sound obvious to most people, but some owners merely take the dog out and let it run, and run and run, then wonder why it injures itself.

Walking is the first step in any fitness programme, and by walking I don't mean stumbling along at a snail's pace whilst your dog ambles gently beside you half asleep.

Walking should be done at a brisk pace, one that a reasonably fit person can maintain for several miles, and at a speed which allows a small dog to trot and a larger dog to jog (simply a slower version of the trot). Many dogs, especially those which are not fit, or those suffering from injury, will pace if the speed at which you are moving is too slow to allow the dog to trot properly.

Pacing is a camel's gait, moving both front and hind leg on one side of the body simultaneously, as opposed to diagonally and as an energy saving action works very well indeed, which is why you see this most often on animals which need to cover many miles in the most economical way possible.

Biking is good exercise but care must be taken during warm weather.

As pacing saves energy you are also most likely to see this in unfit, overweight heavy breed dogs such as Labradors and Mastiff type dogs though the young running dog whose frame is not yet mature is also apt to roll along in this manner.

Trotting involves lifting right front leg and left hind leg at the same time, followed by left front leg and right hind leg and so on, and this requires more energy than pacing.

If you can't walk fast enough for a large dog to move out of the pacing gait and into a proper trot then you have to either jog or get on a bicycle, but do be aware that sustained trotting for an unfit dog is a demanding exercise, far harder for the dog than running free for half an hour when the animal can stop and start as it wishes, thereby easing tired muscles by changing speed whenever it wants.

If I had a dog that had done little or nothing for some time I would start with steady walking, never mind if the dog paces, trots slowly or walks to begin with. I would do this for about three miles per day for two

11

weeks and allow no galloping at all during that time. After the first week I would make sure that the dog was trotting rather than pacing. Galloping stretches muscles to their limit and the twisting and turning which accompanies a happy, mad gallop from a dog that is just dying to run and play is not the best thing for soft muscles.

If you can't allow the dog a degree of freedom without it tearing off at speed, then keep it on the lead for that first fortnight. Remember, I'm talking about a dog that has literally sat in a kennel for months on end, something that no responsible owner would ever do to their dog.

A good example of such a dog would be one that has been sitting in a rescue centre and not even been out in a paddock to run around. (Happily most rescue organisations no longer leave dogs incarcerated 24/7 in a confined space as sometimes used to be the case.)

Another example would be the dog which has fallen out of favour with its owner before they finally decide to part with the luckless creature: I've known of dogs imprisoned in tiny kennels and runs for months on end after the owner had got bored with the animal.

After a fortnight you will by now ideally be trotting the dog three miles in the morning, and walking again in the afternoon, giving the animal the chance to gallop for a few hundred metres as well. Allow the dog to gallop no more than twice a day to begin with, and do this in a place where it won't be encouraged to gallop any great distance after moving objects.

Exercise twice a day if you can, as it is always better split into two sessions daily as opposed to one long hard session. This gives the body time to recover, regenerate cells and grow stronger.

Also, once the dog has lost the couch potato look, by alternating between fast and slow work you are building up overall fitness in the most ideal way; this is known in athletic circles as interval training.

Unfit dogs aren't always fat; severely underweight dogs will have a good deal of muscle wastage where their bodies have been forced to use muscle tissue for energy in order to stay alive. Walk underweight dogs carefully for a month before allowing them to move into a faster gait. The muscles in a previously starving dog take a long time to build up again and galloping is the last thing you want such dogs to do in their weakened state.

Once the dog has reached a state of semi-fitness a good daily walk will involve a little hunting, a few fast, though not too lengthy chases (rabbits are ideal for this) and the rest of the time spent trotting from one patch of hunting ground to the next.

This is the best way to build up overall fitness once the dog has attained about 50% of full working condition. Mooching along hedgerows for rabbits is an ideal occupation as it will encompass both slow and fast work at intervals.

NOTE: The above is easily done over much of the British countryside though inhabitants of wide open areas which are home to larger and faster wildlife will need to take the utmost care if their dogs are not to be drawn into lengthy chases whilst still unfit.

Sending the dog to retrieve a ball several times during the course of a walk will serve much the same purpose as several short sharp chases on rabbits, and of course you can control the number of runs far more easily, though not all sighthound type dogs really get into the fun of chasing and retrieving inanimate objects if they are used to the real thing.

Of course much will depend on what

The ferreting dog may not need the same degree of fitness as the coursing or lamping dog.

sort of work you want the dog to do as well, and a ferreting dog, used only to mark occupied warrens and maybe catch the odd rabbit which has slipped the net, will not need anywhere near the degree of fitness required in a dog which has to catch every rabbit bolted.

Similarly, a lamping or racing dog which is more of a sprinter than a marathon runner, one that must perform numerous fast take-offs during the course of a night's lamping or the heats of a race, needs to be in tip top shape if those repeated fast runs are not to damage the muscles.

Coursing dogs (and I am referring to hare coursing prior to the hunting ban) are often heavily saturated with Saluki blood, (remember those slow twitch muscles) and

whilst they need to have a good ground-work of steady exercise laid down to bring the muscles up to fitness to run any distance, these dogs need to actually course their quarry on a regular basis to really come to full fitness.

The same is also true of the sprinter, but the difference in quarry means that a rabbit will not take a dog three fields away at a flat out gallop as a hare would do, so allowing the owner to limit the amount of running time to just a few rabbits during the early days of conditioning the lamping dog.

I defy anyone to gauge with accuracy the length of time it would take a running dog to catch a hare on big open ground. By allowing an unfit dog to run a hare there is more chance of overdoing things when compared to the dog which runs a couple of rabbits as the amount of energy needed is far greater. There is a world of difference between several minutes of sustained effort on the back of a hare as opposed to a few seconds after a rabbit heading for its burrow.

Very fast Whippet or Greyhound dogs need careful conditioning if they are to run hares, though no amount of play gallops can replicate the real course, which involves a lot of twisting and turning. Running in a straight line is much easier for the dog than bending to left or right during a course, and it is not uncommon for supposedly fit dogs to break down after a prolonged course at the start of the hare coursing season.

NOTE: By 'break down' I mean damage to muscles or tendons due to over-exertion in a semi-fit dog, though even very fit dogs can be over run and break down if run too much. Dogs are only flesh and blood: not machines.

Once a dog can trot three to five miles beside a bike without becoming tired it is ready for some light work in the field. Depending on the breeding of the dog and the weather, I would expect a slightly open mouth and light panting from a fit dog which has just done five miles at a good trot, though of course the thickness of the dog's coat also plays a part in this, so don't expect a heavily coated dog doing a five-mile trot on a warm day to look happy or cool.

In fact, I would never bike my dogs on a warm day unless they were mostly Saluki in make up as it would be both dangerous and cruel: If you ask most types of dogs to run in hot weather they just can't cool their bodies down fast enough to maintain a normal temperature, and the risk of dehydration is also very high. Unless the dog can totally immerse itself in water at frequent intervals during exercise you should avoid hot weather biking completely unless you have a Saluki, though even Salukis can overheat if denied the cooling effects of the wet stuff whenever they need it.

My heavily Saluki-saturated dogs never swim unless they are following prey through water, and the most they'll do to cool-down is to wade a few steps into a river or lake, take a few laps of water, and come out on to dry land again. The hairy lurchers on the other hand would still be swimming about far from shore or lying in the water up to their chins in order to cool-down.

HEART RATE

Something else you should become accustomed to checking is the heart rate of your dog. Place a finger on the dog's ribs whilst it is sleeping and learn to recognise the resting heartbeat. You can also feel the pulse, the transmitted heart beat, very easily in the femoral artery. When the dog is lying down feel with your finger inside a hind leg along the inner thigh: you will feel the femoral artery very easily, it's a bit like a piece of cooked spaghetti under the skin and when you place a finger over it you can feel the pulse as the blood surges through it.

By the way, don't be alarmed if this seems irregular: what in a human might indicate a heart problem is in fact common in dogs and is known as sinus arrhythmia, a condition caused by an irregularity in the heart's natural pace maker. This is unlikely to ever cause a problem even in hard working dogs, and unless accompanied by other signs of ill health (such as exhaustion or heavy panting when doing nothing strenuous), it is nothing to worry about.

You should expect the heart rate to have increased after a half-hour trot beside your bike, but the heart should not be racing. Feel for the heart beat after your dog has had a hard race or run on quarry, (sometimes difficult if the dog is panting heavily), and get to know what it feels like after different amounts of work or running.

Incidentally, you should not run a dog again until its heart rate has settled down, not right down to the resting beat, but to a rate which is normal for the animal either out in the field or at the race track. This will naturally be faster than that of a resting beat as the dog is excited, on its toes and ready for action.

What you should avoid at all costs is running a dog again whilst its heart rate is still very elevated, and whilst some people say that the dog might be ready to run because it has stopped panting, check the heart rate with your fingers on the rib cage and you'll often be surprised at how fast the heart is still beating, especially in cold wet conditions when the outer dog will cool-down quite quickly.

In a really fit dog that has coursed a hare hard for say, three minutes, we'd expect the heart rate to have returned to a normal 'out in the field' rate after a maximum of five minutes, but sensible coursing people would wait at least 20 minutes before running their dog again after a hard course. This is because the muscles need time to relax slightly, the blood to regain its normal steady flow round the body and for the internal organs to cool-down sufficiently so as not to risk overheating when the dog runs once more.

Overheating is a very real problem in the slightly unfit dog which has been asked to do more than it should have done, and lurchers and sighthounds run a very real risk of dehydration if they are not allowed to cool-down properly between runs (see also Hyperthermia page 185).

Sighthounds and their hybrids have far less fat in their bodies than slower breeds, therefore running a greater risk of dehydration after hard exercise or work. Body fat contains water which means sprinting dogs with very little body fat need more frequent hydration. The amount of water a dog needs depends also upon its metabolic rate and Salukis have much lower metabolic rates than Greyhounds, for example.

Saluki-saturated lurchers often pant very little as they don't heat up to the same extent as sprinting dogs which accumulate a lot of heat during the course of a relatively short run or race, but their hearts will still need time to return to a normal 'in the field' rate.

Many dogs have been permanently damaged through being run too soon again after their last race or course if they are not totally fit. Remember the heart is a muscle, not a mechanical pump, and whilst it is one of the strongest muscles in the body, it can still be damaged by over- or misuse.

You may think that the dog is ready to run again because it is pulling at the sight of its prey seen in the distance, but as I've said before, we have so manipulated the genes in our sporting dogs that their desire to chase and run far exceeds anything a wild canine would do, which chases only when it is hungry.

Let's return to the fitness programme ... My Saluki-saturated dogs never even open their mouths during the course of a five-mile trot when they are approaching full fitness during early autumn exercise, and all you can see is a slight blowing from the corners of their mouths as they breathe a little harder towards the end of the session.

My hairy lurchers, which contain much less Saluki and are better suited to lamping rabbits than running hares, always open their mouths to pant when they trot beside the bike, and this is partly due to their thick coats, but also because they don't possess those same slow twitch muscles which are designed for endurance work; they get hotter more quickly.

Endurance work (continuous exercise at the same speed for an extended period of time, such as trotting or cantering beside a bike for several miles) is something which needs to be built up to slowly or you tire out the dog, which then takes far longer to recuperate.

Little and often, in other words daily, is the answer when it comes to a conditioning regime; the other thing that body builders are all too aware of is that it pays to alternate fast and slow work. This allows the muscles to recuperate and regenerate, as each time a muscle is worked hard there is actually a break down of tiny fibres within the muscle. As these heal they grow stronger and bigger, but only if they are allowed the resting time in which to do so. A galloping session one morning can be followed by a steady walk on the lead in the afternoon, or hard work one day will be followed by walking the following morning, with no galloping involved. Fast twitch muscles need a lot more basic training for running

Eight month old pups are of a size where they think they can do anything.

work than slow twitch muscles. You could probably get away with running a Saluki on a hare whilst not terribly fit, though it wouldn't do the dog much good, but it would be less likely to rupture muscles in the same way that a sprinting dog might do if those muscles were soft and flabby.

Running dogs asked to work or race during the warmer months of the year need to be very fit as they are often galloping on very hard ground which is punishing not only to the feet, but to the whole body including the muscles. Running fast over hard ground jars joints, bones, ligaments and affects the whole dog.

EXERCISE REQUIREMENTS FOR DOGS
Under 6 months

Puppies exercise themselves given the freedom to do so and whilst, in theory, running loose in a large garden will provide adequate exercise for a puppy, the confines of that garden will do nothing to prepare the young dog for the big wide world beyond those walls when applied to its mental development.

Once a puppy has finished its course of vaccinations at about 12 weeks of age I take it for a 20-minute walk every day, on the lead down to the local park. There the pup is allowed off the lead to explore, investigate and meet other dogs and people.

Once the pup reaches four months of age I take it out in the field with an older, steady dog or on its own, and I stay away from areas where we are likely to meet up with animals which are likely to run far and fast, such as hares or other large forms of wildlife. Actually a pup of four months is highly unlikely to venture far from you even if a hare gets up, though it has been known to happen!

A slow, interesting walk for about an hour is not too much for a puppy of four months, and by slow, I mean that we walk at the puppy's pace. The pup is off the lead for most of the walk; it can run, walk or stop when it wants to and most pups will spend much of their time sniffing interesting smells in the grass and cover.

If the pup wants to sit down and look at the daisies that's fine by me; if the pup wants to race about like a lunatic for a few moments that too is fine. So long as the puppy isn't over stimulated to run farther and faster than it would naturally do of its own accord I let it do what it wants. This is the reason I never take very young pups out with slightly older and very energetic saplings as these would drag a pup on to do more than it should.

This is why old dogs are such good mentors for young puppies as their prey drive has diminished to the extent that they are almost in their second puppyhood, happy to potter about and take things easy. When an old dog comes alert to a rabbit sitting under a clump of grass, any chasing is likely to be quickly over as the rabbit either disappears down a hole or is snaffled up by the old dog. Either way this is good education for young pups and stimulates their interest in scent and prey.

For those pups unable to access the countryside, be aware that even the local park can host a variety of wildlife (usually squirrels) and I've known young dogs damage their shoulders when attempting to run fast across the mown grass surface of the local football pitch. Summer baked turf is extremely hard on a dog's feet and joints and I never allow my youngsters to play or gallop on this type of surface which is almost like a skating rink to a dog.

At this stage of a pup's life I'm more interested in allowing the pup to become accustomed to the world in which it lives, and if that pup is destined to become a working dog then the field (countryside) is where it should take its daily exercise.

A puppy shows that it is tired by lagging behind, moving more slowly or sitting down and refusing to move. I shouldn't really need to say this should I, but I've seen novice owners dragging a puppy along on a lead when they've already walked several miles. The pup's head is held low, its feet are dragging and its whole demeanour is one of fatigue. If a pup is that tired pick it up and head for home straight away, and remember not to go so far next time you go out.

There's no shame in carrying a tired puppy and I've often taken very young pups out for longer walks than they could manage on foot, carrying them in my game bag which is slung over my shoulder when they've had enough running about. Actually my pups come to me when they want a rest, looking up at me. They seem to really enjoy being out and about without having to try and keep up, their little heads sticking out of the game bag, though of course this only applies to smaller type dogs: you'd be hard put to carry a Deerhound-sized pup of even three months for any length of time!

Six to 12 months
From six to 12 months is the most dangerous time for young running dogs. They are faster and stronger now, love to gallop and chase with other dogs and stand a real risk of doing too much if you put them into situations which encourage them to run, jump and over exert themselves.

Crashing falls, head over heels tumbles, collisions with other running dogs as they play chase-me games, or those first desperate runs at rabbits ... these things can damage young joints and muscles,

not to mention bones, which have not yet finished growing.

Damage sustained at an immature stage of a running dog's life may have no permanent effects as young tissue has remarkable recuperative and healing powers. BUT, (and it's a big BUT) sustained and repeated physical effort in an uncontrolled situation (a dog is only ever really under control when it is on the lead) can lead to problems later in life.

Take a running dog out in the field from say, eight months of age, run it hard and regularly on game or in racing competitions over the course of the next two years and it is highly likely that by the time the dog is three or four years old it will be suffering from arthritic joints, torn or pulled muscles or tendons.

I've been there and done it so I'm not just preaching from an imaginary pulpit. When you see real potential in a pup it is all too easy to let the youngster do too much, and by too much, I mean more than the odd pop at a rabbit or the occasional chase after a lure.

Some people state that their dogs are out catching rabbits and winning races by the time they are six months old, and there's no doubt that some lines and types of running dog do mature far earlier than most. Many of the fast maturing lines of running dogs have been bred lurcher to lurcher for many years; they are often small and lightly built in type as opposed to tall or heavy in build. Generally speaking the smaller dog matures faster than its larger counterparts.

This is why it is so difficult to offer advice to running dog owners: each type of lurcher or sighthound is different depending on the breeds which went into the make up of that particular dog. Whippets generally mature very early, getting their feet as it is called, by the time they are six months old. 'Getting its feet' means that the dog can handle itself at speed, that it no longer runs with the gangly, sometimes awkward gait one sees in large breed pups. My current Saluki bred dog, Reem, matured at nearly 28 inches to the shoulder and at 12 months of age he was still running in a somewhat ungainly manner.

Reem couldn't run fluently until he hit 18 months of age, and I remember how that fluency, that effortless speed just seemed to appear one day out of nowhere. From lumpy 'flat tyre' running one day he suddenly flowed across the ground like oil on water the next time out. Of course it didn't really happen overnight and I expect that I just opened my eyes one day and realised that my big pup could really run.

Hunni, the pup I bred in 2008, contains a fair bit of Deerhound in her breeding, and she took even longer to mature. She was nearly two years old before I saw that flowing running stride come good. Prior to this she seemed to be tripping over her front end when she ran, the reason for this being that the power in her rear end was already there before the front end had matured.

The shoulder blade in the dog is one of the last bones to finish growing (small bones grow first and the largest bones are the slowest to mature). Whilst bone is still growing the tendons and muscles are also immature and the dog shouldn't be asked or allowed to do more than it needs to satisfy exercise requirements.

That is not to say that a pup of under 12 months of age should do nothing, far from it. Bones and muscles need plenty of exercise in order to grow strong and healthy, just not TOO MUCH EXERCISE!

Let's look at a couple of examples, dogs Andy and I have owned in years gone by. Linnet was bred from a ¾ Greyhound ¼

Bearded Collie bitch to a lurcher of many generations, breeding largely unknown. The two pups we kept back were chalk and cheese: mine was more 'lurchery' in type, slower to mature physically and mentally (possible Deerhound influence?) whilst Linnet was to all intents and purposes more Collie-ish in her build and make up. Stocky, sturdily built and much quicker on the take-off than her sister at that time.

Andy started lamping Linnet at eight months of age, just three or four runs over a period of say, an hour or so. Her daily exercise consisted of a good hour's walk every day, during which time she would be walked on the lead for about a mile, hunt along hedgerows for about an hour then walk home again on the lead.

From eight to 12 months of age Linnet was taken out on the lamp about twice a week during that first winter, though at no time did she ever run more than 6 rabbits on any one night.

Collie-bred lurchers do seem to mature fairly quickly, though of course much depends on the dog's sex. Bitches mature more quickly than dogs (males), and I've known male running dogs (mostly sighthound in make up) that were still growing in height at two years of age, albeit very slowly. A Deerhound male isn't fully mature until he reaches three years of age! I know that my first cross Deerhound/Greyhound, a bitch, reached her adult height at 22 months of age but she continued to fill out until she was three years old.

Back to Linnet: had she belonged to the sort of person who wanted to be out catching hundreds of rabbits every night I am sure that she would have been 'knackered' by the time she was three years old, such was her drive and speed. Indeed, I once spoke to someone who claimed that his dogs were always 'finished' by the time they were four years old. He started running (working) them at under 12 months; they were large fast dogs with a lot of Greyhound in their breeding.

We, the owners, are ultimately responsible for what our running dogs do in the field or on the race track. If someone wants three or four years hard graft from a dog before putting it out to pasture (a euphemistic explanation if ever there was one!) that is up to the owner. Some people see dogs as tools rather than individuals with whom they can build a relationship, things to be discarded once they have served their purpose.

Personally I find that way of thinking a real shame, as even when my older dogs are no longer at their best work-wise, their experience in the field makes them invaluable in other ways. The older and very experienced fox dog can provide brilliant back up for a novice, and as speed wanes, so do traits such as common sense and prey sense improve. My old dogs goal-keep rabbits rather than running after them, putting themselves in the right place for a catch, but I digress!

Very fit dogs can better withstand fast work in extremes of heat or cold, conditions which would endanger the lives of fat or unfit animals. Photo: Von

MUSCLING UP YOUNG DOGS

Don't expect to see great bulging thigh muscles on young dogs. Given steady and regular exercise the muscles will show you when they are ready for increased work and it would be a mistake to put a young dog through the sort of gruelling training routine we might plan for an adult coursing dog.

Once you start to see muscle definition in the hind legs of a young dog you know that those muscles are ready to do a bit more: sounds simple doesn't it, and it is. Puppies don't and shouldn't have well defined adult type muscles, but as they approach the six to eight month mark, depending upon size and breeding, you'll start to see a difference in the shape of your dog. This doesn't mean to say that you can gallop the dog into the ground, but it does mean that the pup is now ready for a bit more exercise.

How much more exercise? Once again, it all depends on the breeding, weight and height of the dog. There is no magic formula which you can follow, though as a general rule of thumb I'd say that an hour's walk each day is a good sensible option providing the dog doesn't spend that entire time galloping flat out. If it wants to gallop continuously put it on the lead for 15 minutes at a time three times during the hour's walk and try to find something more productive for the dog to do other than just lunatic charging about.

If you can, take youngsters out in areas which are not wide open: leafy lanes, small fields, river bank walks for example. All these will provide stimulation without temptation to gallop too far and too fast. If you take a keen pup of excitable nature out in the company of older dogs which are doing a fair bit of galloping and hunting and you risk damaging its joints and bones, not to mention the fact that the youngster will become accustomed to tearing about all the time like an idiot instead of watching and learning.

I tend to keep youngsters on the lead when the adults are having a gallop round, only allowing the pup to stretch its legs once the others are back on the lead. If you are walking a pup on its own life is much easier and you'll find that the young dog will spend more time pottering about and using its brain to decipher interesting scents, sights and sounds, providing that you don't allow it to go warp speed after animals it has no chance of catching.

At the time of writing we have in our kennel a 16 month old Collie/Greyhound lurcher: actually he is part Beardie, part Greyhound and part Picardy Sheepdog, an ancient French herding breed. At 12 months of age this dog was very far from being mature as the growth plates in his wrists were still open, which meant that he still had a bit of height to gain. More importantly, this dog is still gangly all over, and although we are now beginning to see some muscle definition in his hindquarters, he won't reach full power until he is at least two years old. This pup weighs in at a hefty 36 kilos and is still very vulnerable to joint damage as a result. Immature puppy muscles plus lots of bone and weight running at speed over rough or uneven ground ... you do the maths!

As a rough guide I would expect a pup which matures at a height of under 25 inches to start doing a bit of work by the time it is 10 months old. A large breed pup which matures at from 25-30 inches at the shoulder should be held back from regular hard work until it is 18 months of age.

I wouldn't bike a dog of less than 12 months for any distance either: remember sustained trotting is hard work on muscles and skeleton. Dogs of less than 12 months should be allowed to stop running and take a breather when they need to, and trotting beside a bike doesn't allow them to do that unless you are a sensitive and very observant owner. Of course half a mile beside a bike won't hurt providing you then allow the young dog to relax off lead for the rest of the walk, though the dangers of biking young, frisky animals that don't have 'bike sense' along a public road should be obvious. Use common sense and don't tire out young animals. Note that it is illegal to bike dogs on public roads.

SOME GENERAL TIPS ON EXERCISE AND WORK

Don't take any dog, young or old, out and start running it hard before the muscles have had time to warm up. People who lamp dogs out of their vehicles should pay particular attention to this because cold, stiff muscles are more prone to injury than those which have been walked to the running ground. The same applies to the dog which is taken out of a vehicle and raced 'cold' then put back into the vehicle without cooling down. Human athletes know to stretch their limbs before they start running hard, which is why you see runners jogging up and down on the spot before the start of a race. Racing Greyhounds are massaged before they race, which achieves the same objective. Walk or massage the dog before it does any fast work and the muscles will be prepared for that work.

All exercise or work sessions should finish with 10 minutes of steady walking before you come home or put the dog back in your vehicle. Heart rate needs to slow and muscles relax before the dog goes back in its kennel or house. A good rub down with your hands also allows lactic acid to dissipate from the muscles, a build up of which causes aching limbs after hard exercise. This cool-down period also allows the dog to become mentally calm as well. It is all too easy to bring home a dog which is still in a state of high alert, with the adrenalin not dissipated. Excitable dogs which wind themselves up prior to racing or work are more prone to cramp and acidosis than calm, laid back animals.

No matter how well we prepare our dogs for hard work, no exercise routine can replicate actual running after prey. Early season hunting brings risks of both dehydration and muscle soreness until the dog reaches the correct level of fitness needed, and I always carry a bottle of electrolyte solution with me so the dog can begin replacing lost mineral salts the moment it has stopped running. *Recharge* (made by Vetsearch) is one of the best electrolyte replacement solutions available as it is designed specifically for dogs (as opposed to other types of animal who can sweat through their skins).

Watch closely when your dog urinates after a hard course. Any sign of dark red or wine coloured urine means that the kidneys are flushing muscle protein along with urine and this is due to the breakdown of muscle fibres which have done too much. Rehydrate the dog immediately in such cases and don't run the dog again for a few days. Whilst rehydrating with plain water is better than nothing, using a mineral replacement electrolyte solution restores the system more quickly, limiting blood imbalance to the minimum. Dogs which do not have access to electrolytes are at risk of getting into a drink/pee cycle as their bodies desperately attempt to regain that balance. This is known as 'coursing thirst' and in severe cases can lead to organ failure and death (see also section on Hyperthermia on page 187).

CHAPTER TWO

Muscles: their function, strains, ruptures and treatment

There are several degrees of muscle damage, with a tightening of a particular muscle being the first sign that all is not right. A muscle can tighten up if worked too hard without proper conditioning, or if it is over extended beyond its natural range of movement. Continue working a dog with a tight muscle and you risk a proper strain, which involves tearing of the fibres and happens when a muscle is over-stretched or pulled beyond its normal range of movement.

A rupture is a major tear of the muscle fibres, often resulting in blood loss and distortion of the muscle shape. Muscles can also be ruptured as a result of a major impact such as being hit by a car, kicked by a horse or even crashing into an immoveable object such as a gate post. In these cases the muscle splits apart at the point of impact and this can be very serious indeed.

Slight tears can take from two to four weeks to heal, but obviously the more fibres torn the longer the healing period, anything up to eight weeks.

HOW TO RECOGNISE AND TREAT A DAMAGED MUSCLE

As many muscle problems involve either the legs or back of a dog you can expect to see either stiffness or lameness, depending on exactly which muscles are affected.

The main problem with lurchers and sighthounds is that whilst they are actually chasing something with intent, it often takes a very severe injury indeed for most dogs to actually stop what they are doing or yelp with pain. This is because the adrenalin pumping through their veins acts as a temporary painkiller, and it is not until later that the true extent of such an injury is really noticed by the animal in question.

Adrenalin is one of the hormones which are produced during life or death situations, and also during times of great excitement. These hormones allow a maximum amount of blood to flow through the veins during phases of intense activity, necessary for the body's ability to carry out whatever action is needed, be that fight or flight, depending on whether the animal is a predator or a prey animal. Even humans, when faced with extreme survival situations have been known to endure horrific injuries without realising how badly they have been hurt until after the immediate emergency has passed.

Most dogs react very differently to internal pain, even quite severe pain, when compared to the sudden shock of externally inflicted pain, such as running into something, or being cut by a sharp object.

If a dog ruptures a muscle, the inner thigh muscle (the gracilis) for example, there is seldom any intense pain response to the injury, though lameness is very likely, lameness which will worsen as time goes by.

As owners of canine athletes we should never ignore any outward signs of pain in our dogs because whilst one animal will let you know immediately it has a cut foot, another dog with a higher pain threshold will carry on running despite a much more serious injury. It is down to the owner to really know their own dog and be on the watch for any sign of unusual movement or behaviour.

Stiffness on rising after resting can of course also be attributed to arthritic conditions, simple exhaustion and a host of other conditions. But we can learn to look for muscle damage, and I watch my dogs like a hawk ... all the time. It becomes a habit, part of life, and when they move away from me out on exercise I am almost unconsciously watching out for any signs of lameness or stiffness.

With practice you can learn to see where the cause of lameness is situated. If the dog seems unwilling to place its paw on the ground you will of course investigate the possibility of a thorn in a pad or a cut to the foot.

However, if the whole leg swings forward at each step in a stiff and awkward manner, this is a different kind of lameness to that caused by a problem to the foot. Try and compare the movement in, say, the left front leg, to that of the right front leg to see if you have a problem.

Similarly, with a hind leg, watch as the dog goes away from you at a trot ... do both legs move soundly without swinging wide or turning in? Does one side of the dog's rear end dip with each stride or do both hips appear to move evenly through each stride? Get used to seeing what is normal so that if the abnormal occurs you are better able to recognise a difference in your dog's movement. I have two lurchers who tore their gracilis muscle (inner thigh) and

both injuries occurred when these bitches were going through their post-season flabby stage. One bitch received a side-on hit from another lurcher as they were both closing with an unexpected rabbit which had got up out of some long grass; she staggered sideways and then carried on running, though a tad more slowly, and as I checked her over once she'd returned to my

Above: Note the swollen, lumpy and discoloured muscle when compared to the left inner thigh which is undamaged. Below: the same injury showing blood seeping from torn gracilis seen as bruising under the skin.

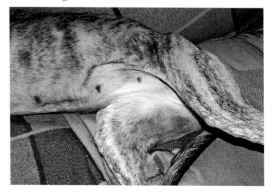

side I could see that the whole shape of her inner thigh had changed.

What was once a normal muscle, albeit somewhat soft due to her post-season condition, now looked as though someone had inserted a bag of soft pulp beneath the skin, with the greater part of that pulp slumped to the bottom of the bag, (just like a sock into which you have poured a bowlful of lumpy mashed potato) and just above the dog's hock on the inside of the leg.

This was a serious rupture, and whilst I wasn't sure if the major tendon which attaches that muscle to the bone, had come away, or if the muscle itself had torn, the initial treatment is the same.

Human athletics coaches call the treatment 'RICE' and it means this:

Rest - Ice - Compress - Elevation

REST: if possible carry the dog off the field and home. If the dog has to walk do it slowly and on the lead just in case more prey gets up and the dog tries to give chase. More running at this stage will make matters a lot worse.

ICE: As soon as you can, ice the area by holding a bag of chipped ice or frozen peas against the muscle which has been damaged. This reduces internal bleeding, and if the muscle itself has been ruptured it will bleed, but under the skin, which makes it more difficult to ascertain the severity of the injury.

Don't put a plastic bag of ice or peas directly in contact with the skin as this can cause burning of the skin: wrap the bag in a tea towel or pillow case first.

Do this, if possible for 15 minutes at a time, every few hours during the first week from the moment of injury onwards, by which time any bleeding should have stopped. Bleeding from a muscle whose sheath has been torn will show up as bruising beneath the skin, turning pink skin bright red and purple, and dark skin a darker shade of purple. This isn't a bruise caused by external impact, but simply the blood which has leaked from the torn muscle. This sort of tear is called an **inter muscular** tear.

An **intra muscular** tear is one where the sheath of the muscle has not been damaged, and this is likely to cause more problems because the blood and fluid from the tear cannot drain away under the skin, thus remaining within the muscle itself and inhibiting healing, also increasing scarring of the muscle fibres.

COMPRESS: By compressing the damaged area you will reduce the amount of swelling and help to stop bleeding, thereby limiting the amount of scar tissue that will inevitably form following such an injury. Scar tissue is not useful in these sorts of injuries as a scarred muscle won't operate as well as one whose fibres are undamaged: normal healthy muscle fibres are stretchy whereas scarred fibres are all knotty and rigid, which hinders normal movement.

In a human, you would bandage the area to apply a compress, but this is not easy to do on dogs as in the case of the upper hind leg any bandage you apply to the upper leg will simply slide down that leg when the dog stands up. I've tried all sorts of ways to hold such a bandage in place, from metres of sticking plaster to a complicated across the back arrangements of slings and webbing!

A pair of support tights has been the most successful device so far, with the excess material pulled right over the dog's back and tied in the middle: I widened the waist band considerably by cutting quite deeply from the waist band both front and back to give me something to tie up.

I put these on to the dog over a bandage already in place over the damaged muscle, and already held up with sticking plaster, just to stop everything sliding down the leg. **NOTE:** don't leave these tights on for too long as the dog won't be able to relieve itself whilst wearing them!

ELEVATION: We humans would elevate a leg with a torn muscle so that it is higher than the heart in an attempt to reduce blood flow to the damaged site. If possible the dog should lie down during this phase of the treatment which is why I would always cage injured animals as 90% of dogs will simply lie still in a cage providing they are used to being confined. We can't make a dog lie on its back with its legs in the air, but we can get them to lie down by confining them to a small, well padded and comfortable area.

I always accustom young pups to a few hours in a cage from time to time as they grow up, and in this way I can confine an adult with no panicking or problem should the need arise.

Kenneled dogs also need to be caged if possible, for you are trying to maintain total rest during the first few days following a bad muscle injury: bed rest, with the only movement being to walk (on a lead) outside to relieve themselves is the best protocol for bad muscle injury.

Make sure that the dog is in a warm, draught free place: I always cover the sides, back and top of a cage with a blanket, not only for this reason, but because a small, cave like den will also help the animal to relax and lie calmly, which is exactly what we want. If your dog has never been caged then now is not the time to start as the last thing you want is a stressed, agitated animal which won't rest or lie down: a closed-in kennel or small, quiet room where the animal feels at peace are options in this case.

MASSAGE

Massage has been used for thousands of years not only to promote a sense of well-being and calm, but also to aid recovery from certain types of injury. Muscle injuries respond particularly well to what we nowadays term as sports massage.

Sports massage is invaluable in helping a strained or torn muscle back to proper function though this type of massage should NOT be carried out on torn muscles UNTIL AFTER THE BRUISING HAS DISAPPEARED. Massage too soon after a rupture and you'll only be increasing the bleeding from the torn fibres which will delay healing as opposed to encouraging it.

There is a vast difference between a general whole body massage that helps promote blood flow to the skin and muscles and sports massage, which targets a specific injury.

Sports enthusiasts, athletes and body builders will know what I mean, but for the person with no experience of sports massage, be warned ... you can do untold damage to a muscle if you are not sure of what you are doing.

I would strongly advise anyone who keeps running dogs to book themselves in to a good sports clinic for a sports massage just so you know exactly what it involves! Even better, ask a canine chiropractor or greyhound vet to show you how it is done.

A flat of hand grooming massage is great for routine dog care and helps to stimulate blood flow to the skin's surface, and certainly won't do any harm to damaged muscles, but it won't really have any curative effect on deep-seated muscle strains or hard knots.

I've found a few very good instructional video clips on the internet on sports massage, for humans of course, where the different massage techniques are shown accompanied by good clear commentary. Try Googling 'sports massage' and have a look for yourselves.

BUT I would still visit a specialist in the flesh before attempting to treat a dog as there is no substitute for real practice. Even today I can still come away from a visit to the canine chiropractor with egg on my face if I've failed to spot a tricky little muscle strain where damage is very hard to find indeed.

Experienced physiotherapists can often detect scar tissue with their fingers, evident as either a little dent in the muscle surface, or in more severe cases, granular bobbles of tissue under the skin. Years of practice are needed for the fingers to 'learn' what they are feeling for, though some people are much more sensitive than others in this field.

Expert sports massage can help to 'straighten out' damaged muscle fibres, soothe out hard knots in a muscle, and promote healing to the torn muscle, providing it is done in the right way by someone who understands the muscle structure and the nature of the problem.

Suffering from muscle problems myself I have learned a lot over the years, and can now apply the techniques of deep sports massage to my dogs. Done correctly, deep massage should never cause more than a certain level of discomfort, not the sort of pain you want to pull away from, and unless your dog is dead it will flinch away from fingers which work too hard on an injury in the wrong way, thereby letting you know that you are not doing the right thing. Most dogs positively relish being massaged, and even when I'm working on

A slip whilst turning can tear a muscle.

Flexing the wrist to check for signs of soreness. Not all dogs have wrists as flexible as this. If the dog shows signs of pain when the wrist is flexed it may have joint or tendon damage.

Extending the front leg to check for tightness and pain in the shoulder area. Note the supporting hand under the dog's elbow in above and adjacent photos.

Extending the hind leg whilst massaging the outer thigh. Tight muscles should be gently stretched whilst massaging to encourage correct extension.

Massaging the thigh muscle using both hands along the length of the muscle.

an injured muscle mine relax fully and seem to appreciate the relief given by the massage. There is a world of difference between the dull, non-spiking discomfort caused by working on a tight muscle and the sharp jabbing pain caused by incorrect massage.

Racing Greyhounds have always been massaged as part of their daily routine, just like athletes, but I wonder just how many running dog owners realise the importance of this: it doesn't have to take long, as little as five to 10 minutes a day, or even every other day (better than not at all) is of real help to the dog.

The other thing that regular grooming and massage does is enable you to find little niggling injuries or sore spots which you might otherwise not have noticed; the slightly strained muscle which could in time become a serious problem is something that you can pick up on whilst grooming with your hands.

Healthy fit muscle feels firm, smooth and has a spring to it: if you press a healthy muscle with your finger the tissue should spring back to shape immediately you remove the pressure.

Tight muscles feel hard to the touch, and don't 'give' in the same way as healthy muscle. They do not stretch properly either. Muscles which have been ruptured may feel lumpy under the skin if the injury is old and has healed with a lot of scar tissue. Immediately after being ruptured a muscle will feel soft and floppy and it will have lost its natural shape; particularly bad injuries make the muscle feel as though there is a bag of jelly inside the skin instead of muscle.

Anyone who has skinned out a rabbit caught by a hard-mouthed dog will have sometimes found a jelly-type mass where there should be firm muscle tissue. This is very similar to what happens when a muscle is ruptured by an extreme movement, a slip or collision.

Due to the different muscle types within lurchers and sighthounds the fully fit muscle of a Saluki won't feel anything like that of a Greyhound, so if your dog is a mixture of breeds, get to know and remember how the muscles feel when the dog is both fit and unfit.

Sprinting dogs possess muscles which are larger and firmer to the touch than stamina runners, though there should always be some 'give' when you press your fingers against a healthy muscle.

Always massage along the length of the muscle rather than across it. Ideally you should work with strokes of your hand away from the heart but this isn't always possible and there will be no problem in massaging the neck, for example, from the head down towards the body. As a general rule, massage in the same direction as the fur grows.

Start by using the palm of your hand without digging your fingers into the muscle and you will, after a few moments, begin to feel the tissue soften slightly. Only once the muscle has begun to soften slightly should you begin to use a kneading motion using your thumbs. Homemade bread makers will know what I mean here.

EXERCISE TO HEAL CORRECTLY

Once the initial bleeding and swelling in a strained or torn muscle has subsided it is important to exercise damaged muscles. Without gentle exercise the muscle risks healing in the 'wrong' shape, or position. Imagine that the muscle in your calf has been ruptured: if you just stayed in bed for weeks on end after the injury occurred, the calf muscle would heal in a 'resting' position, and as scar tissue doesn't stretch and contract like normal healthy muscle tissue, you'd then find it hard to run or walk normally without difficulty or pain.

Damaged muscles should be stretched, exercised and massaged, but this must be done in such a way that more damage is not caused to the healing tissue.

For example, let's say that the running dog has strained a muscle in its hip, a common enough problem in dogs which gallop fast over uneven ground. On the opposite page the photos show how the leg should be stretched, and the muscle massaged whilst in the stretched out position. By extending the leg you are encouraging the damaged muscle to stretch, and by massaging at the same time you are encouraging blood flow to the area which is necessary for healing.

WARNING: At no time should you cause the dog intense pain. If the dog yelps, whips round to bite your hand or in any other way displays symptoms of pain, then you are doing it wrong! Worse still, you may be causing even more damage. I'm not trying to scare people away from massaging their dogs, but do get expert advice before working on your own dog. I can't repeat this too often.

With practice you will learn to recognise tight, strained muscles and be able to ease them. Strained muscles do benefit from exercise, but not from fast work which will simply undo all the good that you have done during massage. Until the muscle feels 'right' whilst resting, keep exercise steady (lead work only) with no fast work until you have resolved the problem.

Incidentally, 'lead work' means just that: on the lead at all times, no jumping in and out of vehicles, no running up and down stairs, no playing with other dogs in the yard, run or garden. Older readers will know what I'm talking about, but to many people under the age of 30 it is hard to imagine just how much a strained muscle affects your overall movement and ability to work. Young muscles, unless severely overstrained by really abnormal amounts of work or serious injury, are far more elastic and better able to withstand abuse from over exercise than elderly dogs and humans.

Give tight muscles a few days off from hard work, massaging every day, then let the dog run a little and see how it performs. Any further signs of lameness or stiffness might mean that you need to see a canine chiropractor.

CAUTIONARY NOTE

Any attempts to diagnose and treat an injury yourself could result in severe and permanent damage to the dog if you don't know what you are doing. Always take a dog to a professional for diagnosis and recommended treatment unless you are yourself an expert in this field in which case I doubt you'll be reading this book!

An injury might present as a torn muscle in your eyes, but if the tendon which attaches that muscle to the bone has been ripped away completely, then surgery is sometimes necessary. Damage to muscles and tendons can result in permanent disability unless correctly treated at the time of the injury.

I have yet to see a working or racing running dog which hasn't at some time or another sustained damage to muscles or tendons, and many dogs continue to work and run almost as well as they did before injuring themselves. However, once a particular muscle is no longer operating to its potential this can start to affect other areas of the body resulting in an overall lessening in performance. No muscle

Above: this 10 month old first cross Bull Greyhound clearly shows the immature muscle of the young dog, whereas (right) at 16 months he has almost attained maturity and the strong muscular condition we expect from this sort of dog at full fitness.
Photos: Phil Jones.

A potentially dangerous jump over wire though these two dogs are well accustomed to this type of obstacle. Photo: Von

operates alone; each muscle is part of a group of muscles.

As one area fails to perform to its optimum efficiency, so does it place more stress on other parts of the body. As an extreme example, a three-legged dog will ultimately suffer from problems in the leg that is doing the work for two!

The back also contains many individual muscles which are responsible for movement and whilst perfect muscular condition is the ideal we strive for in our canine athletes, there is no animal alive which will be 100% undamaged by the time it has raced about on this planet for a few years.

Unless injury to muscles is very serious most animals learn to cope with the odd aches and pains just as we humans do. BUT any damage will ultimately reduce optimum performance in a running dog so be aware that just leaving a strained muscle to heal itself won't cure the problem completely.

MUSCLE DAMAGE TREATMENT IN BRIEF

- *Stop work as soon as you see a problem and take the dog home.*
- *Get a professional diagnosis of the problem.*
- *R.I.C.E. for five to seven days depending on the severity of the injury.*
- *For the next MONTH lead walk the dog twice a day and massage the affected muscle gently to help stimulate blood flow and correct healing.*
- *Severe muscle tears need at least six weeks to heal properly. Allow the dog to run too soon and the muscle will tear apart all over again.*

NOTE: *It is very important to continue massage throughout the duration of healing. Failure to do so may result in the muscle healing in the 'wrong' way, leading to a build up of scar tissue which will inhibit proper functioning of the muscle.*

COMMON MUSCLE INJURIES

Any muscle can be strained or torn if it is stretched beyond its natural range of movement: the same applies to any joint in an animal's body. Whilst there would never be enough space in any one book to describe each and every muscle in the dog body I have listed the most commonly encountered muscle problems.

Triceps

The triceps muscle, also known as the monkey muscle in greyhound circles, is one of a group of muscles responsible for moving the front leg.

Ruptures to the triceps are very common especially when the dog is turning fast and hard, and once torn, often heal shorter in length than they would have been before the injury, especially as the owner is unlikely to notice the damage at the time it happens.

A dent is often visible above the triceps once the injury has healed when this muscle has been ruptured or its tendon over-stretched, but happily even permanent damage is unlikely to affect the running dog from moving relatively easily.

As the triceps is one of a group of muscles which operate the fore limbs a slight lessening in function after such an injury doesn't generally hamper the average running dog too much and I've had several dogs with damaged triceps muscles that continued to work in the field with no real reduction in performance.

Gracilis

The gracilis is the large muscle on the inner thigh of the hind leg and is one of the powerful muscles used to drive the dog forward at a gallop. It is commonly strained or ruptured if a dog is knocked or falls sideways when running, especially if the dog is unfit. Damage to this muscle affects overall speed and manoeuvrability.

NOTE: remember that once a muscle is damaged in any way, it cannot perform to its potential. The inefficiency of a damaged muscle may affect other muscles in the same limb leading to damage to other muscles which will inevitably mean loss of function.

Second thigh or calf muscle

Dogs which do a lot of jumping often suffer from strains to what we call the 'second thigh', which is the muscle below the main thigh, just above the hock (the equivalent of our calf muscle). This part of a dog's leg is often overlooked as the owner tends to concentrate on the larger upper thigh muscles when looking for strain or damage. Massaging a little embrocation or oil into such a tight muscle will go a long way to preventing that little strain from becoming a major problem in the future.

Groin strain

Running dogs are susceptible to groin strains which affect the inside of the hind leg where it attaches to the body. A violent sliding to one side as the dog attempts to turn hard at speed is the sort of movement which can cause a groin strain. These are not easy to diagnose unless you're an expert but an unwillingness to extend at a gallop is one of the signs that your dog may have suffered a groin strain, characterised by a slightly tied in, knock-kneed movement which the dog adopts to avoid moving its leg out to the side. If you lift the hind leg GENTLY away from the body and you meet with resistance suspect a groin strain.

WARNING: When manipulating (lifting or moving the legs on a dog) do so gently and slowly at all times. Learn what is acceptable and comfortable to an uninjured healthy dog so that you can feel the difference if you meet with resistance. A dog will resist any movement which causes it pain, so in the case of a groin strain, attempting to lift the injured leg away from the body will meet with discomfort, and resistance.

NEVER TRY AND FORCE A DOG TO MOVE ITS HEAD, LEGS OR ANY OTHER PART OF ITS BODY IF YOU MEET WITH RESISTANCE. YOU WILL DO EVEN MORE DAMAGE.

Damage to shoulder muscles

The group of muscles which enable the front legs to move are those which attach the shoulder blade to the body. Dogs which do a lot of jumping, especially down from a height (as opposed to upwards only) are more liable to muscle damage in that area; similarly dogs which jump across wide ditches, landing with a jarring action on the further bank.

Neck and back muscles

There are numerous muscles along the neck and back, these interweave and overlay each other along the spine. It is common for one or more of the neck or back muscles to become too tight, which may appear as a slightly raised lump of hard tissue.

BUT IT DOESN'T END HERE!

Because the muscles are attached to bones they may also become tight or strained in response to what is called a subluxation of a joint. Put simply, if a joint is slightly out of place, the muscles' response is to tighten around that joint in order to protect it from further damage by restricting its movement.

If the joint problem is not resolved the muscles are forced to remain in a contracted (tight) state for a long period of time, which can eventually cause chronic problems. Blood flow to the contracted muscle is restricted, toxins cannot be dispersed which can result in pain and loss of function.

For more on joint and bone problems read the chapter on BONES!

WHEN MUSCLES CRAMP UP, TRUE CRAMP AND DELAYED ONSET MUSCLE SORENESS

I'm afraid I'm going to start with the science bit here: those of you who don't want to know the reasons behind cramping can go straight to the treatment part of this section but if you want to avoid such problems in the future then I suggest you read the science bit as well!

Dogs that have cramped up after intense work or exercise are more likely to suffer

Opposite: Lurcher about to pick up her rabbit. Photo: Craig McCann.

further attacks and repeated cramping can severely damage muscles, sometimes to the extent that they never fully recover.

CRAMP: when a muscle contracts and fails to relax again. When a muscle remains contracted longer than it should this causes pain and an inability to move that muscle. Normal cramp usually lasts only a few minutes at the most, but in the running dog which has pushed itself too hard when not properly fit, the condition can last for half an hour or more, during which time the animal will be in severe pain and find it difficult to move.

The most commonly affected muscles are those of the back and hind legs, which are responsible for driving the dog forwards when moving at speed.

BUT if intense hard work (eg extended running) is undertaken by a dog which has not been correctly conditioned for that exercise the muscles will be put under severe strain, such severe strain that they may 'lock up' or cramp in the contracted position, unable to release and move as they should.

Cramp may also occur if the dog is dehydrated and is more likely in the dog which is worked or run hard during hot weather. A deficiency in certain minerals such as potassium, magnesium or calcium may also be responsible for dogs which are prone to cramping.

During the acute phase of cramping up the dog will be unable to move, will stand with its back arched, and if you attempt to touch the back muscles it will cry out in pain. This phase can last for up to an hour in extreme cases, and the back muscles will feel hot to the touch as well as being incredibly painful both to touch and on attempt to move.

During this phase the muscle fibres become damaged, sometimes to the extent that they virtually disintegrate, their protein (all cells are made of protein) passing out of the body and seen as blood coloured urine. Once the cramp has subsided you may, over the course of the next few days, see the back muscles shrivel to less than half their usual size; this condition is known as 'running the back off a dog' because the 'back' muscle literally disappears.

Less severe cases of cramp do not lead to such atrophy of the muscles, though there may be pain and tenderness in the area for several days afterwards. Severe cases can take months to recover from and sometimes the back muscles will never regain their former bulk and strength.

There is also a condition called Delayed Onset Muscle Soreness which can have much more devastating effects than cramp itself. A dog can suffer from this without cramping up at the time of exercise and my little ¾ Greyhound ¼ Beardie lurcher once suffered from this. It can happen all too easily: read on ...

Eight weeks out of season, soft-muscled though I'd been working and exercising Seeker daily, we were out on the fens for a day's fox control. All went well and we'd accounted for a brace of foxes and were heading back towards the vehicles when a hare jumped up from almost under our noses.

I could normally stop Seeker on a hare if we were out after foxes, but only because she preferred them to hares. However, she was still in that heightened state of excitement having just taken a fox and off she went, deaf to my shouts. Luckily another dog came in and helped to finish the course before too long, but Seeker had already put in a minute and a half of strenuous running. She seemed absolutely fine as she came back to me, though panting heavily.

Now for the interesting part ... not that evening, nor the following day did she show any sign of having a muscle problem, but 48 hours later, after running a rabbit, she cramped up: stood in the middle of the field screaming in pain. Her back was swollen and the muscles hard and unyielding to the touch.

This was no simple case of cramp, but something called Delayed Onset Muscle Soreness (DOMS) and an extremely severe case at that.

I got her home, laid warm towels over her back and gave her an anti inflammatory and painkiller. Although the pain abated over the next 24 hours, Seeker's back withered away to nothing over the next two days; she looked half starved, the vertebrae all down her back stuck up as though she'd not eaten a decent meal in months.

It took two full months of careful massage and steady exercise to bring her back muscles up to about 80% of their previous form, and they never did regain the broad, hard-muscled appearance they had done prior to this incident.

I also made sure that she was on a very high protein diet during her convalescence: any healing makes huge demands on the body, and good quality animal protein and fat is necessary for muscular growth.

Yes, Seeker came back from this incident and performed almost as well as she had previously done on rabbits and foxes, though I made sure that she no longer ran hares. I just didn't want to take any chances, besides which she wasn't really a hare dog as such.

Just a little tale to illustrate how easy it is for a dog to do too much; the course hadn't been intentional and the dramatic effect on her unfit back muscles never fully revealed itself until two days after the event. I later learned that the lactic acid build up in over-used muscles can take up to two days to dissipate and for the oxygen debt to be repaid in full; the simple act of running a rabbit the following day was enough to damage the muscles extensively when there was still a large amount of lactic acid in the dog's system, or at least I think that is what caused the problem. To be honest, though I've researched this to the point where I've nigh on killed off my own brain cells and I haven't yet been able to find the exact correlation between lactic acid and DOMS. There seems to be a query as to the exact cause of both conditions.

Anyway, it was a lesson well learned by me: nowadays I monitor my dogs very closely indeed and if I think that they're not fit enough to handle an unexpected hard run they stay on the lead in areas where challenging quarry is likely to be found.

WARNING: Acute cramping can lead to damage of the internal organs and even death; any cramp lasting for more than a few moments needs veterinary attention.

THERAPY FOR DAMAGED MUSCLES
There are various therapeutic treatment devices available. I have only used the Porta-Mag, though there are various other treatments available such as cold laser therapy and tens machines. If you want to use any therapeutic treatment device I would strongly urge you to get instruction from a qualified vet on exactly how to use such a machine. Wrongly used any mechanical device is capable of causing more harm than good.

With regards to the Porta-Mag, make sure that the dog has access to clean fresh water as soon as it comes out of the box. The Porta-Mag has a slightly dehydrating effect and dogs should never be left unattended in the crate either during or after treatment. My own dogs always head straight for the water bowl when they come out of the crate and this is quite normal for most animals.

It is very important to follow the instruction manual properly when using any treatment device and if you are new to such therapies get advice from someone who is well versed in their use.

Porta-Mag or mag box
This uses a pulsed electromagnetic field which is believed to have an influence on the inward and outward flow of ions between the blood, fluids and cells.

Put very simply the electromagnetic pulses encourage healing by stimulating the flow of energy to damaged tissue. Some professionals ridicule the idea that such a device can actually have an effect on the body, but others agree that electromagnetism does work.

I've sat in the Portamag myself and I know that this treatment helps to ease the aches and pains I've accumulated over a lifetime spent pushing my body to do more than it is really capable of.

A well-respected canine chiropractor states that it is particularly useful for hastening the healing of fractures and damaged tendons or ligaments. It is also used to relax strained muscles and I've found that it has a generally calming effect on excitable dogs. I've also found it very useful for arthritic dogs, and whilst there is no actual cure for arthritis the Portamag does seem to make the condition more manageable and less painful.

NOTE: Make sure to use the right setting recommended for a specific injury. Too high a setting will actually prevent healing by encouraging blood flow to an area which is still bleeding, eg a torn muscle. It is not recommended for use on open wounds.

ULTRASOUND TREATMENT
Ultrasound treatment is one of the most widely used methods of repairing soft tissue injuries. These devices produce high frequency sound waves which heat the muscle fibres, thereby allowing dilation of the blood vessels at the same time as helping to break down the blood clots which are one of the most important factors in scarring and reduced muscle function following injury.

Ultrasound therapy should NOT be used on bone injuries (fractures) as the heat produced can permanently damage the bone. Ultrasound therapy should only be used on soft tissue damage to muscle, ligament and tendon, and only after bleeding at the site of the injury has ceased.

NOTE: ultrasound therapy can cause organ damage and should only be used if you have had professional training.

CHAPTER THREE

Bones and joints

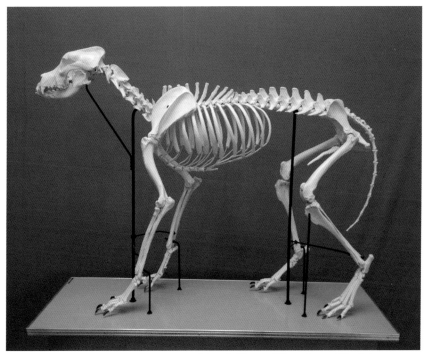

Reproduced with kind permission of the College of Veterinary Medicine, Washington State University, USA.

An animal's skeleton is the equivalent of a vehicle's chassis, and as such, needs to be strongly constructed and able to stand up to the rigours of movement, especially so in the running dog which is asked to perform great feats of athleticism.

Whilst careful breeding from strong, sound stock is all important, just as vital is the diet and care which a puppy receives during the first months of its life.

A dog which has had an impoverished diet as a puppy will, as an adult, have bones which are weaker and less able to support the animal than one which has been fed an optimum diet throughout its life. A diet can be deficient through a lack of one or more important nutrients, though calcium is particularly important for bone growth.

Pups carrying a heavy worm burden may also fail to grow properly because the parasites take vital nutrition from the gut of their host, which means it doesn't reach the places it should. I once knew some people who had bought what they thought was a Deerhound/Greyhound pup, though at five months of age the animal was so undersized that it might have been a Whippet cross rather than a Deerhound bred animal.

It wasn't until they carried out a proper worming programme with the correct wormer that their puppy suddenly started growing properly, and within a couple of months she had reached the normal size for a Deer/Grey. Luckily for the pup the owners were informed in time to correct the problem but had she reached maturity without being wormed correctly her size would have never reached its potential. Regular and correct worming is a must if a young dog is to grow properly.

EXERCISE

Lack of exercise is also responsible for weak bones, and although too much exercise can be equally damaging, all pups need freedom to gallop and play in order to develop to their potential. Weight-bearing exercise increases bone density, and by weight-bearing we mean exercise such as running and walking where the weight of the body puts the bones under a certain amount of stress. This stress is important in making the bones grow stronger. A puppy that is left to sit in a kennel for the greater part of its early life is likely to have weaker bones than one which has enjoyed the correct amount of freedom, playing and running as it needs to.

Don't allow a pup to gallop freely with adult dogs for not only is there a risk of collision (pups don't have very good brakes or steering) which can result in injury, but there is also the very real possibility that the pup will be encouraged to do more than it should. Over-extension and strain to the joints and ligaments as well as to the bones can put undue stress on the growing body,

and most pups will do far too much if they are allowed to.

Striking the happy medium can be a challenge, and whilst there are few people nowadays who would leave a growing pup confined to a kennel 24/7, some breeders who run on litters of pups and fail to put in the time to exercise their charges properly are at risk of producing dogs which may be weak in more ways than one.

A puppy of less than six months of age needs frequent bouts of play during the day, but must also be allowed to rest when it needs to. There is an old saying about children, that they grow when they're asleep, and funnily enough, this is true: young animals do grow whilst they're resting or sleeping.

Energy diverted into physical exercise whilst awake can be used for growth when a young animal is asleep, but it is known that growth hormone production increases when the young animal is resting or asleep. There's often more truth in old wives tales than many would think. Here's another saying: let sleeping dogs lie, and although I take this to mean that a sleeping dog is likely to bite the person who disturbs it suddenly, sleeping puppies should be left to sleep until they wake of their own accord. They know how much sleep they need (sometimes not nearly enough for the owner who wants some respite from the demands of the youngster!) and shouldn't be wakened for any other reason than in an emergency.

How much exercise a young pup needs depends largely on the type of dog concerned, but as a general rule of thumb it is not a good idea to take a youngster of less than six months out for more than half an hour's exercise at any one time. A couple of half hour walks per day is absolutely fine for most pups, PROVIDING the pup doesn't spend its entire time chasing about after adult dogs, which will encourage the pup to do more than it would naturally.

I always reckon that from six months to a year old is the most dangerous time for lurcher and sighthound puppies as their legs are by then long enough and strong enough to gallop at a fair speed.

You shouldn't let pups keep on galloping and galloping, straining every part of their immature body in an attempt to catch anything with four legs, or even keep up with older dogs who are playing at speed. We humans have fine tuned the desire to chase in our sighthound bred dogs, creating an animal which will run and run again after anything that moves, often to the point of exhaustion. Our hunting dogs are very far removed from the wild canine which only chases and hunts when it is hungry.

A wild wolf would never run more than it needed to in order to catch its next meal, but we ask our dogs to repeat that chase

Puppies should not be encouraged to take too much exercise. Note the very large joints in this pup's wrists and toes.

and catch many times over during the course of a night's lamping, for example.

Rabbits may not run as far as hares, but repeated running at prey will tire any dog eventually. An enthusiastic puppy will continue chasing long after its body has had enough, which is why the owner needs to be sensible when working a lurcher, or any dog that has been created by humans for their own needs.

Of course size matters! A great big gangly Deerhoundy puppy needs far less exercise than say, a Collie/Whippet/Greyhound, which will be far smaller and more developed at the same age. To the novice this might sound back to front, but when you consider that the Deerhoundy pup has to grow far more within a similar time frame as the smaller-bred dog, then you'll appreciate that the strain on developing muscles and skeleton is correspondingly greater.

Not forgetting that where a Collie-bred lurcher will have finished growing in height by the time it is about 10 or 11 months old, the Deerhound won't even finish its skeletal growth until it is nearing two years of age.

Small bones grow fastest and finish their growth long before the big bones, which is why a puppy's head often appears disproportionately large when compared to the rest of the body. This is also why some pups appear to have excessively long tails as those tiny bones in the tail are already up to adult size by the time the pup is six months old.

So when you see that so and so's pup of eight months old is running nightly and catching God knows how many rabbits, just keep an eye on that dog and see what shape it is in four or five years old, when it should be in its prime physically.

Chronic lameness especially of the fore limbs, can often be attributed to joint damage from running a puppy too much before those joints and bones had finished growing.

Is it really so hard to wait a few more months before working a lurcher when those few months could see a consolidation in strength? Young joints are particularly vulnerable, and a bad knock or strain can seriously affect a young lurcher's future.

I know it's not easy holding young dogs back, especially if you exercise them with adult dogs, but there is a real need to balance valuable experience in the field with sensible precautions.

Been there, done it! I've had all sorts of problems over the years by letting young lurchers follow the adults on day time hunts in the field, but it isn't until the dog is three or four years old and is prematurely suffering from arthritic joints due to too much strain on those joints at an early age that you realise, too late, that you could have put the pup back on the lead and let it watch instead of tearing about like a headless chicken when a hunt heats up.

Incidentally, a pup will learn a lot from watching from the safety of your side whilst lurchers or terriers are working brambles or uncultivated fields.

Take the following scenario: you are mooching around the edge of a field with a couple of terriers and lurchers, one of which is about eight months old.

Suddenly a rabbit bolts from the hedge, and the adult lurcher takes off in pursuit with the youngster in tow. As the rabbit turns back into the cover the young lurcher takes a swipe, but trips over a bramble and goes head over heels ending up on its back in the hedge!

Pup comes back out, a bit shaken, but apparently fine: after all, young bones bounce better than old ones so you carry on mooching. It is only when you get home that you notice that the pup is limping slightly, though you can't find any obvious injury.

Two days later the pup is still limping on its left front leg, and if you know about heat and inflammation you will have run your hand down that leg and found that the area around the wrist is hotter than the wrist on the other leg, and that there seems to be some slight swelling around that joint.

So you rest the pup for a couple of days, keeping it on the lead while you walk the dogs. The swelling disappears and you think no more about that wrist, letting the young dog have its head once more in the field.

A week later both your lurchers are playing in a grass field when suddenly the pup lets out a yelp and comes hobbling back to you on three legs: holding that same leg up, unwilling to put any weight on it whatsoever.

You rest the leg again but offer no other treatment, and within a few days the pup seems fine again. Well, I could go on describing the same scenario over and over again but I won't!

So what could possibly be wrong with the leg? One of two options spring to mind immediately: the first being that the pup has sprained its wrist. When we speak of 'sprains' we refer to ligaments, which are the 'strings' of tissue which hold a joint together, and if that joint is over-stretched by a fall or a trip (think of putting your foot on the edge of a pavement and your ankle goes over). Worst case scenario is that you have ruptured the ligaments which hold the ankle joint together, much worse than straining and over stretching of those ligaments.

I once severely sprained my ankle, and it was a full three years before I ceased getting pain in that joint if I bent it slightly to one side. I didn't get proper treatment for the sprain at the time being young and thinking that it would heal on its own: we are all invincible in our teens!

Now, I'm no athlete, but had I been a runner, that ankle, not having been correctly treated at the time, would have most likely continued to plague me whilst running, possibly for the rest of my life.

Back to the wristy pup: a sprain needs several weeks of NO straining to heal. Ligaments are a bit like the tendons which hold the muscles on to the bones: they are very strong but have a lousy blood supply and take ages to heal if they are damaged. Suspected sprains of any joint should be iced and rested, using a cloth-wrapped ice pack twice a day for five minutes at a time. Run cold water on the area twice a day if you don't have any ice.

Once the initial swelling has gone down you can massage the joint carefully: no poking and pushing of thumbs into the delicate joint! Just a palm of your hand rubbing motion with a good liniment, which will help increase the blood flow to the area which will in turn help to promote the healing process.

Alternatively, your pup has cracked a bone and if this is only a green stick fracture it might not present as permanent lameness, only causing pain if the dog moves fast, putting extra pressure on that leg. Such fractures happen quite easily and they are just as easily healed PROVIDING YOU GIVE THE DOG TIME TO HEAL!!

Pups crack bones when playing, when falling on to a hard surface, when colliding with an immovable object: the list goes on, but you can't wrap a young active dog up in cotton wool: all you can do is minimise the risks.

For example, don't let a pup of under a year old play crazy chasing games with

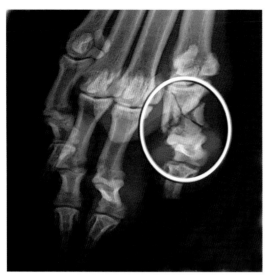

Toe fracture in 4 month old pup.

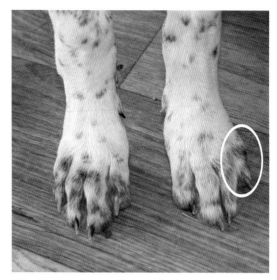

The fracture is not obvious to the eye.

other dogs, especially not in an area littered with fallen trees, garden furniture or slippery concrete paving. Young dogs like to play, and when they're playing tag or chase with another dog they don't look where they are going, their every attention is focussed on the dog they are chasing.

The good news is that young bones heal quickly: four to six weeks, providing the bone is not displaced and you keep the pup quiet. BUT it is essential to find out the exact nature of the problem, ie the cause of the initial lameness, before you embark on any treatment or rest programme. There's not a lot of point in confining a dog to a kennel or cage in the hope that it will get better if it has dislocated its stifle joint (knee joint) for example.

Whilst rest is a good recipe for a lot of problems, a cracked bone needs to be immobilised COMPLETELY if it is to heal in the right position, and a hyper pup in a cage, bouncing up and down with energetic leaps is not keeping a bone immobilised, which is why most broken bones will need to be kept in place with a plaster cast,

or sometimes with a splint and padding bandage.

Toe bones are very prone to breaking, and whilst I'll go into the different types of break very briefly, only an x-ray will give you an accurate diagnosis.

SUNLIGHT AND VITAMINS

Puppies which are kept permanently in dark sheds or kennels with no access to sunlight may also be lacking in Vitamin D, without which calcium cannot be absorbed by the body which in turn may lead to problems such as rickets, a condition where the bones soften and become very painful. Vitamin D is synthesised by the body when it is exposed to sunlight.

Another saying is 'get the sun on its back', often used by old time horse and dog men, and this shows that ever since humans began to domesticate and breed animals, they realised just how important sunlight is to growing animals even if vitamins themselves were unheard of at the time.

A diet lacking in calcium is life-threatening to any young animal, and can lead to bone weakness and possible fractures. People used to add bone meal to puppy meals, but be aware that calcium is destroyed by heat to a certain extent, and as most bone meal is obtained by heat treating and grinding bones, the calcium content may be considerably reduced or altered in such a way that the body fails to absorb it properly.

Calcium is best served in the form of fresh small bones such as are found in uncooked whole carcasses such as rabbits or chickens or in breast of lamb and other non-weight-bearing bones which are softer than the hard leg bones of adult mammals. I've found that even raw leg bones of an ancient rabbit can take some digesting, even for a tough adult dog well used to raw food. Small pieces of hard bone are sometimes vomited back if the dog's stomach has deemed them too tough to dissolve. This is perfectly normal in healthy dogs (see chapter on Nutrition).

PROBLEMS WITH BONES
AND JOINTS
Arthritic conditions

The definition of arthritis is inflammation to a joint. This may be caused by general wear and tear and virtually every old dog that has led an active life will display signs of arthritis when it gets to old age, just like humans. It is useful to understand why a joint degenerates with wear and tear and old age. Read on if you can bear the science bit!

A joint is a natural junction between bones, and these bones are fixed in their correct postitions by ligaments. However, in order to protect the ends of the bones from grating upon each other, they are cushioned by articular cartilage, which provides a smooth, non-frictional surface over which the bones can move easily. Joints also contain synovial fluid (which works like the oil in an engine) to lubricate the cartilage and prevent the joint from drying out.

No part of a body is immortal, and as we get older so do our bodies begin to wear out. Moving parts in any engine will wear out more quickly than those which are less mobile, so the joints of toes, feet and legs in the active running dog are more likely to wear out first.

Whilst there are certain canine diseases that can cause arthritic changes to a joint, excessive wear and tear are the most common reasons for arthritis in the running dog. Injury to a joint is the most common cause of early onset arthritis (see also Puncture Wounds to Joints).

There is no cure for arthritis, but nowadays there are many supplements to help support the joints, Glucosamine and Chondroitin being one of the recommended products. There are also many other types of both natural and synthetic products on the market: as we and our dogs live longer, so does arthritis become a more common affliction.

Glucosamine and Chondroitin work to support the cartilage in the joints, whilst herbal supplements such as Dorwest Herb's Garlic and Fenugreek aid in reducing toxins from the body, a build up of which is said to contribute to conditions such as arthritis.

At the time I was writing this book I started my 11 year old lurcher on a combination of the above-mentioned supplements. Rattis is ancient beyond her years, partly as a result of severe meningitis she contracted as a puppy, which left her joints very stiff. She has also been out hunting every day of her life since her recovery from the illness, so those

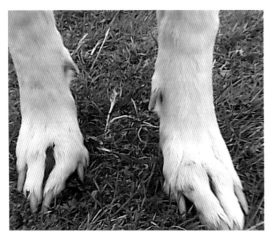

Permanent bony swelling and distortion from dislocation of toe joints. Photo: Sam Coleman

joints really have been through the mill, so to speak.

Nowadays Rattis is still a cheerful old thing who leaps into my van with enthusiasm for her daily exercise, though I lift her out so her poor old misshapen feet don't suffer the impact when she leaps down from the vehicle.

Within a fortnight of starting these supplements I noticed a real difference in Rattis' movement. She'll never be cured of arthritis, but at least she seems to be in far less pain than previously and her swollen joints have far less heat in them.

I have used pain killers and anti-inflammatories in past cases of arthritis, but prolonged use of such medicines can lead to liver damage as well as actually aggravating the condition by creating an excess of acid within the body.

Sometimes it is kinder to resort to modern painkillers during the last few years of an old dog's life if all other remedies fail, but don't ever be tempted to use human painkillers on dogs. Instead, talk to your vet about the various treatments available. I also use electromagnetic pulsed therapy to help ease the pain of arthritic joints.

FRACTURES TO BONES

There are four types of fracture: compound, closed, greenstick and Epiphyseal.

Compound fractures are very serious and immediately obvious to the owner because a piece or pieces of bone will have come through the skin. Contamination and infection are highly likely in such cases and immediate veterinary treatment is necessary.

Closed fractures are less obvious as the skin will not have been broken, lameness and reluctance to put weight on the limb being the only clue to the problem. If a dog shows signs of lameness for more than a few days then professional help must be sought, an x-ray being necessary to show where or how the bone may have been broken as there isn't necessarily any external sign to indicate the fracture.

There may be soft swelling around a closed fracture, swelling which doesn't disappear as quickly as that caused by bruising, so if a dog shows signs of such swelling on a leg, for example, then prepare to investigate further, particularly if pain and swelling last longer than a few days.

Epiphyseal fractures are common in puppies, and affect the bony growth plates at the ends of the long leg bones which are much softer than the rest of the bone and more likely to fracture with hard impact to that place.

Similarly, greenstick fractures affect young animals, normally affecting just one side of a limb bone, and so called because the break is usually found to just one side of the bone, much in the way the young branch of a sapling tree may be broken on one side when bent sharply but remains intact on the other.

The good news about greenstick and epiphyseal fractures is that they usually heal very quickly in young dogs, though immobilisation of the affected limb is necessary.

IMPORTANT: when a cast or immobilising bandage is applied to a very young dog of less than six months of age, this needs to be checked and changed every fortnight (sometimes even more frequently if the dog is under 16 weeks of age) because the puppy's rate of growth is such that the cast may very quickly become a hazard in itself.

One pup that had broken a toe bone at the age of 12 weeks needed the cast removed after 10 days because the unyielding plaster was literally deforming his leg, putting pressure on the fast growing wrist joint and had, in just a short space of time, caused pressure sores on the toe joints and stopper which were already seeping with pus!

I should have taken photos of the grossly deformed and twisted leg once I'd removed this cast, for it looked as though the leg would never straighten properly. Happily, such is the healing power of a healthy body, the leg did straighten out perfectly, though this process did take over three months. Today you would never know that there had ever been any injury to the dog whatsoever.

Most dogs and puppies tolerate plaster casts very well, and hop about quite happily once they are used to the weight and strangeness of their 'wooden' leg, but keep an eagle eye out for any reluctance to put that foot to the ground when walking, or any look of discomfort or pain, a sure sign that something is not right within the plastered limb.

Many vets nowadays prefer to use a plastic splint and rigid foam type of cast rather than the old fashioned plaster cast as these are much lighter in weight and better tolerated by the dog.

If you suspect there is any chance that your dog has broken a bone then immediate veterinary help is the only option, and whilst many dogs do suffer from undiagnosed minor fractures which heal if the dog is allowed to rest for six weeks, anything more than a hairline crack needs professional treatment.

TAIL INJURIES
Broken tail
Lurchers and sighthounds are very prone to tail damage as their long, thin appendages with very little protective flesh mean that furiously wagging tails can be bashed against doors and walls and even broken.

However, more dogs' tails are broken by their owners shutting them in doors than in any other way! My own vet says that she has noticed this in a number of dogs which when brought into surgery for something completely different, have slightly kinked or crooked tails, legacy of an awkwardly healed fracture to one or more of the vertebrae in that tail. The owners hadn't even realised that the dog had broken its tail when the event occurred!

I'm ashamed to say that I am one of those owners, as I once shut one of my dog's tails in a hastily slammed door to an accompanying yelp. I didn't realise that the tail had actually been broken until a lump appeared beneath the skin a few weeks later: bone mass which had formed as the broken vertebrae healed themselves into a shape not quite as nature intended. Even during the healing process the dog showed no signs of pain or distress, which is why I hadn't noticed the injury until much later when I happened to be removing sticky burrs from the long hairs of her tail.

Long thin tails can also become wrapped around wire fences and I've had an exceptionally long and whippy tail wrap

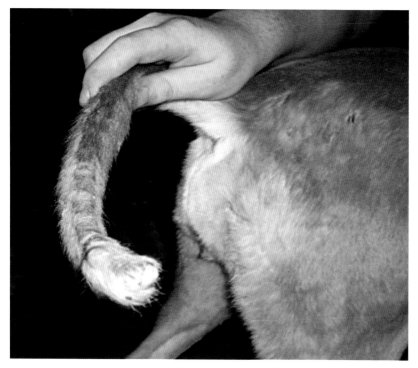

There is no excuse for this sort of tail damage seen in a rescued lurcher.
Reproduced with kind permission of Lurcherlink.

Badly broken tail which has obviously not been correctly treated at the time of injury.
Photo: Jackie Drakeford.

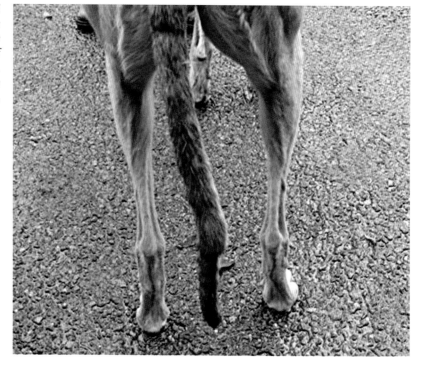

itself twice round a length of barbed wire: this necessitated complete amputation because the bones were shattered and protruding through the skin.

Any open wound combined with a bone fracture needs veterinary attention because infection in and around the break can occur if the damage is not properly treated. I've also had a split tail injury which splintered one of the vertebrae though fortunately this didn't necessitate amputation as we were able to extract the bone splinters and the wound healed fine. But there was a slight kink to be seen in this lurcher's tail thereafter. Check split or torn tails carefully to make sure that no bones have been involved at the time of injury.

Damage to tail tips from over-enthusiastic wagging against walls can also involve the bone, though the damage should never get that far if the injury is treated in time (see chapter on skin wounds).

Broken tails need support and protection until the bones have healed. Bones can't heal if they are constantly moving. A padded support bandage should be used to protect the tail and the dog kept as quiet as possible: preferably caged, as any wagging will only hinder the healing process. I have used foam insulating tubes used to protect outside pipes in the winter with great success as they are both lightweight and rigid, and they can be easily cut to the correct length.

Make sure that the tube is not so tight as to restrict blood circulation. It needs to be snug, not tight, and you'll need to stick it on to the tail with very sticky tape such as Elastoplast Fabric strapping, plus maybe a tiny blob or two of superglue. Tail protection can also be made up of thick foam cut to the right size and secured around the tail with tape. You'll need to stick it to the fur of the tail as well.

DISLOCATED TAIL

A rather more unusual injury is when two adjacent vertebrae in the tail become dislocated rather than broken. I have seen this happen with large lurchers playing rough and tumble with one another. This also happened to one of my young dogs which I believe was caused by another dog running into her rear end whilst they were playing. The dog in question yelped and stood stock still, back slightly arched with her tail hanging straight down. It was obvious immediately that something was not right with the tail as that appendage is only ever completely floppy when the dog is asleep or resting.

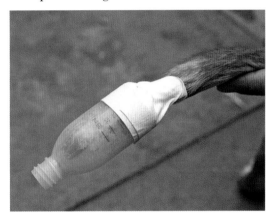

Above: Cut down small plastic bottle leaving end of tail open to the air.
Below: Water pipe lagging is only suitable for the end of very thin Whippety tails.

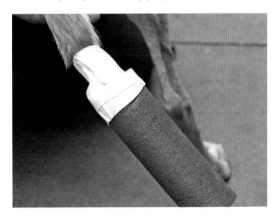

I took the root of the tail in my hand, supported the rest of the tail in my other hand, then pulled, slowly and carefully away from the body, and was rewarded with an audible 'click'. The tail still hung immobile, but there had been a slight twitch to the very tip after I'd pulled it straight. I put the dog on the lead, walked it carefully home, and wrapped the whole tail in a support bandage made of foam and Vetwrap and kept the dog very quiet for 24 hours. The next day I removed the bandage and as soon as I'd done so the dog wagged its tail again! Relief!

It is very important to support any joint which has been dislocated then relocated for at least 24 hours following a minor dislocation. Relocated joints often need weeks of support as the ligaments holding the bones in the correct place will have been damaged to some extent, even a minor injury such as the one I've just described. I kept this dog quiet for a week following the accident, but had she dislocated a toe she would have been restricted to lead exercise only for at least a month afterwards (see chapter on Feet).

However, I don't recommend any home treatment of this kind if you have neither seen the procedure done by a professional nor if you are unfamiliar with the structure of the dog's skeleton. Pulling a broken tail will do nothing to help it in any way whatsoever and a dislocated tail is very different to a weight-bearing joint or one in the delicate neck area.

DISLOCATED JOINTS

I was once obliged to have a young and promising lurcher euthanased after she completely dislocated her stifle (knee) joint during the pursuit of game whilst running through a tree plantation. As I approached the dog to get her on the lead she spotted more game in the distance and attempted to give chase, albeit on three legs, with the damaged leg flapping uselessly to one side.

When I eventually got her back to me I could see that there was a serious problem and the vet only confirmed what I had suspected. Unfortunately the ligament damage was so severe that amputation of the leg would have been the only solution and I wasn't prepared to allow such a young and hard-driving lurcher live the rest of her life unable to do what she loved best: it would have broken her heart.

It can be very difficult to recognise even serious damage when there is no external wound, but any injury which results in deformity or loss of use of a limb needs professional attention immediately.

Any dislocation is potentially a very serious injury, as not only is the joint forced out of place, but there will nearly always be a degree of damage to the ligaments which would normally hold the joint in place.

A dislocation is normally caused by a hard, sudden impact to the joint resulting in immediate loss of use to the limb. Lurchers and sighthounds are for the most part soundly constructed, with problems such as hip displasia being very uncommon indeed, but running dogs can dislocate their hips, hocks or any joint in their legs if they run into an immoveable object or are hit by a vehicle. It depends upon the amount of ligament and soft tissue damage as to whether or not the joint can be successfully relocated.

Dislocation of the delicate bones of the wrist or hock are also very serious injuries which can affect running dogs, and again,

Opposite: dogs that work in woodland run an increased risk of toe injury.
Photo: Craig McCann.

a complete return to full function is a doubtful prospect in many cases. The sheer speed of lurchers and sighthounds means that the joints come under tremendous strain when the dog is turning or twisting when running at speed. Dogs which have previously dislocated joints may only be suitable for light tasks in the future.

Obviously immediate veterinary treatment must be sought with any such injury. Immobilise the affected limb with a soft padded bandage, wrapping a scarf around the joint if possible and inserting the leg affected into the sleeve of your coat or shirts as an emergency measure in the field. Prevent the dog from standing or moving whilst on your way to the vet. The more you can do to restrict further ligament damage the better.

Dislocated toe which clearly shows surrounding tissue damage. Photo: Sam Coleman

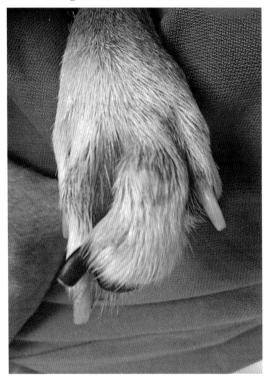

Any surgery involving severe ligament or tendon damage can take many weeks, even months to heal, and it is important to follow medical advice to the letter in all such cases. Toes are amongst the most commonly dislocated joints in running dogs (see toe dislocation in the Feet chapter).

SUBLUXATION OF A JOINT

A subluxation is where one of the bones in a joint is not correctly aligned with its neighbour; for example, if one vertebra is misaligned with the vertebra on either side. A subluxation is not a complete dislocation and may appear to cause little outward sign of pain in the dog. However there will always be some drop-off in performance; the dog may run less enthusiastically, less fluently and be reluctant to pick up a rabbit or a thrown ball.

Subluxation can happen as a result of a fall, a collision which jolts the joint out of place, and even over-extension of the joint in question. Repeated actions such as twisting when running, for example, striking at quarry over and over again: a common scenario in rabbiting and coursing dogs or those who run flat out snatching at balls etc.

Subluxations can lead to trapped nerves, so read on to find out more about this relatively common problem in running dogs.

TRAPPED NERVES

Anyone who has ever suffered from a trapped nerve will know that this can be a debilitating and painful condition, in extreme cases leading to loss of use of a particular limb and even muscle wastage.

But what exactly is a trapped nerve? And how does it become trapped? To understand this we need to examine the construction and function of the spine.

The spine is made up of individual vertebrae which are designed to protect the spinal cord which passes through them, rather like a bundle of wire fed through the protective outer layer of rigid cable.

Each vertebra is cushioned from the next by a strong but rubbery pad of tissue known as a disc, and in mammals which walk on four legs this disc is situated beneath the spinal chord itself, so protecting the vertebrae from impacting on each other when the animal moves.

Individual nerves exit the spinal chord through special openings in the vertebrae, but if there is a misalignment of one vertebra this can cause pain and impairment of use to a limb (see subluxation already referred to above).

Although we refer to nerves being trapped it would be more accurate to say 'pinched'. The nerve can be pinched between the misaligned vertebrae and the surrounding muscle which tightens (seizes up) in order to protect the misaligned joint.

The over-tight muscle can also go into spasm, which means that it is permanently contracted, something that no muscle is designed to do. Muscles cannot function properly if they are in spasm, and this causes acute discomfort in a dog.

Dogs which regularly throw themselves, rugby tackle style, at their prey, somersaulting over and over as they strike, are particularly prone to trapping nerves in their necks and backs, something I learned many years ago when one of my useful lurchers stopped striking at her quarry properly whilst running.

My first visit to a 'bone man' was a real eye opener, and within minutes this expert had 'clicked' my lurcher's neck and back, provoking only a small yelp as a reaction. The real reaction though was quite dramatic, for only seconds later this dog shook herself all over more vigorously than she had done for a long time.

As we walked back outside the treatment room her back actually appeared longer than it had done for many a month for no longer did this dog have to hold herself tense and awkward in an attempt to protect her injured back. The real evidence was apparent a few days later on the coursing field when she ran and caught with real enthusiasm, rather than just following the hare tentatively across the fen without attempting to strike.

The most common symptoms of trapped nerves in back or neck are: hunched appearance, where the dog holds its back into a slightly rounded shape. Any attempt to depress the spine when the dog is standing will be met with resistance as the animal attempts to protect the painful portion of its back. There may also be intermittent lameness in front or rear limbs, usually only on one side of the body. Most dogs enjoy a good shake, starting at the head and ending with a shudder right down the spine to the tail. Dogs with trapped nerves in their neck or back are often reluctant to do this. Giving the dog a good brush along its back, finishing by brushing the fur the wrong way, towards the head will normally encourage a dog to shake itself 'right', and I can usually tell if one of my dogs has trapped a nerve by its refusal to shudder right down to the tail after I've 'annoyed' it by brushing the fur the wrong way.

Dogs may also be reluctant to put their heads down to a food bowl on the ground if they are suffering from neck pain, which also shows if you try and bend the animal's neck to one side or the other. You should be able to ask a healthy and normally constructed running dog to touch its flank with the end of its nose. Use gentle hand pressure only on one side of its muzzle. If you meet with any resistance at all DO NOT ATTEMPT TO FORCE THE DOG to turn its head into this position. If resistance is met there may be a neck or back problem.

NOTE: never attempt to manipulate your dog unless you are a trained chiropractor as you could end up doing permanent and irreparable damage to the animal.

A specially trained Greyhound vet, qualified chiropractor or physiotherapist is the only person who should treat your dog if you suspect any joint problems. Most good general vets will offer you a referral to a specialist chiropractor, many of whom will only treat dogs upon such a referral. There are however, a number of very good Greyhound vets for whom you do not need a referral as they are qualified veterinary practitioners who specialise in the treatment of racing Greyhounds. Such vets often employ canine physiotherapists, and various forms of treatment are often carried out in the same clinic. Your local greyhound track may be able to put you in touch with a vet near you.

When 'untrapping' a nerve, the practitioner will make a quick forceful, though very controlled push, at the affected joint, which, put simply, shoves it back into the right place. Many years training are needed in order to do this safely and even after watching chiropractors at work I would never attempt to copy them as I simply don't know quite enough about the way the skeleton and muscles cooperate and link together.

Whilst many humans and animals routinely visit the chiropractor or osteopath, it is important to realise that manipulation of joints should only be carried out once any possibility of fracture to bones has been eliminated by correct professional diagnosis. It is quite possible for dogs to suffer from non-displaced fractures to vertebrae which could be made worse by manipulation if the wrong treatment is carried out in ignorance of the injury's exact nature.

BROKEN BACK OR NECK

Whilst a broken neck or back often brings instant paralysis, some dogs, just like some humans, can crack a vertebra in their necks as a result of such a collision without the owner suspecting anything more than bruising.

This is a difficult one and many's the time I've known a dog crash to the ground as a result of a collision, only to jump to its feet, shake itself down and get on with life with no problems at all.

Unfortunately, if there has been damage to vertebrae a later collision or fall could see fragments of bone impinge on or even sever the spinal chord which can either kill the dog outright or cause irreparable damage which necessitates euthanasia.

It's hardly possible to get a dog x-rayed every time it collides with another dog, or does a somersault after tripping, and the only comfort I can give is that when we own running dogs we do so with the knowledge that we are sharing our lives with some of the most beautiful, charismatic and useful canines on the earth. We can never know when they shall be taken from our care and we can only do our best to make their time here as good as we possibly can. They are a precious gift, on loan to us for however long or short a time fate has decreed it.

I went through a very bad patch where I lost four dogs to freak accidents in as many years, two of which broke their backs. For a while after this I refused to allow my dogs to work anywhere that I deemed dangerous,

The 'neck like a drake' referred to by Dame Juliana Barnes in The Book of St Albans c.1480.

(rather impossible as the very nature of running fast across country is dangerous in itself!) which curtailed my activities somewhat to say the least. Time went by and as I added newcomers to my pack I gradually became a little more fatalistic in my outlook, BUT I made sure that I was now breeding in a small but essential trait ... that of self preservation and common sense.

The reckless and unthinking pursuit of any quarry, or indeed a race lure, may ultimately result in heartache for the owner. The fact that our dogs live for the chase should not blind them to the dangers that spring up all around them whilst running, and I firmly believe that it is better for a dog to lose what it is chasing than to die trying.

It's one thing living each day as a tiger and not as a mouse, but living only for the very short lifespan of a mouse is hardly a good thing either.

This section was supposed to be about broken necks and backs, but such severe injury demands a look at the whole life and death subject. Veterinary science is pretty good, but even modern medicine can't fix a severed or badly damaged spinal chord. Minor damage to vertebrae can be fixed, but be aware that the spine is a delicate and complicated pathway through which the whole nervous system operates. Any damage to such a finely balanced system may not meet with the sort of prognosis you hope for. Some people might try to give a partially paralysed dog some sort of a life, but this author would never attempt to burden these fleetest of canines with such a handicap. Better, in my opinion, to give the victim of such horrendous disability the dignified end it deserves rather than force such an animal to lead a painful half life where the memory of running free and graceful is no more than a twitching dream which can only be lived whilst asleep.

BRUISING TO BONES

As a result of a very hard impact a bone may be bruised but not broken. Bone bruises are very painful indeed and can take several weeks to heal properly. The heavily built dog is more likely to suffer from bone bruising than a lightly built animal which 'bounces' off obstacles much better. Fast work or exercise should be restricted during the healing period, though lead walking is beneficial because it increases the circulation.

NOTE: If you find any unusual lumps or bumps on bones get them checked out by a vet because a severe impact may cause a fracture, rather than mere bruising.

HELPFUL REMEDIES FOR BONES

Comfrey has long been known as 'knit bone', and has been proved helpful in the healing of bone fractures and bruises. Comfrey should not be taken internally but you can make the leaves into a poultice and apply them to the injury site (as long as the skin isn't broken). To make a poultice from comfrey leaves simply mash the leaves before adding enough purified water to make a paste. Apply to the injury site and bandage. It is safe to leave this poultice in place until it has dried out. Homeopathic Symphytum is also recommended for bone healing.

GENERAL TIPS ON MAINTAINING HEALTHY BONES AND JOINTS

- *NEVER continue to run a dog if it shows any sign of lameness.*
- *If lameness is still present after two day's rest then seek professional advice.*
- *Feed good quality food from birth, making sure that the pup has adequate essential nutrients in its diet (see chapter on Nutrition).*
- *Exercise dogs daily but restrict fast work if the dog is recovering from injury. Always allow sufficient healing time after an injury before working the dog.*
- *Do not attempt to manipulate (or pull about) limbs, neck or back if you suspect a problem unless you are professionally trained. You could make matters much worse.*

Photo opposite: Chris Doyle.

CHAPTER FOUR

Feet: no foot no dog

"No foot, no hoss" is an old saying amongst horse men and women. The same can be said of the running dog for without tough and hard wearing feet a lurcher or sighthound's working life is likely to be a short one.

Let's start with a look at the different types of feet commonly found in lurchers, long dogs and sighthounds, and see just how they differ according to the job that a particular breed has evolved to do.

Ever since Greyhound track racing began, these dogs have been bred pretty much for speed and speed alone, and whilst a coursing Greyhound's feet have to be sound to course hares, the type of ground that a track Greyhound would normally run over is flat with no stones or hard lumps in its surface.

Compare a flat wheat field or a race track with the northern moors or the southern flint covered fields, and it is easy to see that the delicate long boned toes of the Greyhound would be damaged in double

Feet come under tremendous strain whilst turning at speed. Photo Mike Bridle.

Racing on hard ground during the summer puts tremendous pressure on the feet.
Photo: Chris Doyle.

Note how the Whippet's far hind leg does not appear to be moving in harmony with the nearside leg.
This may indicate a muscle or tendon problem. Photo: Chris Doyle.

quick time, not least because of their great speed. That said, Greyhounds SHOULD have good, strong-boned feet, and well bred dogs from sound ancestry will have far better feet than those which have been bred indiscriminately from substandard stock.

The quality of an animal's feet, like everything else, is something which is inherited not just from the immediate ancestors, the parents, but from generations before that as well. Just because the dam and sire have good feet doesn't mean to say that there won't be a substandard foot in previous generations. This is why it pays to know the lineage of a dog and to breed only from those animals whose bodies have been tested fully in whatever line of work they have been bred to do.

Now compare the feet of the Greyhound to those of a Collie, or working sheepdog, dogs which have been bred to cover all types of rough, unforgiving terrain, often for hours on end as they gather and herd sheep on mountain, hill and moor.

Collies have some of the strongest feet to be found on dogs, and by strongest, I don't mean that they necessarily look like fists of iron, such as the feet you'd see on a Rottweiler or Labrador.

A Collie's feet are strong because their tendons, bones, pads and skin have all evolved over hundreds of years to cope with the work they do: dogs with feet that couldn't stand the strain would have gone by the wayside in old times, and would not have been bred from.

Similarly, a Deerhound has large, strong feet, with strongly arched toes and great toughness to enable them to run through heather and similarly rough vegetation. A Whippet's feet would be shredded in no time at all if they had to cope with this type of ground. Saluki feet are also incredibly strong despite their more elongated appearance, and they should have thick juicy pads covered in tough skin, extremely supple toes and strong bones to enable them to run on hard packed ground in desert conditions. I watched a video of Salukis coursing in the desert, and the ground resembled a moonscape: dotted with rocks and sharp stones. I shudder to think what that sort of ground would have done to a fast Greyhound.

So you see that all modern dogs have evolved to handle the conditions in which they evolved, and we, when creating lurchers to do a particular job, should pay just as much attention to the quality of the dog's feet as to its stamina, intelligence and hunting ability.

It also pays to remember that a heavily built lurcher will need exceptionally strong feet, far more so than its more lightly built counterpart, as the amount of weight coming down on each foot will be correspondingly greater. Lurchers with light bone and muscle mass will escape foot injury far better than the heavy animal, and some of the Bull crosses we see nowadays are sadly lacking in the foot department.

Bull terriers of whatever type are heavily built animals, with massive muscles and thick bones; they are really at the opposite end of the scale when compared with a typical sighthound, an animal which has evolved for speed in the pursuit of game.

When we cross a bull terrier with a Greyhound there is always a risk that the progeny will inherit the more finely made feet of the sighthound parent, at the same time as inheriting the bulky muscle and bone of the Bull Terrier parent.

Delicate feet combined with a heavy body are a recipe for foot problems as great body weight atop a sprinter's toes will mean that the feet are far more likely to be damaged as a result.

Some of the line bred Bull lurchers (Bull cross Greyhound over many generations) do have very good feet, and this is surely testimony to careful breeding, but far too many lurchers of this type do not have the correct type of foot for galloping at speed over rough ground.

This problem is also exacerbated by the fact that many lurcher owners do not exercise their dogs regularly, and there are some who will leave their dogs sitting in kennels all week only to run them hard over a weekend before shoving them back into the kennels for another week of doing nothing (see Chapter on Muscles for more information on conditioning and fitness).

The fact that most Bull cross lurchers also have a high pain threshold and immense prey drive, a drive which enables them to continue working despite damaged toes means that all too often we see these dogs with virtually flat feet as a result of tendon and ligament damage once these dogs have a few season's work under their belts.

A foot which has become flat through damage must not be confused with the traditional 'hare' foot, long and seemingly delicate and often found on lurcher to lurcher bred dogs containing a fair amount of sighthound. There is still an arch to the toes on a hare foot which is quite different to a completely flat toe where the ligaments have been over-stretched, cut through or ruptured.

These hare feet can be tough, and my own line of lurchers possess this type of foot which is sufficiently robust providing that the dog runs like a cross country runner and not with the pounding action of the sprinter. A sprinter's feet hit the ground far harder when running than the dog which 'floats', such as the Saluki, the ultimate marathon runner. The best feet I've seen on

my own lurchers belong to Starlight, who at nine years old has not a toe out of place, and only a small amount of swelling on one toe joint as a result of a minor dislocation.

Unless a dog has unbelievably tough and damn near perfect feet, (and a great deal of luck) I'd say that great speed usually equals damaged toe joints by the time the dog is three years old and has done a fair amount of fast work in the field over most types of ground.

Deerhounds, though large, are extremely light footed in their running style, whilst Whippets, for all their light weight and small size, have a sprint-type pounding action that hammers the ground hard as they run. The fact that Whippets weigh so little does of course help to render their pounding action less punishing to the feet, but just imagine how much damage can be done if a dog has Whippet type feet and a heavy body!

When you cross different breeds together to create lurchers, you can be lucky or unlucky in just what genes influence what bits of the resulting lurcher.

One of the reasons that Collie cross Greyhounds are such a tried and trusted cross is the soundness of their feet and most of these lurchers have feet that are as tough as old boots.

As far as hare dogs are concerned, most of the very best come from generations of dogs with a fair amount of Saluki in their blood, not just because of the legendary stamina to be found in the Saluki, but because dogs bred from animals which have been tested to the full in the field are those which have been used for breeding.

Most good hare dogs will never have seen the inside of a show ring and they have been bred for one reason only: that they could catch hares, and to catch hares not only do they need stamina, they have to possess the physical properties needed to run over rough plough, drilling and all types of land, and to do that week in, week out they need superb feet, amongst a whole host of other attributes.

However, no matter how brilliant a dog's feet might be, accidents and injury can and do happen. It's the risk our dogs take when they run, and the harder they run and the more they try, the more they are likely to be injured: the dog that doesn't really try is far less likely to injure itself than the one that takes up the challenge when the quarry throws down the gauntlet.

BASIC FOOT CARE

First we need to feed, rear and condition the dog correctly. A dog left standing in a kennel all week and only taken out at the weekend and run hard on game or even just racing on grass, is almost guaranteed to damage itself. It is not just the muscles and heart and lungs which should be conditioned to do a particular job, the feet too need to be in tip top shape before we ask a dog to run hard over ground that won't have been raked smooth like a Greyhound track.

Good feet can be obtained by correct breeding, but even small puppies need exercise for their bones and muscles and tendons to develop as they should.

Pups (and adult dogs) restricted permanently to a back yard will never develop the right kind of foot if that yard is made from slippery slabs or cement. I've seen lurchers which have seldom been out of such a yard, and their feet, without exception, were flat toed and splayed: the only way these animals could keep their footing when playing on such a smooth surface.

Apart from the obvious benefits of socialisation which will greatly improve

Running on hard gravel can cause sore pads.

their mental development, young lurchers need to be able to gallop, twist and turn on grass - that's the stuff you used to have in your back garden before you had lurchers, providing you've given them the freedom and exercise they needed as little pups.

However, I'm hardly suggesting you take a 14 week old lurcher pup out in the field and let it gallop around on rough, hard plough as this will undoubtedly lead to strains and sprains of growing joints.

A combination of lead walking and free running on relatively safe ground is needed, and as the pup grows, so will its feet become stronger. No exercise equals weakness, and weakness leads to greater risk of injury.

It is absolutely vital for pups to learn how to run, and if you've bred your own litter and allow them to run riot in your back garden you can see just how much their instincts lead them to gallop, even at six weeks of age, as they chase and stalk each other and pounce on butterflies and anything else that moves.

Miles of road walking with a pup that strains continuously on the lead does no good for a puppy's feet either, as those feet are developing, once again, in the wrong way, planting themselves on the ground and pushing against it as they pull on the lead, which can lead to flattened toes and strained tendons.

Miles of road walking in the adult dog is a different matter, and whilst road walking doesn't increase galloping stamina or running muscles, it can do wonders for flat and unfit feet as well as toning up the whole body.

Some types of lurcher, no matter how hard you try to improve things through correct diet and exercise, will always have feet that are not up to seriously hard work. A design fault, if you like, which may show as thin skinned, soft padded feet or thin boned and weak jointed toes. This is yet one more reason to breed only from animals which have been tried and tested in the field over several seasons of hard work; those that have come through these tests still sound and able to function properly.

Continuous and steady exercise will tone up and strengthen the part of the body you are working on: keep-fit enthusiasts and body builders will understand this! Road walking exercises the toe muscles and joints, as well as generally keeping the whole body in shape, and done for several miles each day, helps to build up foot strength, not to mention the increased toughness of the pads.

Walking is, however, not the gait at which you should be exercising the dog on the road, as trotting is the best speed at which to tone up any dog. A small dog will have to trot as you walk briskly, but you will need to run or cycle for a big lurcher to break into a trot.

A steady trot either beside the jogging owner or next to a bicycle (actually against the law on public roads in the UK though many people do it!) will help tone up tendons, strengthen muscles, and generally toughen the whole foot. Trotting also increases stamina as it makes the

A small, lightly built lurcher with fine, but very tough feet, bred from generations of coursing dogs.

heart beat faster over a prolonged amount of time and is a very good all round way to increase a dog's general fitness on the build up to really fast work in the field.

A word of warning though: too much road walking can actually wear down the surface of the pads if the dog is very unfit, overweight or heavily built, so you'll need to keep an eye on the state of the pads every day.

A worn pad is smooth and shiny, as opposed to slightly rough and matt in appearance. The skin will actually feel too thin if you press the pad, and if the dog winces then you've definitely gone too far (literally as well as metaphorically!).

CLAW MAINTENANCE

Let's start with the claws. All the road walking in the world won't keep the claws short if the foot isn't the right shape for the claw to come into constant contact with the ground. Unless the dog's toes are very arched the tip of the claw is unlikely to touch the ground hard enough to keep it worn down to the correct length.

Strongly arched toes are said to be the best, but once again, much depends on the breeding of the dog and for what ground that type of dog was originally developed.

White claws are easy to trim correctly, and black claws are the devil as you can't see the tender quick inside the claw, but first you'll need a good pair of claw clippers, and there is some real rubbish on the market that masquerade as dog claw clippers these days, bits of metal that would be hard pushed to cut a length of spaghetti in two.

I must admit to using the same pair of clippers for over 15 years as I've been unable to find anything better! Many people use the guillotine type clippers as they don't pinch the dog's claw before cutting it, but I've found that the 'cigar cutter' type of clippers are better for big, hard claws.

Many lurchers are complete wimps when it comes to having their feet handled, and it pays to accustom a pup to having its claws cut from a very early age: start at 10 days old with a pair of human nail clippers to nip off the needle sharp tips of those claws, being very careful not to touch the quick.

By beginning to cut a pup's claws this early on in life you not only accustom the pup to having its feet handled, but you also make life a lot more comfortable for the bitch who is rearing the pups. Those tiny sharp claws can scratch and tear the delicate skin on her teats, and a large litter of strong pups can force a bitch to quit feeding her pups or even bite at them when they hurt her. I use human nail clippers to clip small puppies' claws.

LIGAMENT DAMAGE
AND DISLOCATED TOES

Over-long claws can also be a factor in foot injuries, leading to knocked up (flattened due to torn or over-stretched ligaments) and even broken toes. When the tip of the claw comes into contact with a stone or

> TIP: *many dogs panic far less during the claw cutting process if you allow them to stand whilst you do this. Stand over the dog and pick its feet up as though you are shoeing a horse: not recommended if you have a bad back! But I've found that this practice makes the dog feel far less threatened by the procedure than if it had been forced to lie down.*

hard lump in the ground when the dog is running at speed, an over-long claw can literally force the toe out of its natural shape, putting undue strain on the joint and ligaments. The ligaments are what hold a joint together, and whilst they are very strong, they can rupture or over-stretch, which leads to a break down in the stability of the joint.

Imagine that the ligaments are like wires, holding the bones together in the correct place: snap or distort those wires and the joint becomes unstable or collapses all together. This is what happens when a dislocation occurs.

Ligaments are also very difficult to re-attach to their moorings, have a poor blood supply, which makes healing difficult and once damaged will often be prone to further injury if sufficient time is not allowed for the healing process to be completed properly. Keeping the feet in good working condition goes a long way to maintaining the whole thing in a state which will be more difficult to damage, so once again: regular exercise is a must in the working dog.

The right kind of food also plays an important part in maintaining the feet in good condition, and as most of you know, I'm a dedicated disciple of raw feeding! This is not to say that there are not many dogs which survive on all sorts of rubbish food and never suffer injuries or other health problems, but one thing's for sure: since my dogs have been fed almost totally on a raw diet, the healing time for all sorts of injuries and wounds has nearly halved, and more to the point, they seem to suffer less from those irritating working injuries such as pulled muscles and stiffness after a night or day's work. Before I knew better some of my dogs used to suffer from dry and cracked pads and splintery soft claws. Not any more! A decent quantity of animal

fat in the diet, along with good quality animal protein in the form of beef, horse, rabbit and chicken with the occasional bit of venison thrown in for good measure nourishes the whole body and maintains the dog in optimum health.

However, what you are seeing when you catch me side tracking is the undeniable fact that everything in the animal body is linked. We can't just look at feet without considering breeding, exercise and feeding when there is a foot problem, and similarly we can't just look at diet without considering what sort of work we are asking the dog to perform.

So, I'll drag myself back to the running gear, without which we don't have much of a working dog at all, and as with any maintenance programme, we need to keep those feet healthy, exercised and well nourished.

Take a look at your dog's feet: are they long toed and relatively flat? Or are the toes high arched with the claws growing downwards to the ground? Are the pads themselves thick and spongy like a well filled cushion, or are they soft and seemingly deflated as though someone has let out too much air?

Now look at the length of the claws: does your dog clatter across hard surfaces as though it's wearing castanets on its feet? Time to cut those claws! But be warned, if you have neglected this job over a period of time, then the quick (the nerve and blood supply to the claw) inside the claw will have also grown down further than it should have. You'll need to trim the claws every single week, a little at a time until the quick has receded to the correct level.

NOTE: some dogs have claws where the quicks are naturally far down inside the claw and all the trimming in the world won't give you the perfect shape; the same goes for claws which fail to come into contact with the ground at the correct angle, either through injury or inherited shape.

Now look at the pads: check their sponginess, look for cracks and worn smooth patches. By the way, if for example, just one pad is severely worn, say on an outside toe, this can tell you that the dog is not distributing its weight evenly across the foot, which could indicate an injury further up the leg, even in the shoulder.

Just as we stand awkwardly if we have a back or pelvic problem, so does the dog, and if the claws on one front foot appear to be longer than on the other, then that is another good indication that the dog is not putting the weight on that leg properly.

The dog might not actually be lame to your eyes, but it may not be moving level, as they say in the horse world, and it takes a trained eye to see if an animal is not using one leg as much as the other as this can be an infinitesimally small difference, but enough to make a difference in the length of the claws.

Over time, that pulled muscle or other injury, the slight and unnoticed injury which is making the dog put less weight on a particular foot, could become a serious problem to the running dog.

It is by taking note of the small things that we can nip any future problems in the bud, and the earlier we can pick up on a problem, then the better chance there is of reducing the amount of long-term damage to the part affected.

Now check between the toes for any thorns or bits of mud which might be irritating the skin. Bend all the toes back and forth (gently!) to see if they move correctly. Are any of the joints thickened, swollen or warmer to the touch than their neighbours? Does one toe refuse to bend as it should?

If that is the case then you've probably got a dislocation, which doesn't mean to say that the joint is still dislocated, just that it has been dislocated. Dislocation can be total, or partial, depending on just how badly the ligaments were stretched, or at worst, ruptured.

It is very common for lurchers to snap a joint out in a toe when running on hard, lumpy ground, but you won't know anything about it at the time if the joint snaps back into place immediately at the next stride: apart from a faltering stride or two. This is providing that the ligaments were not actually broken.

Unless the ligaments holding the joint together have completely ruptured, the toe will look much as normal, that is until the following day when inflammation and swelling will have set in around that joint.

And that is part of the great problem with lurchers. The adrenalin high when they are chasing prey stops them feeling pain immediately, so we don't realise that they've damaged themselves unless the injury is severe, and this is particularly so in the case of knocked up and dislocated toes.

What should you do when you discover that your dog has dislocated a toe? First you need to establish if the toe is still dislocated and that will be easy to recognise as the toe will be held at a very odd angle, out of line with the other toes on that foot. Pulling gently but firmly, away from the body in a straight line, will sometimes be enough to click the toe back into place, but if you are unsure see an expert. Usually in these cases the toe will have returned to its rightful place by the time you notice a problem, and the following steps should be followed to minimise permanent damage.

Get it cooled down: apply an ice pack or bag of frozen peas to reduce the swelling and inflammation, or failing that stand the foot in a bucket of cold water. This should be done for at least 10 minutes three times a day to begin with.

Much will depend on the severity of the dislocation and how soon you can get the joint back into place BUT, if the dog then keeps running on that foot, already tender and slightly inflamed, and the damage re-occurs, making what was a relatively minor injury into a more severe problem you may end up with permanent damage.

After the initial cooling down of the injury which will help to prevent excessive inflammation, you should apply a good liniment such as *Bone Radiol* for three days, then leave for three days before using the liniment again for a further three days.

Liniments such as *Bone Radiol* work on the principle that they are actually an irritant, and by their action they bring a greater blood supply to the area of application. Blood heals injuries, and a good supply of the red stuff is what you need to enhance the healing process. Ligaments and tendons have a very poor blood supply so it makes sense to try and improve that supply whenever there is damage to either.

You should never apply such a liniment or embrocation to areas where the skin is broken, no matter how slightly, and you shouldn't bandage the area after application either as this can cause intense irritation. Keep an eye out for any adverse reaction such as serious reddening of the skin or hair loss. If either of these occurs then rinse the area thoroughly with clean water.

Witch Hazel is a more gentle and natural type of liniment, and is excellent

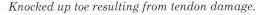

Knocked up toe resulting from tendon damage.

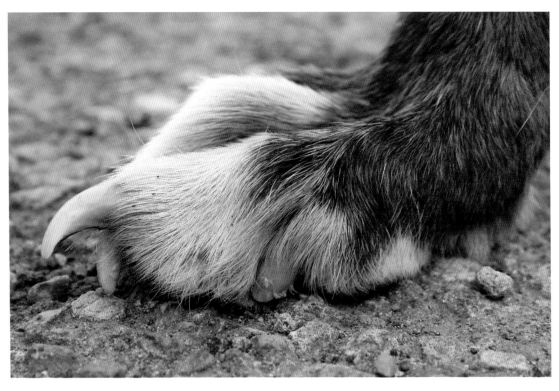

for minor bruising and swelling. This can be bought from most chemists and applied daily for several days.

Lead walk the dog for a minimum of three weeks after such an injury, and in some cases this could be longer depending on the severity of the injury. A good greyhound vet will advise you on the length of time a particular case needs before running the dog again.

What happens if we do nothing at all bar rest the dog in such cases? The swelling will eventually form a mass of scar tissue around the injury in an attempt to protect the joint, but this will in all likelihood render the joint either less mobile or completely immobile. There won't be any movement in it at all which will in turn render that toe more prone to damage at a later date.

All bar one of my older lurchers, the wonderful Starlight dog whose feet just have to be the best and toughest in the world, have got at least one hard swollen toe joint on at least one foot, and this is testimony to the fact that when I've discovered the injury its been too late to treat from fresh, the damage making it irreversible.

Sure, a lurcher can still run on a foot when one of the toes has become rigid due to such scarring around a joint, but I've noticed that over time, a dog with one such damaged toe often seems to be prone to damaging the others on the same foot, until sooner or later depending on the amount of work you give the dog and on the type of ground, the other toes end up damaged as well.

Once a toe is really badly affected there's not a lot you can do apart from removing it completely! Personally I leave those calloused toes attached to the dog and only contemplate actually having a toe removed

if it is: a) completely dislocated and flapping about; or b) it becomes infected, and this can happen if there has been an open wound to the joint when it first slipped out of place.

Removing one or more toes on a running dog is always a risky procedure, but I know of several dogs which still work well despite having fewer toes than they were born with.

The inside and outside toes on a dog's foot are used mainly as props when turning at speed, whilst the middle two toes are the power toes, used for propelling the dog forwards.

If you remove middle toes you lose speed, though probably not enough to affect the working ability of a lurcher; of course it would be a different matter if you are talking about a racing Greyhound where milliseconds count on the track.

Once again, much depends on how a dog runs, its action and weight etc. When you assess the possibility of removing a toe, the only way to get a satisfactory assessment is to get the dog to a Greyhound vet, one who sees these sorts of injuries on a regular basis. Be guided by this specialist vet.

FLAT TOES AND HOW TO LOOK AFTER THEM

Let's move on to flat toes. Toes whose ligaments have been permanently over stretched or torn. This can happen either as a result of a cut to the underside of the toe, usually happening when the dog runs over flinty ground or is unlucky enough to run over broken glass or other similarly sharp objects. There might be no external wound at all which means that the ligaments have been stretched beyond what nature intended.

Cut ligaments can be stitched back together, but they have a poor blood supply which doesn't help healing at all (they are

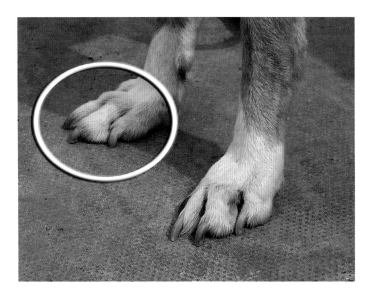

Multiple damage to tendons causing flattened toes.

white in colour which tells you something about the amount of red blood that gets to them, or not ... in their case.

I've had several dogs whose cut ligaments have been stitched back together by the vet, but the repair has never held satisfactorily and sooner or later the toe has flattened permanently, which reduces the speed of the dog very slightly but doesn't seem to bother them unduly when they are running over anything except very rough stony ground.

If a dog bruises the underside of its flat toes and goes lame for a couple of days, rest the dog and apply Witch Hazel to the area. Ibuleve is also useful as both a painkiller and an anti-inflammatory, and should be applied topically just as in humans.

Sparrow, my Collie lurcher, has a flat toe on her hind foot which happened when she was running rabbits on the old landfill site: a deadly place to run dogs, full of cracks in the ground, stones set cement like into the clay topping, and it's either fast running uphill or a mad dash downhill. I didn't even realise she'd damaged the foot until we came off the hill (well, it is a hill to us in East Anglia!) and I noticed she was limping a bit. On examining the foot I saw immediately that one of the middle toes on her hind foot was flat, though there was no sign of any wound.

What Sparrow had probably done was to impact that toe whilst running, probably hitting a stone hard with the tip of the claw, which forced the toe up and back to an impossible angle, thereby over-stretching the ligaments which allow the toe to flex and straighten.

Total rest of such an injury is needed for at least a month if there is to be any chance of those ligaments healing, and I'm afraid to say that I've had dogs damage their toes in this way so often and not return to their rightful position even after weeks of rest that I now tend to let nature take its course.

One year on and Sparrow's flat toe has caused her absolutely no bother at all, but you do need to pay attention to the claw on a flat toe as it will stick straight out rather than coming into contact with the ground when the dog walks on it. (This type of toe is also known as a 'knocked up' toe in the Greyhound world.)

Note completely flat front feet probably due to lack of exercise and incorrect housing. Reproduced with kind permission of Lurcherlink.

Keep the claw on a flat toe as short as you can and if the dog seems prone to stubbing it on hard objects then get to the vet and discuss having the offending claw removed permanently, which of course will have to be done under general anaesthetic as the entire nail bed will need to be removed. I've had dogs minus claws and have never had a problem once the area has healed completely.

SORE PADS

Run your dog on hard ground, either frozen hard or summer baked hard and you're asking for all sorts of foot problems. Sore and over-worn pads are just one of those problems, and as I've described earlier, the surface of an over-worn pad is smooth and shiny compared to the matt surface a healthy pad should possess.

First, stop running the dog on hard ground! Then set about curing the problem by: a) making sure that the dog has enough good quality animal protein and fat in its diet; and b) applying a healing ointment or cream to the cracked or worn pad.

Padnasol is one of the best old fashioned foot creams on the market and it helps heal cracks by softening the hard edges to the pad and promoting new skin growth. It's available from the Greyhound Megastore.

I actually use *Padnasol* on my own hands in the winter when my thumbs become cracked and sore through prolonged contact with cold and wet, and I can vouch for its effectiveness!

STOPPER PAD AND ASSOCIATED PROBLEMS

The stopper pads are also often damaged when running dogs on hard ground, and for those people who are desperate to run their dogs as soon as the corn is cut, short stubble causes just as many problems as hard ground, though at that time of year the ground is likely to be rock hard anyway!

Dogs which run on stubble often suffer from grazes and cuts to the backs of their lower legs, and if the owner is stupid enough to carry on running a dog in this state, these grazes may often become infected as more and more hard earth is ground into them.

Injuries to the stopper pad itself vary from knocking a bit of skin off the end of the pad, to serious cuts which occur where the stopper is attached to the leg, almost always on the underside of the stopper.

These can be the devil to heal. First, the stopper acts as a shock absorber when the dog is running hard: look at the photo of the running dog and you can see that the stopper is in direct contact with the ground, whilst the bend of the leg below the stopper shows just how much strain the skin and underlying tissue is subjected to when in that position.

If the tissue is cut at precisely the point where it needs to be strongest, where the stopper is attached, you have some idea as to how important it is to allow sufficient time for that cut to heal.

The problem we also have is that scar tissue doesn't stretch like normal tissue, so every time the dog runs hard with scarring around the area which needs to stretch and contract whilst running, that tissue could break down, cracking under the strain, and I've known dogs that opened up old injuries in this way every time they ran and had to have their stoppers bandaged each and every time they were worked.

If the stopper itself hasn't been sliced into, and the cut appears to be just below and into the base of the stopper, then the dog absolutely must not be allowed to run whilst the wound is healing.

However, the wrist does need to flex a little as the wound is healing or the scar tissue will bind into the position the leg has been held at during the healing process. Look at just how much upwards bend the lower leg is subjected to when the dog turns and runs flat out: the stretch on the back of the wrist is tremendous, so complete immobilisation is not a good idea when you're allowing this sort of wound to heal as it will only split open again the moment the dog runs.

Yes, it will take longer to heal if you allow the dog to move about: lead walking only, but the resulting scar tissue will at least have grown over the place in such a way that whilst it might appear to be slightly raised in comparison to the rest of the surrounding skin, there will be enough tissue there to allow movement.

If the tendons have been cut this is definitely not a do-it-yourself job, and whilst there are many tendons running down the backs of the legs which can't all be reattached, the major tendons need to be repaired by a vet under anaesthetic. Tendons and ligaments are what hold the whole muscular skeletal system together so just leaving a major tendon severed is not an option.

If your dog does sever a major tendon you may well see something which looks like a thin white piece of pasta or very narrow tape inside the wound. You will probably only see this immediately after the injury has occurred though, as a cut tendon will shrink back up or down the legs very quickly. A word of warning here: tendons take a very long time to heal: months in some cases due to their poor blood supply. Like ligaments they are very tough but once cut they do need at least six to eight weeks to heal, sometimes longer, and sometimes fail to stick back together which is not good news for the running dog.

SEVERED STOPPER PAD
If the stopper pad has been almost sliced off, which can happen if the dog hits flint or broken glass at an unlucky angle, it is probably just as well to remove it completely as it will never 'glue' itself back to the right position again satisfactorily.

If the stopper is dangling by a thin piece of skin you can just snip it off completely, but I'd still go to the vet just to make sure that there has been no tendon or bone damage as well. The very important flexor tendon runs down the back of the front legs and if this is damaged severely the dog won't be able to run again.

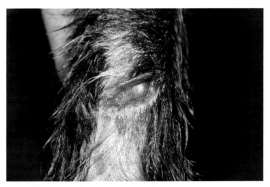

Small cut on hind leg which exposes though does not damage the tendon which can be seen as a small patch of white tissue.

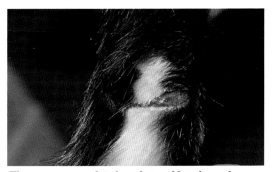

The same wound 7 days later. Note how the tissue is starting to granulate inside the wound.

I know of one very good coursing bitch which had to have both her stoppers removed as her running action continually shredded them on stony ground. From then on her owner had to bandage her wrists to protect the area where the stoppers had been removed, which didn't affect her running at all.

You can buy special stopper protectors, but I've seen them in use and wouldn't advise them for work in the field, for the following reasons:
   a) They allow grit and muck to filter down against the skin as the dog runs which could cause abrasion.
   b) To my mind they don't fit snugly enough to really protect the dog's wrists and if affixed too tightly (they have a Velcro fastening) they would either hamper the dog's movement or cut off the circulation!

Far better is to use Vetwrap, with a pad of sponge against the skin where the stopper has been removed. Wrap round the wrist with the Vetwrap, tightly but not too tightly. Then finish off by wrapping round with Elastoplast, top and bottom of the Vetwrap to make sure it doesn't slip and doesn't allow dirt to slide beneath the bandage.

SORE NAIL BEDS
Some dogs suffer from sore nail beds (quicks: where the claw joins the end of the toe). I have found no particular reason for a dog to suffer from this, some of mine do, most don't so I can't really put a reason to this one. What happens is this, when some dogs run on earth or sand, their running action forces dirt up under the delicate skin that covers the bed of the claw. Left untreated this can cause serious problems with the nail bed becoming sore, infected, oozing and swollen - very painful indeed.

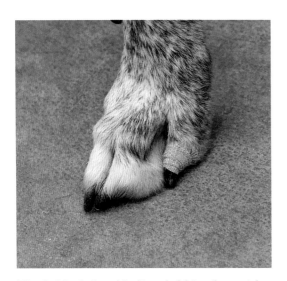

The finished claw binding, held in place with a dab of Superglue. Note the end of the plaster is on top of the toe, not underneath where it would come into contact with the ground.

Always check your dog's feet when you have been out in muddy conditions, and wash them carefully on your return home. I use a bucketful of warm water with a splash of Dettol in it, though a tablespoonful of salt is just as good for everyday use. Use a soft brush, I use an old toothbrush, to clean the softened dirt from around the claws. Don't brush upwards towards the dog's foot, always brush away from the nail bed, or in line with the skin. Don't try and do this if the mud is hard, stand the dog's feet in the bucket for a few moments first if the mud has set hard. Our clay sets like concrete by the time we reach home!

Make sure every speck of mud or dirt is removed from the nail beds, and if there are any signs of soreness apply an antiseptic cream round each nail bed. If your dog is prone to suffering from trapped dirt under the nail beds then it is a good idea to cover them before working the dog in muddy conditions. This might sound a real fiddle, but believe me, with practice it can be done

quite quickly, and the bonus is that for day time work, you can do it the night before. For night time work try and bind the nail beds several hours before you go out as the sticky stuff in the tape sets better over a period of time. I used to use Elastoplast fabric strapping, but have since learned that Zinc Oxide tape is even better, being less bulky and very sticky.

Don't forget to remove the tape as soon as you return home. Washing the dog's feet in a bucket of hot water soon loosens the binding and the whole lot normally slips straight off if you get a finger nail under the top edge.

You should also check underneath the dog's feet as well when you wash them Lumps of mud, even stones, can get trapped between the pads, once again setting like little concrete chips between the toes, and fastened there by the fur. Don't try and pull these off if that is the case as you'll not only hurt the dog but pull out the protective fur as well. Always soak mud off feet.

You can finish the feet by applying *Padnasol* around the nail beds and on the pads, which is a brilliant ointment and stops pads drying out and relieves soreness round the nail beds.

If the dog's nail beds have become swollen, oozing and infected it is ABSOLUTELY VITAL that you DO NOT attempt to bind them until healing is complete. Binding infected nail beds will seal in the infection and be incredibly painful to the dog and prolong the problem one hundred fold! You need to keep the dog on a lead and out of mud until the healing process is complete, and if the problem has been allowed to continue this could take several weeks after you start treatment.

An antibiotic cream can be applied to infected nail beds once the initial cleaning has taken place, and to clean infected nail

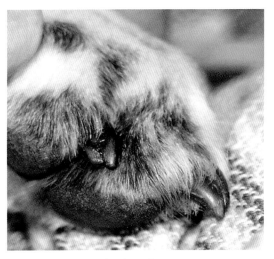

Quick showing in broken claw.

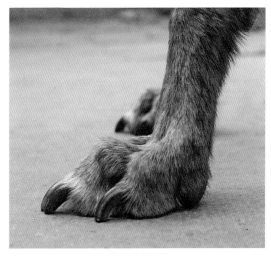

Claws too long. Note how the toe joint is being forced back and up.

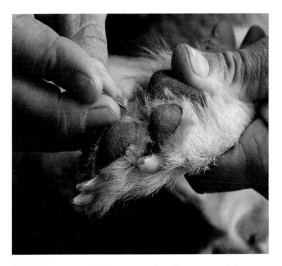

Sudden onset of lameness is often caused by a thorn in the foot.

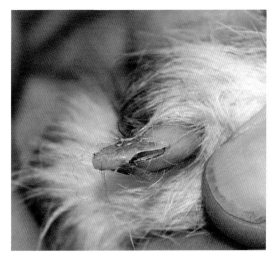

The broken flake of claw can be pulled or snipped off.

beds you need to make sure that all pus and dead tissue, as well as fur, is removed from the area.

Hydrogen Peroxide 6% vol is a good way of removing the muck from infected nail beds as it seeps into the wound, and by its oxidising action, bubbles the infection and trapped dirt to the surface. If the problem has become really severe you will also see dead tissue sloughing off leaving behind healthy pink flesh. If there is any sign that the claws are hot and tender, or that swelling is apparent on the toe itself I'd get straight to a vet as that sort of infection can travel up the leg to the whole body and make the dog very ill indeed.

NOTE: Do not use Hydrogen Peroxide more than twice at the very most as it does damage healthy tissue as well as helping to remove infected tissue. Hydrogen Peroxide has a slightly cauterizing effect which inhibits healing if used too often.

Any infection to the foot should not be ignored as without correct treatment you could find yourself, or rather your dog, in deep trouble. Remember? No foot: no dog! (at any rate, no dog capable of running!).

THORNS, PUNCTURE WOUNDS AND ABSCESSES

And as if the previous problems weren't enough, a dog's feet are also at risk of being stabbed by thorns as they work through cover. Blackthorns are the worst, almost immediately setting up a reaction in foot, so the moment you notice your dog go suddenly lame, inspect that foot carefully.

The worst sort of thorn is the one which has snapped off level with the pad, the sort where you can't even get your fingernails around it to pull it out.

I discovered a handy tool for these problem thorns the other day: a pair of human nail clippers! Swift came hobbling

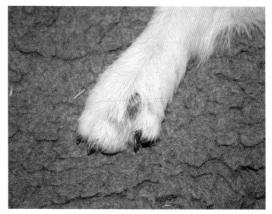

Very swollen foot with inter-digital abscess about to burst.

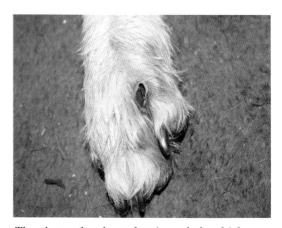

The abscess has burst leaving a hole which must be cleaned and drained.

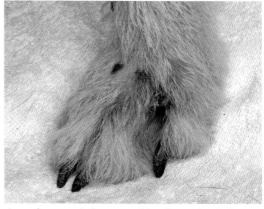

A week on and the wound is almost healed.

76

home with one such thorn, barely visible against the surface of her pad, and Andy had the bright idea of using the toe nail clippers when ordinary tweezers just couldn't get hold of the head of the thorn.

By pushing down into the pad slightly, with the clipper jaws ajar, then gripping very gently, I was able to sink the clipper jaws into the sides of the thorn just hard enough to extract it. You need a steady and gentle touch not to cut through the thorn though, which would leave you in even more of a pickle as to how to remove it.

Squirt a little antiseptic ointment or Tea Tree Oil into the puncture, which might well have sealed over already due to the shape of the thorn as it entered the pad. If you've lost the entry hole, then slop the antiseptic or whatever you are using over the pad and massage in a little.

A healthy dog will heal with no problems providing you have left no bits of thorn in the pad. Strangely enough I've never had a typical blackthorn problem when such a thorn has entered the pad as long as I've been able to remove the whole thorn quickly. I think that this is probably due to the thickness and toughness of pad tissue, which seals off potential infection from the rest of the body.

Similarly, foreign objects, including thorns, bits of glass, and even twigs sticking up from the ground, can all impale a dog's foot, often between the toes.

If a thorn or similar has gone into the toe from underneath, you will often be unaware that this has happened during the heat of the hunt, and even when you examine the foot at home later on you will most likely find just a small hole, often just to one side of the big back pad on a dog's foot.

Clean such wounds out using salt water or Hydrogen Peroxide squirted into the

hole with a syringe (minus needle!), but be warned ... it is usually impossible to see if there is any dirt or debris left inside, and if there is, you will see swelling of the toe, often accompanied by a red, angry looking swelling usually to one side of that toe bone. Such swelling usually appears within hours of the injury.

This is the body's method of pushing out foreign objects, by forming an abscess around the invading object or dirt. This sort of abscess nearly always bursts on top of the foot or toe, taking the path of least resistance, the skin on the underneath of the foot being much tougher than the skin on top of the foot.

Don't attempt to lance the abscess yourself as you can do more harm than good. If the dog is happy in itself and not in serious discomfort you can apply a poultice which will help to draw the infection from the foot, and by applying a poultice on to the abscess direct the skin will soften which allows the abscess to burst less painfully than it might were you to wait for it to happen naturally.

Various kinds of poultice can be used, but I like *Animalintex* which is designed for horses. You just need to be careful and not leave the poultice in place for more than four to six hours. This is because a dog's skin is much thinner than a horse's and the poultice would soften even healthy skin too much, almost melting it!

Bread poultices and kaolin poultices are also good old fashioned remedies and don't have such a dramatic effect on a dog's skin so no harm will be done if you forget and leave it on overnight. Make a bread poultice by soaking a slice of wholemeal bread in hot water, squeeze out the excess water and place over the abscess, holding it in place with Vetwrap. As long as you can see that the abscess is darkening in colour at the upper most point, and that the skin is becoming shiny and stretched looking and that the dog is quite well in itself with no sign of swollen glands or undue discomfort, then allow the abscess to burst and drain naturally. The poulticing will help this process to complete itself, and once the abscess has burst you can help the dog by cleaning out the hole thoroughly with a syringe or two of boiled, cooled salty water. I wait until the water is blood temperature as it seems to be less painful to the dog than very cold water.

All you have to do now until the hole has completely healed is keep the foot ultra clean and dry. Your dog will do any further cleaning of the area itself and I never stop a dog licking at such an injury unless it seems to be obsessed with the problem spot. Most lurchers and sighthounds aren't stupid or obsessive in their behaviour and I have never been forced to put a 'lid' (Elizabethan collar) on a lurcher to stop it over licking a wound of any kind.

However, you must keep a close eye on the foot and monitor it closely for signs of further infection, which could appear as heat and swelling around the burst abscess. I don't like to put dogs on a course of antibiotics unless absolutely necessary as too frequent use of antibiotics does a dog's immune system no good and is likely to lessen the effectiveness of future antibiotic treatment if and when needed.

What you can do, a halfway house of a sort, is to use an antibiotic ointment of the type designed to treat mastitis in cows. This comes in a syringe (no needle) and the nozzle of the syringe can be inserted into the wound where the ointment can wipe out any bacteria locally without flooding the dog's whole system with antibiotics. The site of any burst abscess needs to

remain open whilst it heals from the inside just like any puncture wound, as healing externally first is likely to seal in bacteria and provoke further infection. You can flush out the hole daily with a salt water solution, but don't use antiseptics as these actually slow down the healing process a little.

It took Hunni's foot three full weeks to heal properly before I let her off the lead or allowed her to run through mud. The skin needs to be completely reformed over the area before you dare allow the dog to come into contact with bacteria and possible contamination. The skin also blackened around the area for a while due to tissue dying as a result of the infection. This skin regenerated itself over a further few weeks, and once the fur had eventually grown back you wouldn't have known she'd ever had a problem with that foot.

NOTE: If at any time the dog appears unwell in itself or that the swelling seems to be increasing in overall size and moving up the foot, then get the dog to the vet straight away.

Warning: If the abscess doesn't come to a head after 24 hours the dog will need to be put on a course of antibiotics because a toe joint or the whole body could be infected.

CUT PADS

Whilst the pad on a well conditioned and fit dog is surprisingly tough, it is unfortunately no match for a piece of flint or glass. The running dog's foot hits the ground with considerable force when it is moving at speed and if there happens to be a broken bottle or piece of sharp stone in the way of that foot then there is only one outcome. Out at night in the dark, and unless the injury is particularly serious we are unlikely to know that the dog has been injured until we are on our way home and if your trusty hound has been running through mud you are unlikely to be aware of the injury at all until you enter your abode!

Five minutes in the back of your vehicle will, however, allow the dog to tastefully adorn the back seat or boot with paw-shaped puddles of blood, likewise your house upon your arrival home. Unless the blood is spurting or gushing from an artery or vein don't worry! Blood is good, and a decent flow of blood is cleaning the wound of dirt, debris and bacteria with which such a wound is surely contaminated.

Cut pads are very unlikely to 'gush' as there are no major blood vessels within the actual pad. However, they can seep quite well, and of course that seeping can seem to continue for rather a long time, partly because of something called gravity, and also because the pressure of the dog's weight when standing on the wound forces it open.

A vertical slice into the pad will bleed more than if a chunk of pad has been shaved off completely, and such vertical cuts can take a long time to heal, even in really fit and healthy animals because healing needs to take place deep within the cut to begin with, only finally sealing the outside layer of skin once the inside has 'filled up' with new flesh.

Split pads can be stitched, though I'd not attempt this surgery at home. Contamination and the thickness of the outer skin on the pad combine to make this a 'vet job' under anaesthetic, and of course it goes without saying that a course of antibiotics will be necessary as well.

Unless a pad had been cut almost in two I prefer to let nature do the healing, though we are looking at almost a month of lead work only for deep pad cuts. Incidentally, even if you have had the pad stitched at the vet's, you will have to wait almost as long before you can run the dog again, this has been my experience at any rate.

Treatment

Wash the whole foot thoroughly using cooled boiled water to which a teaspoon of salt has been added, or a general purpose antiseptic, one that you would use on your own cuts. If the wound is still bleeding freely then initially hosing the foot down with cold water can help to slow the bleed, but laying the dog down and raising the affected limb will also help bleeding to stop.

In any case, you will need to up end the dog somewhere comfortable in order to examine and dress the wound: I use the sofa!

Once you have washed the foot you need to examine the wound carefully. I use a small bright torch to highlight the area and if necessary to peer inside the wound in order to make sure there are no foreign bodies or bits lodged deep in the flesh.

If you have a very calm dog, a steady hand and preferably someone else to hold the dog and foot immobile, then you can attempt to retrieve fragments of debris from within the wound with a pair of blunt ended tweezers.

If you have a nervous, worried dog, a shaky hand or no tweezers you must then seek professional help if you suspect that there is a foreign body in the wound, for it cannot heal properly if a foreign body remains inside.

Once I'm happy that the wound is clean I bandage the foot. It is important to dry the foot thoroughly first or you will leave the foot warm and damp which is the perfect breeding ground for bacteria. You will need a roll of cotton wool, some Vetwrap bandage, some fabric sticking plaster, and a pair of scissors.

Cut pad showing slightly dry edges.
Photo: Matty Jones.

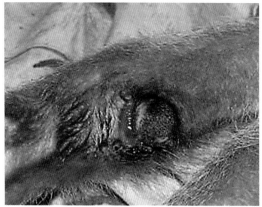

Typical injury below stopper pad.
Photo: Jackie Drakeford.

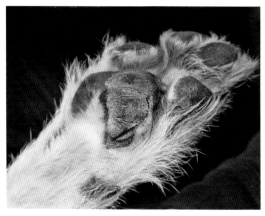

Shallow gash on pad which should take about 3 weeks to heal providing the dog isn't allowed to gallop during healing.

You can buy all you need to bandage a dog's leg at your local chemist, with the exception of the Vetwrap, although most chemists do sell a human equivalent which is not quite as good and very expensive!

Place a small wadge of cotton wool between EVERY toe and a further wadge behind the toes and in front of the big pad. It is very important to make sure that the toes aren't being pressed together inside the bandage which could create sores and dampness.

The pads on a dog's feet are the only areas of its body which can sweat, apart from the tongue, and these release heat and moisture when the dog is hot. Covering the feet with a bandage is to place those pads in an unnatural environment (a bit like a human wearing plastic socks) so it is essential to use breathable bandaging materials to help in the prevention of infection.

Place a piece of non-stick sterile gauze or a piece of lint (the type that doesn't stick to tissue and blood) over the wound itself. I find the silver lint pads very good for this purpose.

Finally wrap the whole foot with the Vetwrap bandage, ending just below the wrist. Finish off by taping fabric sticking plaster around the top of the bandage and on to the leg itself so the whole lot doesn't slide down the leg and off the end of the foot.

It is standard practice to bandage the whole foot and leg (if the stopper, for example has been damaged). Bandaging tightly around the wrist but leaving the foot free for example, is likely to cut off circulation to the foot and this can all too easily lead to serious infection and even gangrene, amputation or death. I have seen the results of too tight bandaging which left the toes unbandaged. Gangrene set in within days and the dog had to be put down, so take this possibility very seriously and NEVER bandage a dog's leg without also doing the whole foot.

Vetwrap and cotton wool will allow the foot to breathe, but will also let in damp, so each and every time the dog goes outside to relieve itself you will need to put the foot in a plastic bag secured with an elastic band.

You will of course need to remove plastic bag and band on return to the house or kennel. It is very important that a bandaged foot is not allowed to become wet at all or the bacteria will have a field day breeding like wildfire in that damp, warm climate of damaged flesh that is your dog's cut pad.

NOTE: I can't say this too often. CHECK ALL WOUNDS EVERY DAY WITHOUT FAIL!

If the wound is clean (no bad smell or discharge) then you can leave the gauze patch in place because it is acting as a glue to keep the wound sealed and safe. Don't worry if it is stuck in place with dried blood, healing will be going on beneath the 'scab' so leave well alone and don't be tempted to pull or wash it off.

Other than checking the wound daily all you need to do is wait, though if all goes well you should be able to do away with the bandage after about a week. You'll still need to plastic bag the foot every time the dog ventures outside though, and if the dog is kenneled you must make sure that the kennel and run are kept spotlessly clean and dry (yet another reason to house your dogs in a covered run).

Don't worry if the dog licks at the wound once the bandage is removed for good, and if that piece of gauze is still in place it won't be for long. Let the dog lick it away, but keep an eye on things to make sure that the wound doesn't re-open and start bleeding.

Pad between each toe when bandaging the foot to avoid pressure sores.

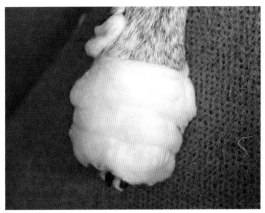

Don't forget to pad under the dewclaw as well.

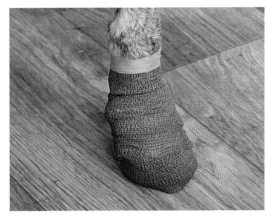

Foot bandaged with Vetwrap and held on with Elastoplast.

Most lurchers are very sensible when it comes to keeping their own wounds clean, so don't stop the dog from following its instincts. If you do notice that your dog seems to be 'nagging' at a wound incessantly then suspect either infection or a foreign body that you have missed. Of course, if things don't go according to plan and an infection does set in, or there is any other sign that all is not well, then you'll need to see a vet straight away.

TIP: *using a good foot cream such as Padsanol once the wound is almost healed, will help to prevent hard, horny tissue appearing at the edges of the cut. If you allow this hard tissue to build up whilst the skin on the pad is regrowing then it can make the pad very sore when the dog runs.*

Total healing time for a cut pad depending upon the depth of the wound I'd say about three weeks, and that is only if you are sensible and keep walking to a minimum. The more the dog walks on a split pad the more the wound will be kept open. I know that three weeks sounds like a long time but even if you'd had the wound professionally stitched you'd be looking at a similar length of time before you could let the dog off the lead.

SHAVED PAD

Equally as common as a cut into the pad is the lump sliced off the outside of the pad. The large pad behind the toes seems to be most prone to these injuries with one of the 'corners' of this pad being most commonly either completely or partially removed, usually by coming into contact with broken glass or sharp flinty stones.

It is usually futile to try and sew or stick such a lump of pad back into place as it invariably refuses to seal itself back on to the rest of the pad and eventually dries up into a hard, leathery flap which continually irritates the dog and actually prevents the whole thing healing.

Far better to snip that flap off immediately, but I'd only advise doing this at home if the flap is merely hanging on by a shred of skin. If it is attached along one side of the wound then it is unfair on a dog to do this without a local anaesthetic, so you'll need to get this done at the vet's.

Once the loose flap or chunk of pad has been removed then cover and follow the same procedure as with a cut pad. Healing time is the same: about three weeks.

In any type of injury to the pad I would always advise smearing *Padsanol* over the whole pad once the first week of healing has passed. Do this daily to prevent a build up of hard, dried tissue around the wound. *Padsanol* also protects the raw flesh from airborne bacteria by providing a protective barrier. Apply this after washing the foot.

SPLIT OR CUT WEB

As if the previous foot problems and injuries weren't enough, lurchers and sighthounds may also suffer from a split or torn web, the skin between the toes.

This usually happens as a result of impact with a sharp object, but the web may also be torn if the toes are forced apart excessively when the dog is running at speed.

The web is extremely tough, with the outer edge forming a band of gristly tissue which is thicker than the rest of the web, difficult to cut and even more difficult to heal once it has been injured.

In severe cases a vet may need to cut the damaged web away completely, but I'd not recommend this except in extreme cases. Most split or cut webs will heal fine PROVIDING you allow enough time for healing to take place.

The web comes under great pressure in active dogs. Note the extreme stretch on the web between the toes on the rim of the tank. The web is both flexible and strong.

This might sound obvious, but such injuries can take weeks to heal, and any attempt to run the dog before the web is COMPLETELY healed will result in the injury re-opening.

Unless the dog is kept indoors throughout the healing period you will need to cover the foot with a light bandage and sock whenever the dog ventures outdoors. I don't like to bandage these injuries as a rule, and the dog will lick and clean the wound when appropriate, also keeping it moist, a condition essential for healing as all wounds left to heal as nature intended should not dry during the healing process.

If the wound does look as though it is drying out too much with hard dry crispy edges then you will need to apply an antiseptic ointment such as Sudacream or

Padsanol AT LEAST TWICE A DAY until healing is complete.

What you should NOT do is keep the foot covered all the time as this provides a superb breeding ground for bacterial infection. Use a bit of common sense and only cover the foot as needed when the dog goes outside.

If the web has had to be surgically removed you might find that the toes tend to splay too much when the dog is running even once healed. In this case you can tape the toes together on either side of the missing web whilst the dog is working, but be sure to remove such tape once the dog has finished running each and every time. Failure to do so can result in sore toes and once again, a damp breeding ground between those toes which encourages bacterial infection. Use a strip of fabric sticking plaster and place a small wedge of sponge between those toes first. Some Greyhound trainers use the equivalent of a very strong rubber band to hold the toes in place. Bind the toes firmly but not too tightly: practice on your own fingers first to see how tight is comfortable! Some dogs cope quite well in this way, but it is of course a less than ideal solution, and whilst racing Greyhounds might manage during the few seconds they run on a prepared track, working lurchers would be at far greater risk of damage when running across farm land or hill.

AMPUTATION OF TOES

If a toe bone is badly broken, infected or irreversibly dislocated there is sometimes only one option, that of amputation. Amputating a toe is something which should be done, in my opinion, only as a last resort. Whilst amputation of a hind foot toe is less likely to affect the dog's running ability, the removal of toes on the front feet can cause problems.

The front feet are the feet which enable the dog to turn sharply, brake equally quickly and as such they take a lot of punishment, especially when running over open countryside as opposed to a smooth and rock-free race track.

Removal of an inside or outside toe may alter the dog's turning ability, but more importantly can put extra strain on the shoulder, which is lacking an important prop on the side where the toe is missing. Removal of one of the middle toes may also cause problems as the remaining middle toe is now doing the work of two. Nor does it have the support it should, which can mean that the toe may bend to the side which in turn can lead to an increased risk of dislocation when running hard.

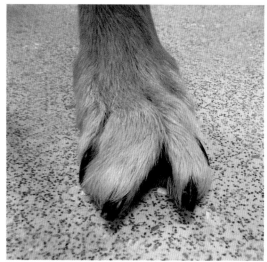

Badly torn lateral ligaments necessitated removal of this toe. Photo: Paul Nightingale.

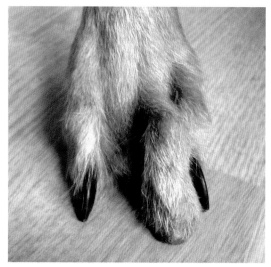

Toe removed, note the claw on the adjacent toe has also been removed to reduce stress on the remaining middle toe. Photo: Paul Nightingale.

I've known some people strap two adjacent toes together with a rubber band whilst the dog is running in an attempt to keep the toes in the right position. This can help but great care is needed to make sure that earth and grit do not lodge between the two strapped toes, causing chafing and open sores. It goes without saying that any strapping must be removed immediately the dog has ceased running.

I've not had much experience with toe removal, and the only dog we had whose outside toe needed amputation suffered with shoulder problems almost immediately she started running again. However, I've also heard of dogs with fewer toes than they were born with that worked and ran with absolutely no problem at all.

Much will depend on the type of dog and its running style as to whether or not the dog suffers from ongoing problems due to toe amputation. A slower, less aggressive style of running will put less pressure on the feet than a hard-hitting sprint type of running style.

I would always advise referral to a good Greyhound vet when considering the amputation of a toe. Greyhound vets are vastly experienced in this area as they treat racing dogs, which need to be able to race efficiently, unlike the pet dog whose speed is irrelevant to its quality of life.

Many Greyhound vets will take the toe off at the joint then round the joint off to prevent seepage of joint fluid; they may also save the pad and sew it back over the end of the amputated toe in order to provide more protection against knocks. As I've said before, I would never decry the knowledge of the general practitioner but when dealing with specific running dog injuries it makes sense to see a specialist orthopaedic vet, specialist, one who understands the increased stresses and strains on the body of a working running dog.

FOOT MAINTENANCE NOTES

- *Always wash a dog's feet on return from any hunting trip on to farm land as you never know just what spray or chemical your dog might have come into contact with.*
- *Check feet thoroughly every day after exercise, walks or hunting.*
- *Wash mud off as soon as you get home making sure there is no dirt lodged in the nail beds.*
- *Apply Padnasol or similar to pads if they are dry or cracked paying particular attention to the edges where the cracks begin and under the base of claws at front edge of pad.*
- *Check for broken or split claws: trim back as necessary.*
- *Check between toes right up to the deep crevice between the toe joints for grass seeds or thorns which may become embedded. These can actually pierce the skin, enter the body and 'track' up the leg under the skin, and on occasion even penetrate internal organs. Rare, but it does happen.*
- *Pay particular attention to feet during cold and wet weather which can cause cracking and splitting of pads.*

CHAPTER FIVE

Skin

The skin is the largest organ in the body, and as such, reflects the general health of an animal. Jackie Drakeford, in her excellent book *Essential Care for Dogs,* wrote that the great thing about skin is that when something goes wrong with it there is either something trying to get in or something is trying to get out. This is so true, and can explain a lot of hidden problems

Toxins are eliminated through the skin which is why dogs suffering from digestive problems due either to disease or incorrect feeding will often smell musty, greasy or just plain doggy. The so called 'doggy' smell that has apparently affected canines throughout their domesticated history can often be caused by yeast infections though dogs which delight in rolling in rotting carcases and faeces won't smell any too great either!

Yeast is a fungus which thrives on cereals, though it contains large amounts of vitamin B. I once bought a yearling Whippet which had been fed large doses of yeast tablets by her well-meaning owner. The dog positively stank of yeasty sour dough and although her general health appeared to be OK her coat was very greasy, her faeces were slimy and smelt like the bottom of a rotten beer keg.

Within a month of no yeast tablets and far fewer cereals, the young bitch was happily tucking into real meat and bones.

She doubled her energy levels and no longer smelt like a run-down brewery. Her coat had also lost that greasy feel that you often see with cereal-fed dogs which are wheat intolerant.

As science progresses and we learn more about what dogs and humans should and shouldn't eat there are many 'traditional' methods of feeding which can be firmly binned along with the more outrageous claims that such and such a food is essential to good health.

Whilst yeast does contain many of the B vitamins essential to health, I don't believe that supplementing the canine diet with this type of made-for-humans tablet does them any good whatsoever. Many will disagree with me, and yes, some human supplements can be good for dogs as well as people, but in my opinion yeast is not one of them.

Skins and fur can also suffer if there is something wrong internally, disease or worms for example, and if fleas or mites are present you will also see signs that not all is well.

This is why daily grooming, not necessarily a marathon grooming session, just a quick brush over and general check up, is so important. Dogs which live in your house alongside you are more easily monitored than animals which are permanently kenneled because you are instantly aware if the animal begins to smell unpleasant in any way. It's a sad fact that some kenneled dogs just aren't given enough attention, seldom handled and even more rarely groomed, if at all.

Rough or long coated dogs obviously need more grooming than smooth coated animals, and certain types of fur tend to smell different as well. The coats and skins of lurchers containing Bedlington terrier blood are more likely to be dry to the touch than many others, whilst dogs with coarser fur, often those with pastoral or earth dog ancestry, may feel greasier when stroked.

Dogs which evolved to work in wet and cold conditions have greasier hair than most sighthounds because they need that waterproofing oil if they're not to lose undue body heat. And this type of coat quite naturally has a stronger smell than typical sighthound fur, though Deerhounds, which originated in damp, cold Scotland, are predisposed to an oilier coat than Salukis, for example.

MOULTING

Most types of dogs moult, naturally losing dead hair at certain times of the year, though certain breeds such as Poodles and Bedlington terriers are what is known as non-shedding. They don't moult at all though do lose the odd hair now and then.

The most obvious moult takes place in the spring when the heavier winter coat is shed, and whilst it is natural for dogs to lose a certain amount of fur throughout the year, excessive moulting can be a sign that not all is right with the internal workings of the dog.

Most dogs have a double coat with a finer, softer undercoat beneath the courser outer layer; the undercoat is usually moulted completely during the warmer months of the year though dogs which are ill, (this includes depression) pregnant or very old may have difficulty in moulting successfully.

Whilst wolves and other wild canids rub themselves against trees and rocks to dislodge the dead fur, domestic dogs don't seem to do this to the same extent, though I've noticed that my own dogs love to roll on rough grass far more during the spring than they do at any other time of year. I assume that they are doing this partly to relieve the itching caused by irritating loose fur.

Here's an important fact to remember ... when you keep an animal in a confined space for most of its life it loses the instinct and ability to behave naturally. I've sometimes seen dogs which don't have the opportunity to run, roll and play as nature intended because they spend 90% of their lives stuck in a kennel and run with a concrete floor. Many such dogs, if not groomed or fed correctly, sport what I call a 'teddy bear coat'; a dull, fluffy layer of dead fur which seems to resist moulting properly.

The skin needs a good blood supply to remain healthy, and regular exercise which gets the blood flowing well round the body is essential if the fur is to 'behave' normally, moulting at the correct time of year and shedding properly.

Daily exercise is a must for any dog to maintain good condition, both internally and externally.

Some rough coated lurchers shed both under coat and the longer guard hairs, appearing almost smooth coated during the summer months, and whilst loose guard hairs can be hand stripped you must be careful not to over do things and make the dog sore.

There are so many grooming tools on the market nowadays that I'd be listing them for pages if I described them all. I've found that the Furbuster is brilliant for removing both loose undercoat as well as the longer outer layers which do shed on some dogs, but use it carefully. Don't go over and over the same place during one session as this rake is really aggressive and will make the dog's skin sore if you use it too often.

The 'teasel', which is made up of fine hooked wires, is also very useful in dragging out loose fur, but shouldn't be used on smooth coated or very thin skinned dogs as the wires can literally scratch the skin.

Smooth dogs benefit from being brushed with a short haired brush, such as the 'body brush', which is designed for horses.

Some so called 'working dog' people might sneer at the thought of brushing their dogs, seeing this as a pointless indulgence beloved of pet and show dog owners. If the sneerers realised that the benefits of grooming extend beyond the outward appearance of the dog they might see that grooming is actually a very useful tool in their range of maintenance skills, a tool which has real health benefits to the animal as a whole.

I don't groom my dogs every day, maybe twice a week at most, though I'm careful to comb through my rough coated animals each time they've been out in summer grass. I often find grass seeds embedded in their coats, and occasionally one which is actually working its way into the skin.

These barbed grass seeds can cause serious problems if they remain unnoticed, and can track through the body ending up in an internal organ where infection and sepsis can even result in death.

I once lost a superb lurcher because a tumour had grown between her lungs, and although I couldn't bring myself to have her body autopsied the vet felt that her problem might well have been due to a rogue grass seed which had entered her body.

I've had two dogs which developed large abscesses on their flanks, just behind the ribs. Once again, we can't say for certain that these were caused by grass seeds, though foreign bodies which attempt to exit the dog often do so in this place, where

Excessive moulting in ungroomed dog.
Photo: Gavin Evans.

The same dog after a week's grooming which has got rid of the dead fur.
Photo: Gavin Evans.

there is less muscle and tissue to work through.

The first dog was subjected to extensive surgery, with a portion of tissue excised in an attempt to remove the cause, though the abscess 'blew up' again shortly after the incision had healed. This time I left it to burst and drain naturally whereupon the whole thing healed perfectly.

Having experienced this first problem I decided to let the second such abscess run its course, which it did without problem, though the dog was under veterinary supervision to make sure that it was not in danger throughout the process which took three weeks from start to finish.

In this photo you can see an open wound where the dog has licked extensively, literally wearing away its skin and flesh in an attempt to be rid of a grass seed which no doubt entered between the toes before tracking upwards towards the leg.

Dogs groom themselves daily, but if you notice that your dog is niggling away at one spot more than it should, then check out that place immediately.

Grass seeds for all their tiny size, can kill a dog if they get into the body and they don't show up on x-rays either, which means that any surgery is very much a 'needle in a haystack' affair and not guaranteed to bring about a successful outcome (also see the foot chapter).

NOTE: Allowing or encouraging an abscess to burst naturally should only be done under veterinary supervision and if the dog is in optimum health in the first place.

Whilst an abscess is nature's way of walling off an infective agent, dogs which are not in the best of health are often unable to bring this process to completion. I'm afraid I'm going to say it again: dogs which are fed largely cereal based diets don't always have such strong immune systems as those which are fed meat and bone based diets.

FLAKY DRY SKIN

It is normal for skin cells to be shed along with dead fur when a dog is moulting, though excessive and permanent dandruff may indicate an internal problem, often of dietary origin.

Dogs also seem to become scurfy when under stress, and I've seen many lurchers enter the show ring covered in white specks whilst their owners remark that the dog isn't usually like that. If you haven't groomed your dog much in the past then expect to see a fair amount of dead skin cells come away with the brush during the first few weeks.

Persist with the grooming and you'll see a gradual lessening of scurf as time goes by just so long as there is no underlying cause for this condition.

Evening Primrose Oil given as capsules is often used to combat a flaky skin, but

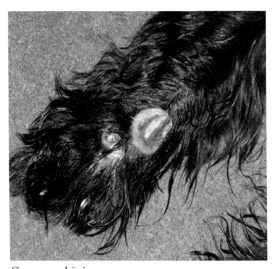

Grass seed injury.
Photo: Jackie Drakeford.

I've never found it necessary to supplement like this just so long as the dog gets enough animal fat in its diet. In fact I never add oils or extra fat to my dogs' meals, but they do get breast of lamb and chicken carcases nearly every day. Commercially bred chickens are full of fat, so I'd say that on average, about 10% of what I feed my dogs is animal fat.

Feeding animal fat will not result in a greasy skin, quite the opposite, and I've never seen flaky, scurfy skin in the fur except when a dog is moulting heavily or being fed an inadequate diet. REMEMBER - The state of your dog's skin and coat reflects its internal health.

Barbed wire is a common cause of skin tears and dogs which work round wire need to learn its dangers early in life.

SKIN TEARS AND CUTS IN RUNNING DOGS

Many running dogs will at some time or another in their lives suffer from a skin tear or cut. It's not surprising really as these fast dogs have much thinner skin than a terrier or gundog breed. Dogs which have evolved to run and catch their prey by speed carry no excess fat which could slow them down. Speed generates heat too, so running dogs don't need a layer of subcutaneous fat to keep warm: just look at human athletes, not a spare gram of fat to cover their muscles!

Correspondingly greater muscular development also means that the skin is more tightly stretched over the muscles than in slower breeds of dog, particularly so in the sprinting types such as Whippets and Greyhounds, which in turn renders that skin more prone to tearing when the dog runs through or into sharp things like barbed wire.

Laceration just below stopper pad. This size wound should really be stapled or sutured but this was allowed to heal by secondary intention (naturally) to show the healing process and just how long this takes even in a healthy and fit dog. At no time during the healing process was the dog in distress or pain. He was allowed to lick and keep the wound clean as he wished and he never over-licked the site. The whole process took just under six weeks; had the wound been sutured or stapled the dog would have been running again in a little over two weeks. As it was, he had to spend nearly six weeks on a lead, which obviously reduced his fitness level considerably, as well as being irksome for both dog and owner!

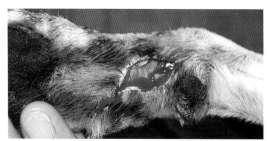

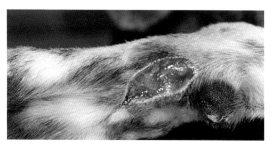

Fresh laceration. There is minor damage to the underlying tissue and a small blood vessel near the stopper was severed which explains the amount of bleeding. A skin-only tear would not bleed to the same extent. This wound was bandaged lightly for 24 hours after the incident, mainly to prevent the small blood vessel losing its clot as the dog moved about. Once clotting was successful I could allow the dog to clean the wound as he wished.

Five days after injury. The tissue within the wound is granulating well and the edges of the wound have started to grow inwards. Note how clean the site is, though there is some swelling beneath the site.

Three weeks after the injury. Note slightly discoloured tissue at right hand side of wound, and slight swelling in that area. This is because the dog escaped my attention and ran down the garden and charged about forcing dust and dirt into the injury! This caused a slight and localised infection which set back the healing process by a week. The dog continued to clean the wound several times a day and the injury continued to heal as it should once the infection had been neutralised.

Finally healed six weeks after injury. Only a tiny scab remains in this photo and soon the hair will completely cover the site. Today I can't even feel where the wound was.

NOTE: It is not ideal to leave an open wound on the lower part of the leg to heal by secondary intention. There is an increased risk of infection due to contamination from dirt at ground level, plus the length of time spent with an open wound could increase the risk of infection from other sources. I have included these photos in the book purely to show the differences in healing time when compared with a sutured wound. The reasons and benefits of closing a wound with sutures or staples are obvious.

No sighthound possesses the thick layer of subcutaneous fat which is found in breeds such as Labradors, and to a lesser extent in German Shepherds, Collies and the Bull breeds.

Thickness of skin also varies within the sighthound breeds, with Whippets and Greyhounds topping the list of those with 'tissue paper' skin: not really a great combination when a dog has tremendous speed and skin which splits apart when barely grazed by a barbed-wire tine.

Many lurchers with Collie or Terrier blood in their veins have much thicker skin, though some pure breeds such as Deerhounds are blessed with far tougher skin than Whippets. Very fast dogs with tunnel vision, those intent on what they are chasing, will always be at more risk of injury from barbed wire than slightly slower dogs and those which think whilst they're running.

Ex-racing Greyhounds are the worst when it comes to crashing accidents as they have never had the opportunity to learn how to negotiate obstacles when young, having spent their lives either in safe paddocks or running on smooth, obstacle-free tracks. It can take months and months to educate such a dog to the dangers of the countryside, and people who take on ex-racers need to treat their dogs in the same way as they would a puppy, taking plenty of time to introduce the animal to all manner of situations whilst on the lead.

Barbed wire! The curse of the running dog owner, is found throughout the world, and I don't possess a single dog which hasn't, at some time in its life, become hung up or torn on those vicious tines of steel, though only once did such an injury result in the death of the unfortunate dog and this was a freak accident which resulted in an important muscle being completely torn away to the extent that reattaching it was impossible.

A dog is normally considered to be safe when it is on the lead beside you, but even then, watch out for the over keen dog that is waiting for you to crawl through a barbed wire fence and then tries to jump that fence whilst still on the lead!

Teach the dog the 'wait' command, preferably in a sitting position (a dog can't jump if it is sitting down) then call it to you after you've negotiated the fence. Or you can send your dog through the fence and then tell it to wait as it is less likely to become impatient and attempt to jump as it sees you leaving it. This is especially useful with worried or nervous pups that see you 'leaving' them if you go first.

Barbed wire tears commonly occur on the deepest part of the chest just behind the front legs, or on the back, even across the front legs, though I've seen tears on almost every part of a dog, including the removal of a patch of skin just above the hock on the hind leg when the lurcher flicked its hind legs up as it jumped through two strands of wire, catching the leg on the upper strand as it did so.

Most barbed wire injuries are not life-threatening though they can be messy and quite nasty to see, varying from a tiny nick in the skin to a major tear with a large flap of skin pulled away from the body in a typically triangular shape, or where the skin has been torn and also slipped down the leg. This is known as 'de-gloving' and is a case where immediate veterinary attention is needed if the wound is to be stitched back together successfully.

Even with professional suturing some very large skin tears do 'break down', which means that the skin surrounding the stitches has died off because there was too much tension when the edges of

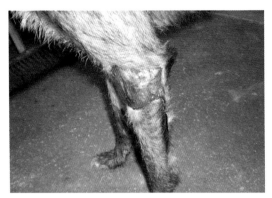

A bad 'de-gloving' tear on front leg.

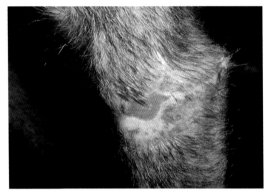

The wound was successfully sutured but subsequently broke down due to skin tension leaving an open patch of raw tissue which was allowed to heal naturally .

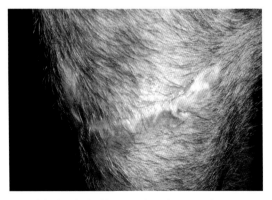

Freshly healed albeit with substantial scarring which lessened with time and never hampered the dog's working ability. Photos: Karen Marr.

the skin were pulled back together. If only a small part of the wound breaks down it is normally left to heal by what is called 'secondary intention', nature's method, whereby the gaping hole in the skin slowly heals from the edges in towards the centre of the gap.

That large wound, if left to its own devices may well have healed by secondary intention, albeit with an increased risk of infection due to the size of the injury. The main problem, apart from the suffering caused to the dog and the obvious cruelty in leaving such a wound untreated, would be that the mass of scar tissue accompanying such a healing regime could prevent the dog from moving properly once the injury had healed.

Scar tissue doesn't stretch like normal healthy skin, and such a large amount of scarring can seriously hamper a dog's movement when running. There would also be a possibility that the scarred tissue could tear open if put under great strain, such as when galloping, not to mention the fact that there would never be any hair growth over such an area which means that the bare skin would be at greater risk of being damaged. The fact that lurchers and sighthounds have very little subcutaneous fat also means that many otherwise minor skin wounds will also affect the underlying muscle, something which needs to be carefully assessed if you are considering treating your own dog.

At the time of writing it is legal to treat your own dog if it has suffered an injury, but beware, if you are found to have caused any unnecessary suffering to your dog, or any animal through incorrect treatment then you will be rightly prosecuted for cruelty or neglect.

Experience is a wonderful thing, and the minor skin tears that my lurchers obtain through their work no longer have me running to the vet because years of treating such injuries have shown me that most small cuts and tears heal very well with no veterinary intervention.

However, when considering home treatment of any skin wounds I always look at exactly WHERE on the dog's body the injury has occurred, and the SIZE of the injury.

Some wounds with jagged edges on very moveable parts of the body such as the groin area and under the 'armpit' of the front leg, really do need specialist attention, and it goes without saying that major traumas of whatever kind mean you need to see your vet as quickly as possible.

WOUNDS WHICH NEED SUTURING OR STAPLING

Many years ago, when the first veterinary staplers came on to the market my own vet kindly gave me a small field stapler to try out, and I was so impressed with this wonderful gadget that I've never been without one since.

If you take a lurcher to the vet for minor wound suturing, the chances are that the vet will use a stapler, and unless the patient is highly sensitive or too much time has elapsed since the accident, he or she will more than likely staple the edges of a clean cut together without using a local anaesthetic.

Local anaesthetic injections can really sting, as well as prolonging healing time a little in some cases as they actually slightly damage the tissue into which they are injected. However, if there was a choice between sedation, general anaesthesia and a local anaesthetic injection before suturing a wound I would choose the local injection every time, though of course major surgery demands a general anaesthetic.

Skin stapler and staple remover.

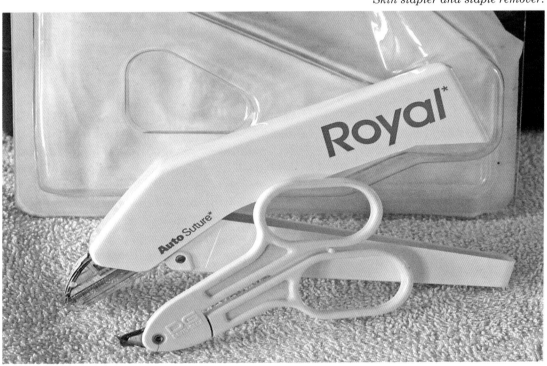

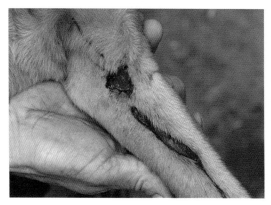

Skin tear, not full thickness. Cleaning with salt water was the only treatment needed.

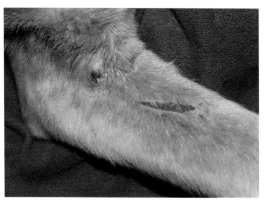

The same wound ten days later and almost healed.

However, there are some big 'BUTS' when it comes to DIY treatment of your dog. The important thing to remember about using a stapler at home to mend small cuts is that the wound must be ABSOLUTELY CLEAN and free from debris, hair or any other foreign bodies, as any of these can cause infection in the wound site.

I use Hibiscrub to clean out wounds before stapling. Hibiscrub is an anti-microbial skin pre-operative skin cleanser which needs to be diluted before using on open wounds.

NOTE: When using antiseptics or disinfectants remember that a disinfectant is stronger than an antiseptic. Disinfectants are commonly used to remove bacteria from inanimate objects (hard surfaces) and using a disinfectant on skin can cause hardening of the skin, lesions and even erosion of the skin.

If you do use a disinfectant on a wound then always dilute according to the manufacturer's recommendation and be very careful not to over use. Always check label to see whether or not a disinfectant is a skin irritant: many are not suitable for use on the skin even if diluted.

Antiseptics are designed for use on skin and are much safer to use on wounds, though should always be diluted as per the manufacturers' instructions. Always read the label on any disinfectant or antiseptic before you attempt to clean a wound.

I would never advise anyone to use a stapler unless they have been shown how to use one correctly, and I wouldn't use one if there has been underlying damage to muscle or tendon. At the risk of repeating myself, that is a job for the professional.

Staplers must be used for skin tears and cuts ONLY, unless used by a vet following a surgical procedure under sterile conditions and usually accompanied by a course of antibiotics.

The edges of the wound must be fresh, and ideally you will be stapling a wound less than 30 minutes after the injury occurred or the tiny blood vessels in the skin will already have started sealing the cut edges of the wound and will then find it more difficult to make the connection with the opposing side of the wound.

The sooner you can staple these minor skin tears and cuts the better from the dog's point of view as well, because for about 30 minutes after the incident the dog will usually feel very little pain in and around the wound site due to naturally-occurring chemicals produced in the body which are called endorphins. These act as nature's painkillers, blocking the body's response to the pain temporarily whilst the body does what it needs to in order to survive: fight or flight depending on the type of animal and the dangerous situation in which it finds itself.

As an aside, scientists now believe that people who self-harm do so in order to feel the 'high' produced by the endorphins when cutting themselves! Luckily dogs aren't likely to suffer from the same affliction but running dogs come into contact with sharp objects often enough in the course of work or play without deliberately seeking pain!

It is also of vital importance to hold the edges of the wound together, and raised upwards, so that the two cut sides are facing upwards away from the body, but held in contact with one another whilst you insert the staple.

If you don't do this correctly you will not only cause the dog intense pain as the staple penetrates beneath the skin layer and into the muscle or underlying tissue, you will also run the risk of introducing infection into that subcutaneous tissue where there was previously none.

Another thing to remember is that once you have closed a wound with staples you might well have sealed in a potentially infective agent despite your best efforts at cleaning the area, which is the reason a vet prescribes antibiotics after any kind of surgery.

If I am sure that the wound is clean and has been caused by a relatively clean object and also bled a reasonable amount (which helps to flush any debris from the wound), and that there has been no subcutaneous tissue damage, then I would use a stapler, and then only if I feel that the wound warrants any intervention at all.

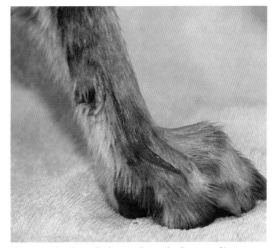

Cut washed and cleaned ready for stapling

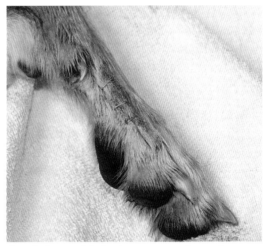

Stapled cut with drainage gap at base of wound.

Not even a scar remains to show the place.

Expect to see a small amount of clear fluid leak from the wound, This is Serum. Serum is made up of white blood platelets, the infantry in the healing war, and it is they which are vital to the healing process, so a clear or slightly pink coloured discharge from the wound site is normal.

There should be no nasty smell from a healing wound, and the skin around the edges of the wound should never look dark red or inflamed: if it shows any other colour than a healthy pink then infection is present, infection which could invade the whole body and lead to septicaemia and death. Slight reddening, bruising and swelling are normal around wounds which are the result of impact, but this must not be confused with inflammation caused by infection. I'm not trying to put anyone off using a stapler, but it is important to be aware of all the possible problems that could occur when you treat your own dog.

Equally important as the stapler is the staple remover, without which you will be up the creek without the proverbial paddle. Staples are removed with a special tool which 'undoes' the staple, which has formed a box like shape on insertion.

Any attempt to use pliers or other incorrect tools could well result in breaking the staple, leaving a bit under the skin which could cause more problems and still necessitate a trip to the vet! Staples should be removed about 10 days after insertion, by which time the skin edges should have grown back together. If they haven't you should suspect some type of infection, so you're off to the vet anyway!

NOTE: Barbed wire tears are often found on the legs of running dogs and as these legs are usually slim, thin skinned with very little underlying tissue to protect tendons and bones, you need to be very careful when stapling or stitching such injuries.

SKIN WOUNDS WHICH CAN BE LEFT TO HEAL BY SECONDARY INTENTION

If a tear or cut is a full thickness skin wound and doesn't exceed two centimetres in length, I'd usually allow the wound to heal naturally (by secondary intention) providing that the wound is not situated on a part of the body where there is a lot of movement such as the 'armpit' on the front leg or the groin area at the hind end of the dog.

First you need to make sure that there is no dirt or hair or other debris under the loose triangular flap of skin, the point of which will be facing towards the head end of the dog, unless the dog was going backwards at the time of impact!

Flush the wound out carefully with warm saline solution (cooled boiled water to which a teaspoon of salt has been added). Incidentally, I use warm saline solution simply because the dog doesn't react so sharply to liquid which is the same temperature as its body: very cold, or hot, liquid will obviously cause more pain.

Clip away the surrounding fur carefully with a very sharp, preferably round ended pair of scissors. Pointed scissors can cause more damage if the dog suddenly moves while you're doing this.

Any wound will seep a small amount of serum, a clear fluid, as it heals. This is nature sending white blood corpuscles (platelets) to the site, the first step in healing, and there will be seepage around the wound site so you need to clip the fur so as to keep the whole area as clean as possible.

DO NOT BE TEMPTED to use Wound Powder on these sorts of wounds. Whilst wound powder is great for drying up oozy grazes which are not full skin thickness, a full thickness skin tear, cut or puncture needs to remain moist and should not be allowed to scab up immediately. If such a wound does dry up too quickly it will start to contract uncomfortably before the tissue has started to granulate in the middle of the wound, pulling at the edges, becoming sore and irritating to the dog.

If anything other than very small cuts scabs over too fast, infection can arise if bacteria have been sealed in under the scab, so watch for any signs of infection once the skin has closed over the wound.

A wound heals from within and the body knows what sort of tissue to grow where. It starts off by forming new subcutaneous tissue within the wound before finally sealing the area with new skin to finish off the healing process. Such wounds heal far better if they remain moist. If the dog can reach the wound so much the better, and I've never known a working dog or sensible sighthound lick excessively at wounds to the extent that they make things worse or inhibit the healing process though some non-working pure breeds which have been genetically over-manipulated by Man are predisposed to become obsessive over such things.

Most dogs will lick and clean the wound several times a day which is just what the thing needs to stop it drying out prematurely, but unless you can see that the wound is getting larger in size or that there is sign of infection, don't stop the dog doing what it needs to. I've had several fairly large tears on the underside of dogs' chests, and it's surprising just how far back under their chests a lurcher or sighthound can reach to clean such a wound.

Tears on the back of the neck which the dog cannot reach to clean with its tongue will need more help from you to stay clean and moist. You can do this by bathing the site gently with saline solution (salt water) every day. It is very common for wounds to the back of the neck, top of the shoulders and back to become quite messy as they cannot drain naturally and the dog can't keep the injury free of debris by itself.

In rough coated dogs it is also not unusual for such a wound to be unnoticed unless you spend time grooming the animal every day. I don't groom every single day and I've sometimes come across hair clogged scabs on my dogs' backs some days after they had rushed incautiously through a barbed wire fence.

Nine times out of ten this type of wound causes no problem, though occasionally you may find that a slight and localised infection is present due to the fact that hair has clogged the site allowing bacteria to be sealed into the wound. All you need to do is soak the scab and hair with warm salt water then snip the clogged hair carefully away, removing the gunky scab before cleaning the wound.

If you have several dogs which live together it is quite common for one dog to help in keeping a wound clean and moist if one of their companions suffers such an injury. I have some such 'nurse' dogs in my pack, and most injured animals are only too happy for these canine medics to help out especially if the wounds are in hard to reach places. Just make sure that the medic dog doesn't get carried away in its duties, exactly in the same way you would check that the patient itself doesn't over-lick a wound.

If you have to tend to the wound yourself you can either use Intrasite Gel, Aloe Vera Gel or honey to keep out airborne bacteria and hold in moisture once you have cleaned the injury with salt water. Just a blob on the end of your finger of any of the above can be applied to the raw tissue. (Don't mix them together!) Don't worry if it spreads a bit as you'll be cleaning the whole thing again the next day anyway.

A typical wire tear often leaves a loose flap of skin, usually triangular in shape. Don't try to press this flap back into place as it will almost certainly fail to do so properly and will often trap an infection if it does stick back down. If the dog can clean the wound itself that flap of skin will gradually dry up and shrink back, either to die off or become reabsorbed, though it might appear to be rolling into a sausage shape for a while, especially on leg wounds if the only way that the dog can lick the wound is downwards, taking the flap of skin along with its tongue.

Once the flap has become blue or grey in colour and looks to be shrivelling up I often snip it off as dogs find this dangly bit of skin really irritating and will sometimes nag away at the place. The shrivelled bit of skin won't have any feeling in it by this stage and once you have removed it the dog will revert to just keeping the wound clean a couple of times a day.

For the first couple of days after your dog has incurred a skin tear you probably won't see much change, but after about three days you should see that the edges of the torn skin are thickening slightly, and that the centre of the wound is becoming slightly granular.

This is the start of healing where the new cells are growing to fill in the wound. Keep the site moist and clean and over the next 7-10 days you will see that the wound is shrinking in size, though remaining open.

Only when the wound has reduced to about the size of a one pence piece can you allow it to scab over. Allow it to scab over prematurely and the chances are that you'll see pus seeping from under that scab: usually only a slight localised infection and nothing to worry about, but monitor such wounds very carefully.

NOTE: If a dog is on medication of any sort (some drugs can compromise the immune system, steroids being one such example) I'd recommend taking the dog to the vet as soon as possible after any accident. An immune system which isn't working properly will leave the body open to infection which can flare up in a frighteningly short time. Large doses of antibiotics are often needed to combat such infections.

Normal healthy scabs must NOT be picked off as they are protecting the new tissue beneath them, and they'll fall off when the time is right, often taking the surrounding fur with them but not to worry. Sometimes you may need to snip the fur very carefully to allow the scab to come off completely, but don't do this unless the fur is stopping the by now loose scab from falling off.

Any sign of dark red or purple tissue around the wound, an unpleasant smell or signs of pus means that you must remove the scab and thoroughly clean the wound site again.

Providing that the dog is in good health and is being fed a good diet high in animal protein the whole healing process of a minor skin tear should take three weeks maximum.

TIP: Any injury makes demands on the body as a whole, and a good diet is important in aiding healing. Research tells us that an injured body uses much more protein than normal to help in the healing process and I know that my own dogs, on a raw meat and bone diet, heal much faster now than they used to when I fed a more cereal based diet which was lower in animal protein.

LARGER SKIN TEARS AND CUTS
When should you take the dog to the vet for a skin wound? Depending upon your

level of expertise and experience I would say that anything needing more than three or four staples or an injury which involves damage to muscles, tendons or bones needs specialist treatment immediately.

The sooner a serious wound gets the right sort of attention the sooner it will heal. There's no point coming home with a badly torn dog on the Friday night and waiting until the Monday in the hope of saving some money by not calling the vet over the weekend! The longer a bad wound is left without treatment the greater the possibility of permanent damage, especially where muscles and tendons are concerned.

THE BUBBLE WRAP SYNDROME

Sometimes a rather strange thing happens when a dog's skin is punctured or cut, one which I call the bubble wrap syndrome! The correct term is subcutaneous emphysema, and whilst alarming when first seen is not usually a problem if it has been caused by air getting under the skin through a skin wound.

When a dog cuts or tears its skin and carries on running, air can sometimes be forced under the skin through the wound and as a dog's skin is only very firmly attached to the subcutaneous tissue at certain key points on the body, (mainly the feet, head and root of tail) any air which enters a wound can seep a long way under the skin.

This is commonly seen in foot punctures where by the action of the dog as it continues to run, reopens the wound at every step, forcing air, along with mud and debris, up into the wound. Even without infection, and a well washed out wound, you might find that your previously slender legged running dog wakes up the following morning with a 'fat' leg! Experience once again comes into play here: how do you tell

Barbed wire tear before stitching note how the dog does not appear to be in any great pain. Photo: Sam Coleman.

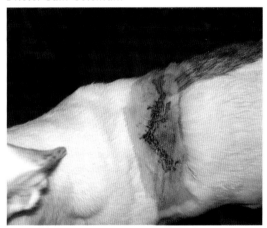

Professionally sutured skin wound. Photo: Sam Coleman.

the difference between a 'fat' leg which is full of air, and one that is swollen because of rising infection? First, a 'fat' leg full of air will not contain any of the heat that we associate with infection, so the leg won't feel hot to the touch. Second, an air-filled leg will feel almost as though there is bubble wrap under the skin, hence the name I've given it!

There is a subtle but distinct difference between a liquid-filled swelling and an air-filled swelling. Liquid, either from blood or pus (more of that later) will feel firmer

101

to the touch under the skin, whereas air can be dimpled more easily under finger pressure, almost as if you were pressing an air bed: one touch pushes the air to the side. This dimpling also corrects itself easily once you have removed the pressure and you can sometimes feel a 'crackling' beneath the skin with your fingers.

Although the dog may well be in some discomfort from the original wound, it is unlikely to be in pain from the bubble wrap syndrome unless it covers a large part of the body, in which case you need to see the vet FAST just in case there is another underlying cause, such as a punctured lung!

My worst case of bubble wrap was when my young Saluki lurcher hung himself over a barbed wire fence at the age of about 11 months. Balanced awkwardly across the top wire with his feet resting on the lower strand, I had to untwist from the tines the web of skin that joins the hind leg to the body. Brave and sensible dog that he was he remained still and relatively calm and luckily for me a fellow dog walker was passing by, who supported the dog whilst I untwisted the tine.

There was only a tiny hole in the web of skin between the front of the hind leg and his abdomen but the next day the dog's back was strangely swollen and upon examination his entire left side, loins and left hind leg were covered in bubble wrap syndrome.

Each time the dog walked the movement of that web of skin sucked air in through the wound between skin and underlying tissue. He looked really uncomfortable, but as I knew that he had sustained no other injury all I could do was keep him quiet in the kennel and wait for the air to be absorbed into his body, which it did within a few days with no ill effect whatsoever.

So the good news is that air is reabsorbed by the body with no problem: the only difficult bit for those of you who haven't seen such a phenomenon before is recognising the syndrome correctly. Once again: if in doubt, seek the advice of a vet.

PUNCTURE WOUNDS

Puncture wounds can be quite a bit more troublesome than open skin tears and cuts, and are usually caused by pointed objects which have driven deep into the underlying tissue.

Teeth and thorns are two of the most common objects to cause puncture wounds to running dogs, and both are often heavily contaminated with bacteria. Whilst thorn punctures are usually located under the pads and between the toes, bite wounds are more usually found around the face and neck, though also on the legs. I'll deal with thorns and teeth separately for reasons which will become clear later on.

THORN PUNCTURES

To begin with, thorns, and in particular, blackthorns, contain alkaloids which react quickly upon penetration beneath the skin. There is some debate as to whether the very small amount of alkaloid present in a broken-off thorn tip is solely responsible for the acute and dramatic infection that nearly always follows such a puncture, but it does seem to be fact that most blackthorn punctures 'blow up' alarmingly within a very short space of time.

As most dogs puncture their pads or between their toes on thorns that are lying on the ground still attached to broken branches, it is more likely that the thorn has been contaminated by animal faeces or other bacteria which, coupled with the long length of such thorns, enables them to set up a breeding site deep beneath the skin, even if the thorn itself is no longer in situ. See chapter on Feet for details on how to look after puncture wounds to feet.

VERY IMPORTANT! It is possible for a thorn, nail or other sharp and hard object to actually penetrate a bone in the foot, and this can introduce bacteria into the bone itself. If this happens you absolutely will need to see the vet for a course of antibiotics, or risk ultimately losing the dog's toe.

Infections within the bone usually need a special type of antibiotics for what are known as anaerobic bacteria, bacteria which live without oxygen, and it is they that are responsible for deep seated infections within the bones or internal organs. Just using a broad spectrum antibiotic which has been designed for 'surface' bacteria will not do the job.

You can use a good broad spectrum antibiotic for most skin wounds but anaerobic bacterial infections need a specific antibiotic (such as those used by dentists to treat root abscesses) to beat them into submission.

Long acting Penicillin injectionable solution is a commonly used method of combating an infection caused by bites, and is injected subcutaneously (under the skin on the back of the neck).

Don't try and attempt intra-muscular injections yourself unless you have seen this done and have experience of this type of injection.

Basically, if you have a dog which remains lame after an abscess has burst, or a toe or foot which is constantly hot and swollen and refuses to heal, then suspect some type of internal infection, or a broken bone and get the dog to the vet immediately!

Puncture wounds from inanimate objects do occur on other parts of the body, such as the dog running into a barbed wire fence and simply bounces back off that fence. These are usually not serious as of course there will be no broken off bits remaining in the dog.

Lurchers which run through woodland are at risk of impaling themselves on broken branches, which can be far more serious if part of the twig or branch breaks off inside the dog's body. Punctures like this must be seen by a vet if you suspect that there is any internal damage whatsoever, and bits of twigs and branches sometimes need major surgery to be removed. Happily these incidents are far from common, though running through woodland on a regular basis with a hard-driving dog will of course increase the chances of this sort of injury.

WOUNDS FROM BITES
Rat bite

Bite wounds generally fall into two categories: punctures or rips. A bite from a rat's chisel like incisors is always a rip type wound, and although sometimes out of all proportion to the size of the animal that has bitten your dog, generally flushes out quite quickly with the natural bleeding that accompanies such a bite. Rat bites usually bleed very well due to the slashing action of the rat's teeth, which is just as well as these rodents come into contact with all manner of bacteria as part of their lifestyle. Always wash rat bites well with salt water or antiseptic solution: Hibiscrub or a human antiseptic diluted to the maker's recommendations for open wounds. Monitor rat bites well whilst healing just as you would any other wound, and make sure that the dog is up to date with its inoculations for Leptospirosis.

Here's a fact: whilst fewer people are boosting their dogs on an annual basis nowadays, it is true that the Leptospirosis vaccine only remains effective for six to

Rats deliver slicing bites as opposed to punctures.

12 months, so if your dog is ratting on a regular basis it would be advisable to keep at least that part of its inoculations up to date. It has been estimated that 55% of all rats carry this disease, often known as Weil's Disease.

It is also unfortunately true that a number of dogs do die each year from Leptospirosis even though they had been recently vaccinated as sometimes the vaccine doesn't 'take'. The only way to ensure that a dog is fully protected by a vaccination is to get a titre count done by means of a blood test which will ascertain whether or not the vaccine has done its job properly.

Bites from carnivores
Bite wounds from the canine teeth of predators are usually puncture wounds, and deep puncture wounds are common in dogs used in fox control. Although the current hunting ban makes it illegal to use dogs to control foxes in the UK, accidents can and do happen if a fox jumps up in front of your rabbit-hunting dog, and if the dog does come into contact with that fox and is bitten, you should always search for and check the type of wound and its location on the dog.

If the dog has been bitten on the leg you will need to check just how many punctures there are on the leg. A fox has four canine teeth, just like a dog, two in the upper jaw and two in the lower. A fox's canine teeth are out of all proportion to the size of its jaw, and much sharper than those of most dogs, with the result that a puncture wound from one of those teeth can go a long way into the victim. As the fox is an opportunistic scavenger its teeth are laden with bacteria, and unless the dog has accumulated a good immunity to these bacteria through regular contact with foxes, infection will invariably follow a fox bite. I usually find that the first encounter with a fox results in infection, which I combat with topical antibiotic cream. Subsequent bites don't provoke infection nearly as much because the dog has acquired some degree of immunity to a fox's bacteria.

When inspecting the leg of the dog which has been bitten by either a fox or another dog you need to find all the puncture wounds in order to clean them out properly. Incidentally, a dog's teeth are much blunter than a fox's, which results in much more bruising to the surrounding tissue.

Dogs which have been involved in a fight with another dog invariably suffer from extensive bruising to the area surrounding the bite. Invasion of any joint by sharp bacteria-laden pointy things needs careful and thorough treatment if infection is not to set in immediately. Due to the shape of a fox's canine tooth this sort of wound doesn't often bleed much either which means they are unlikely to be flushed out well by flowing blood unless a blood vessel has been punctured. In the field you can start by flushing the wound immediately with saline solution (salt water) which you will of course have in a handy squeegee bottle in your first aid kit.

All joints are protected by something called synovial fluid, which acts a little bit like oil in a car engine, helping the moving parts to remain mobile. A joint can become dry if this fluid drains away due to injury, causing permanent problems such as arthritis when the bones receive undue wear from grating against one another.

This is why it is very important to give

such injuries a long period of recovery: a month is not too long in the case of a bad bite to the wrist. Providing there is no infection present, the wound will heal and the synovial fluid will replenish itself.

However, this will not happen overnight, and you MUST NOT ALLOW THE DOG TO WORK THE JOINT EXCESSIVELY if you want it to heal properly.

IMPORTANT FACT! Cartilege (the stuff that helps cushion the bones within the joints) has no blood supply of its own. Tendons and ligament also have a poor blood supply, hence their whitish colour: no red blood in there! Unlike muscles which are bursting with red blood cells.

Any damage to joints, cartilage, tendons and ligaments can take up to 12 weeks to heal satisfactorily depending on the severity of the injury. Rest is vital, the healing power of rest is greatly under-rated!

At the risk of banging away on the same drum and sounding like a cracked vinyl record, HEALING CAN'T TAKE PLACE IF THE JOINT IS HAVING TO WORK HARD, and a leg that is bearing a quarter of the dog's weight shouldn't be running at all. Lead walk only until there is absolutely no sign of heat, tenderness or lameness.

Rest it for as long as it needs and FOLLOW THE ADVICE of the person in charge of your dog, be that the physiotherapist or the vet. Don't just say to yourself: "My dog's had a month on the lead and it'll be fine now because it's stopped limping." A great number of running dogs have been forced into early retirement because their owners were too impatient and wanted to get them working again too soon.

Let's get back to that bite to the wrist: clean it out thoroughly by syringing (no needle!) salt water into the wound. Do this

Fox bites can be tears as well as punctures.

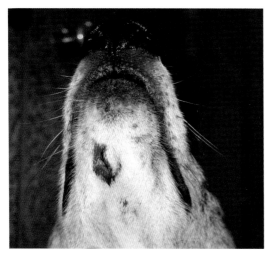

Check for bite wounds on both sides of jaw or legs.

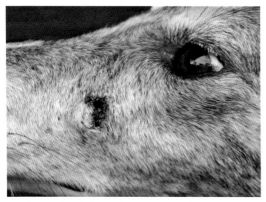

10 days after injury, healing well from within and washed daily with salt water, treated with honey.

several times. Hydrogen Peroxide at 6% vol. the sort you find in the chemist, can be diluted one part HP to five parts boiled cooled water, and this syringed into the puncture wound will oxydise and bubble up as a froth, bringing with it any debris.

Don't be tempted to keep using either Hydrogen Peroxide or antiseptic day after day because these products will slow down the healing process; this is because their action cauterises the tissue to a certain extent. Once should be enough. If infection sets in despite using HP, then you can apply a poultice to help draw out any infection lurking in the depths of the wound.

Once again: two applications of a poultice, 12 hours apart, should be sufficient to do this. If a poultice hasn't been successful in removing infection then you'll need antibiotics.

Many people routinely give a dog an injection of long acting Penicillin in the case of fox bites but I've found that this isn't necessary providing the dog's immune system has learned to recognise and cope with those particular bacteria. Dogs which only come into contact with foxes or other biting animals once in a blue moon will have far less resistance to infection.

TOPICAL ANTIBIOTIC TREATMENT
Whilst I don't use oral or injectable antibiotics unless absolutely necessary, I do use topically applied antibiotic ointment. You can get an antibiotic ointment syringe, the nozzle of which is introduced into the wound.

Since using such products I have never had to use either oral or injectable antibiotics for fox bites. Flooding an animal's system with antibiotics on a regular basis can cause antibiotics to lose their efficiency over time, and the fact that they also kill the intestinal flora (the good bugs in the gut) means that the animal's general health could be compromised through prolonged use.

By using a locally applied antibiotic ointment in the wound itself you are attacking the infection at source, which seems to me to be a far more logical way of doing things. Having said that, if you have been negligent in attending to any wounds in the first place you might well find that a generalised infection sets in, which will require a course of antibiotics.

I've never had a puncture wound go bad when I've used this method of treatment, and the stickiness of the cream also helps to stop the wound drying out prematurely.

Wash out bad puncture wounds every day with saline solution and insert enough antibiotic cream to fill the hole: most such wounds will heal within a couple of weeks: if they don't then suspect a foreign body deep within the wound. Once again, if healing doesn't take place as it should you will need to see a vet as some bacteria are very resistant to antibiotics and need special treatment in order to kill them.

TIP: It is often easy to find the main puncture wound or wounds to the front or side of the wrist or leg, but search carefully on the opposite side of the dog's leg to find the corresponding holes from the opposing canine teeth of the attacker, be it a fox or other carnivore. All predators have similar dentition, and a bite from a cat can be just as nasty as that of a fox. Missing the smaller puncture wounds can result in just as severe an infection as if you missed the larger ones in the first place.

NOTE: Mastitis ointment is not licensed for dogs so you may find that your vet is reluctant to prescribe it. I have never, over the many years that I have used this type of antibiotic cream, encountered an adverse reaction but this is my experience only.

DO NOT BANDAGE UNLESS ABSOLUTELY NECESSARY

Puncture wounds of all but the very largest (the type that would have you running like a scalded cat in the direction of the vet, such as impalement on farm machinery or branches) are best left open to the air as they need to drain freely, and once again, if the dog can lick the place so much the better.

Just keep an eye on the site for any undue warmth (the place will be slightly warmer than the undamaged surrounding areas anyway due to localised inflammation of the surrounding tissue) but watch for excessive heat, swelling, pus or severe discolouration of the skin.

NOTE: If you are interested in natural and homeopathic treatments and remedies you might like to have a look at Jackie Drakeford and Mark Elliott's book *Essential Care in the Field*, which offers a host of useful advice and treatments both in first aid situations and for more long term conditions and problems.

It would have been foolish of me to have included everything that Jackie covers in her book, and there is only so much room in any one book!

Gentle physiotherapy of a healing joint is also useful. Note the word GENTLE! Gentle rubbing with a slightly cupped hand can promote increased blood flow to any damaged area, and you can also VERY GENTLY flex the joint a few times during the course of the massage.

Do not attempt to massage if infection is present or if the massage causes pain to the dog. After the first week, all being well and if healing is progressing satisfactorily, this form of physiotherapy will help to 'remind' the joint of how to move correctly and also helps to reduce potential permanent stiffness.

Just as human accident victims are encouraged to get moving as soon as possible after surgery or injury, so can we encourage our dogs to walk gently: twice a day during the period of convalescence.

Keeping the blood flowing well round the body and raising the heart rate very slightly are important factors in any recuperation. Just leaving a dog lying in a kennel for days or even weeks on end will prove counter-productive in the long run.

BITES TO THE FACE

Bites to a dog's face are often a combination of punctures and tears, the tearing occurring when the dog attempts to pull away from the animal which is doing the biting. Bites to the face should be treated primarily as for puncture wounds, and then as for skin tears. Just as with leg bites, even if you can see an obvious bite on the top of the dog's muzzle, you need to check for punctures under the dog's chin as these will correspond with the bite from the opposing incisors of the fox.

Failure to clean and treat these bite wounds correctly, whilst unlikely to be life-threatening to the dog, can leave a good deal of swelling around the area. If the dog is healthy and strong its body will seal off infection in the area surrounding the puncture, and this swelling, often very hard to the touch, can take many weeks to subside, and be painful to the dog if you press the place with your finger.

Hard swellings such as these are simply infected tissue and pus, which in the healthy dog is gradually reabsorbed by the body, but if the wound had been properly attended to in the first place it shouldn't have got to this stage.

It is very important that bite wounds to the dog's face are not allowed to scab over until the site has filled up with new healthy tissue or infection will arise. If a scab does form prematurely you can soak it off with warm salt water, swabbing at it with damp cotton wool, thereby leaving new tissue underneath. Don't be tempted to try and pick the scab off whilst dry as you will cause undue pain. A scab is simply dried blood, and will soften and dissolve if soaked in warm water, though if the underlying tissue has become infected you will see pus oozing from beneath that scab.

You must clean away any pus and infected tissue very carefully (this is known as debriding a wound) and make sure that there is no spread of the infection beyond the wound itself.

Anyone who has ever suffered a cut to a finger will know that there is bound to be a certain amount of inflammation surrounding any break to the skin, but experience is needed to tell the difference from normal inflammation and the onset of a more serious infection. If in doubt see a vet!

Bites in the area surrounding the eyes must be very carefully monitored and if you suspect that the eyeball has been damaged you will need to seek professional help immediately.

TEARS TO EARS

A dog's ear bleeds profusely if cut, and then some! The fact that the dog is usually running when it catches an ear on wire, thorns or something's teeth also exacerbates the problem as the blood is flowing faster round the body during physical exertion.

The ear tips and front edges are commonly the most often damaged, and the first thing to do is to stop the dog from running if the blood is flowing freely. Dogs which work bramble patches are often at risk, emerging from their work place looking as if someone had attacked them with a chain saw! And then of course the dog shakes its head as the sticky blood irritates its ear and neck, spraying blood everywhere and coating both sides of its head as well! You can apply pressure between finger and thumb to stem the bleeding and if you are near a clean source of water liberally dousing the ear in cold water will also help to slow down the flow of blood.

To be honest, I don't usually bother about washing ears and heads until I return home as even whilst walking on the lead the dog is likely to shake its head from time to time which sets off the bleeding all over again.

The one good thing about so much blood is that any dirt and infection is almost always flushed away from the wound very quickly, so all you have to do is immobilise the ear so that the blood can begin to clot and seal the wound.

Do make sure to wash away all the blood, which will by now have soaked into the dog's fur on head and neck. If you leave

Even a minor tear to the ear can bleed for ages if the dog has been running.

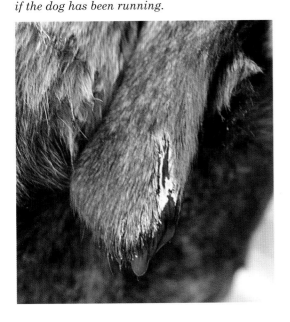

dried blood encrusted in the fur you will lose the fur from that area, albeit temporarily; dry blood also irritates the dog which will scratch incessantly possibly making its skin sore as well. Dry the area as much as possible, trying to hold on to the ear in the mean time because all dogs want to shake their heads after being saturated in water.

Use a roll of cotton wool and tear or cut off a piece which is large enough to completely cover the ear. Fold this in two and wrap it around the ear, then fold the whole ear gently on top of the dog's head. Fix the ear on top of the head with Vetwrap going right round the head and under

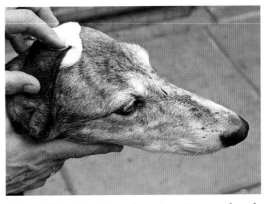

Above: Wrap the injured ear in cotton wool and fold on top of the head. It helps to have 4 hands when bandaging ears.

Below: Wrap Vetwrap in front of and behind the free ear to help it stay in place

the throat, several times. Finish off with Elastoplast fabric strapping if necessary.

Make sure that the bandaging isn't so tight that the dog can't drink, eat, swallow or move its head. I've often had to resort to using dabs of superglue to keep even sticky fabric strapping in place as the amount of force generated by a dog shaking its head is quite extreme.

Yes, you may have to eventually cut the fur to remove the glue, but fur grows back. Just be sure to only use tiny spots of glue which won't seep through the fur and stick to the skin. You might not have this option with very fine coated dogs such as Whippets, but I've never had a problem doing this with the average lurcher be it rough or smooth coated.

Whilst we do hear scare mongering tales about superglue, hot water removes hardened superglue from human skin with no damage, and of course superglue was first developed to seal the edges of the liver during surgical procedures so it is highly unlikely to cause a problem externally.

Try and leave bandaged ears well alone for at least 24 hours following wrapping an ear, though if bleeding continues you may have to change the whole bandage.

Check daily to make sure that the ear doesn't feel abnormally hot (infection) though try to avoid removing the inner cotton wool wrapping as dried blood will have stuck this to the wound.

Minor damage to ears takes no longer to heal than any other part of a dog, and after three days I would normally remove bandage and cotton wool, BUT I carefully snip away the cotton wool from around the wound, leaving what is stuck to the injury site in place. This shred of cotton wool can stay there, acting as part of the scab, until it comes away naturally once healing has finished.

SPLIT EAR

An ear flap which has been severely split takes a lot longer to heal than a minor laceration because the ear is made up of a flap of gristle covered on both sides with a thin layer of skin. If the gristle has been cut or split the skin then needs time to grow to cover both edges of the split. The longer anything takes to heal, the more likelihood there is of the possibility of infection.

One of my dogs once tangled with a fox which split one of her ears from tip to about two centimetres up the ear flap and this took a full month to heal completely. The area was tender and hot for at least three weeks, though not infected. It could have been stitched, but would definitely not have been a DIY staple job. Now I have to feel both ears to remember which one was damaged, even though fur has never grown inside the split.

TAIL WOUNDS

Lurchers and sighthounds' tails are far more at risk than most other types of dog, being long, slender and very whippy. In smooth coated animals there is very little to protect the skin and bone.

There are two classic types of tail wound: one is a split tail, often caused by catching the upper side of the tail as the dog is going through barbed wire, the other being the result of the dog beating the tip of the tail against walls whilst wagging said appendage.

Split tail

Usually a split or cut on the upper side of the tail, and along its length, and often caused by speeding through a barbed wire fence. Treat as for any other skin tear or cut, then bandage using Vetwrap held in place top and bottom of the bandage by fabric strapping.

These normally heal with no problem though do be aware that the bones in the tail can be broken at the same time as the wound occurred, especially if the dog was running at speed at the time of injury. If the wound fails to heal within normal healing time (a fortnight) suspect bone damage; I once had to pull bone splinters from such a wound which wasn't healing properly, though the tail didn't appear broken and had full function both during healing and afterwards.

Damaged tail tip

This is a more difficult proposition because the end of the tail needs protecting until both skin and hair have regrown. If the dog is happy to see you then it will wag its tail, though kenneled dogs can be trained to sit until you let them out into the open where they can wag without damaging their tails, and house dogs ignored when you re-enter the home until you can call them to you in a safe open place to wag.

By ignoring the dog as it rushes to greet you when you come back home, not only are you re-establishing your status as top dog, you are preventing that insane wagging which causes the whole tail damage syndrome. Believe me, it really does work, though you have to be iron strong in your behaviour and simply walk past the dog, using your knee to push it out of the way if it attempts to block your passage. Don't make eye contact with the dog as you enter your house, just act as though it wasn't there, and although some people might find this hard to do at first, you'll end up with a much calmer animal, and one which will allow you to get into your house without all the hysteria you may have had in the past. More to the point, you won't be cleaning blood off your walls any more either!

Tails which have suffered a lot of damage to the tip over a period of time tend to suffer from thickening and scaling of the skin nearest the damaged tissue, and this can take some time to regenerate properly though very occasionally amputation is the only cure to this problem.

TIP: Once again, full healing of any wound is greatly helped by feeding the dog a top quality diet, and here is a tale of how good diet resolved two such problems.

I once took on a rescue lurcher which had not only a bald and bleeding tail tip, but also an open sore on his hock, which I was told just wouldn't heal. It was obvious from first glance that the dog's diet was not good as his coat was dull and fluffy where it should have been smooth and shiny. Getting this dog to eat raw meat took over a week as he just didn't recognise meat as food, and preferred the cheapest, most additive filled commercial dog food that I could find!

However, by the end of week two this lurcher was wolfing down raw meat, whole carcases, and although I did nothing to treat the sore hock or the tail tip bar smearing a little antiseptic ointment on to the raw flesh, within a month both had healed completely to the extent that you would have been hard pushed to know that there had been any damage to either site.

Just as importantly, this dog's coat now shone like glass and was smooth and sleek to the touch with new hair covering both the damaged hock and the tail tip.

A good diet is about much more than keeping a dog healthy: good diet actually encourages wound healing, and a natural (ie meat) source of protein will aid in healing not just skin wounds but internal damage as well, including broken bones.

SEVERE BLEEDING

Any bleeding which pumps, spurts or gushes from a wound and doesn't stop within a few moments must be classed as severe. Arterial bleeding spurts out to the rhythm of the beating heart and is the most dangerous. Bleeding from a vein pumps out more slowly and is darker red in colour than arterial blood which is typically bright red.

Pressure must be applied immediately to any bleeding which pumps, spurts or flows with no sign of stopping. Use any material you may have to hand and worry about infection later, for there will be no later for a dog if it continues to bleed out uncontrollably: it only takes a few minutes to bleed to death if an artery has been severed.

Bleeding always seems more severe if the dog was running at the time of injury because the heart is pumping blood around the body at a faster rate than if the dog had been doing nothing. Minor blood vessels can drip quite alarmingly fast when the heart rate is raised, but stop altogether once the heart rate subsides.

Try and elevate the damaged part of the dog so it is above the animal's heart: blood travels more slowly uphill. Hold the dog on its side with the damaged leg in the air if a leg is affected. If the body is damaged then keep the injury uppermost whilst on your way to the vet, and KEEP PRESSURE APPLIED TO THE WOUND AT ALL TIMES UNTIL YOU REACH THE VET.

The most frightening accident I have encountered was when a lurcher tried to kill one of my terriers, ripping the jugular vein out of the dog's neck in its attack.

By immediately pinching off and holding on to the torn end of the jugular vein nearest the body, which was clearly visible in the gaping wound, we were able to save the dog's life, along with the help of a blood transfusion from my largest lurcher once we'd reached the vet.

Incidentally, the vet made no attempt to suture the jugular vein back together, the torn ends of which had by then shrunk back inside the wound,. It was then that I learned that there were three separate paths for the blood to travel back to the body from the head! The torn ends of the jugular sealed themselves off during healing and the dog was able to go back to work within the month. The body is truly a marvel of survival techniques!

NOTE: If your dog experiences major blood loss and you have more than one dog, take the uninjured animal to the vet with you as it might be possible for the vet to take blood from the uninjured dog to provide enough for a transfusion. Don't expect the vet to use a terrier to provide blood for a Deerhound: the donor should be a lot bigger than the receiver of blood. Twice I was able to use my large Deerhound/Greyhound to provide blood for smaller dogs with no ill effect to herself whatsoever.

Incidentally, dogs do have blood groups just like humans, but the first transfusion can be of any type. Subsequent transfusions, if needed, must be matched to the recipient's own type because the body will have made antibodies against 'foreign invaders' after the first transfusion.

AND ONCE AGAIN!
If any bleeding doesn't stop within a few moments, take the dog to the vet. Slow seeping from a minor wound is no great cause for concern but if you are worried don't take any chances.

I've had deep cuts to my own fingers that seeped for a couple of days, especially after I'd banged them a few times! Don't allow injured dogs to run about at all until a minor skin tear or cut has started to granulate and there is no further risk of bleeding.

USEFUL ALTERNATIVE TREATMENTS FOR SKIN WOUNDS

Arnica is one of the most useful Homeopathic remedies there is and even if you are not normally a disciple of Homeopathy I'd recommend keeping Arnica in your first aid kit.

Arnica pillules taken orally are very useful in reducing bruising of any sort, whether or not the skin is broken. Do not use Arnica ointment in any form on cuts or wounds where the skin has been broken.

Tea Tree Oil is a brilliant natural antiseptic, but in my opinion it should not be applied neat to open wounds. Always dilute as per the manufacturer's recommendation before using to clean wounds.

Tea Tree Cream (contains Tea Tree Oil) is very good for inhibiting bacterial infections in wounds but do not use on deep wounds as it should not be taken internally. Deep wounds may allow a product to enter the blood stream. Calendula Cream is very good for all minor skin wounds and helps to promote healing.

WARNING: never apply neat Tea Tree Oil to open wounds. It is much stronger than any man-made antiseptic.

OINTMENTS AND ANTISEPTICS

I keep a whole stock of bits and pieces in my medicine cupboard and many human products can be safely used on dogs.

Savlon, an antiseptic cream, is a good example and can be used on minor cuts and grazes to stave off infection and keep such wounds moist.

Sudocrem is another such ointment which both soothes and protects minor skin damage. It contains zinc oxide which helps to prevent damaged tissue from drying out and can be used on many skin conditions. I've also used it on pus filled spots which some dogs get inside their hind legs and along their chests after they've been running through long grass and thistles.

Hibiscrub can be bought in a bottle and needs to be diluted, though is also available in small plastic vials ready diluted and useful for first aid use in the field.

Arnica 30c and Arnica 6c can help with bruising and is a homeopathic 'first aid' remedy.

Rescue Remedy is one of the Bach Flower Remedies and is excellent for shock, both physical or emotional.

SOME GENERAL TIPS ON WOUNDS AND THEIR HEALING

- *Keep all wounds clean and monitor wound healing every day.*
- *If the dog appears quiet, listless, off its food or in any other way unwell, take it to the vet immediately.*
- *Dogs kept in damp conditions are more likely to suffer infections than animals housed correctly in dry, airy surroundings.*
- *Don't become stressed as this will be picked up on by the dog which will in turn become stressed as well! Stress can inhibit healing.*
- *Feed a good quality raw meat diet as this promotes fast healing of wounds.*

CHAPTER SIX

Eyes, ears, noses and throats

I've lumped eyes, ears, noses and throats together in this chapter for although they suffer from very different types of injury they are all found on the head which is usually at the forefront of most problems in the running dog.

EYES
Similarly to feet, if the dog can't see properly it can't catch! Eyes in running dogs are usually fairly soundly constructed and I've yet to see any sign of entropion (inturned eyelids) in any lurcher.

However, many sighthounds have fairly protuberant eyes which leave them at greater risk of injury if they hunt hard in deep cover of nettles or brambles, when they are prone to impaling themselves on thorns and the like.

Whippets especially with their high drive attitude and somewhat bulbous eyes are often at risk of damaging their seeing equipment if they follow their prey into cover which often consists of brambles or nettles.

It is fairly obvious if a dog has damaged its eye in any way as it will be in considerable distress immediately, either pawing at its

Small lurchers are good in tight situations but risk their eyesight in dense cover.

The forward facing eyes of the predator able to pinpoint a moving target at a distance.

eye or rubbing its head along the ground in an effort to get rid of the pain.

Rubbing a damaged or sore eye is of course the worst possible thing to do, and in some cases can make the damage far worse by pushing a thorn deeper into the eye ball. The moment you see your dog pawing at an eye you must stop and examine that eye carefully. (This is where it pays to keep a small torch in your pocket.)

Foreign objects in eyes

If you can see a foreign body of any kind sticking out of the eye ball DO NOT ATTEMPT TO REMOVE IT YOURSELF. Pulling out a thorn that is deeply embedded in an eye ball can result in the partial or total loss of the eye fluid. This is a job for the vet and any do it yourself attempts at amateur eye surgery could result in the loss of the eye.

Put the dog on the lead immediately and get it to the vet as soon as possible, meanwhile doing everything you can to stop the dog pawing at its eye. Don't attempt to bandage the area tightly as any pressure could well force a foreign object more deeply into the eye though a pad of cotton wool gently placed over the eye and lightly fixed in place with Elastoplast can help to stop a dog pawing at its eye. Similarly, a light covering of a scarf or towel wrapped carefully around the dog's head can sometimes help to calm the patient until you get to the vet. The eye is a remarkable organ and usually recovers from small thorn punctures very well BUT immediate treatment is necessary in order to save the eye.

Scratched eye balls

Far more common than something actually penetrating the eye ball is a scratch to the surface of the eye, and these can be initially very painful. Several of my dogs have tiny white specks on the surface of their eye balls where a scratch has healed and left a tiny scar.

At the time of the injury I make sure that there is nothing embedded in the eye ball by carefully examining the eye with the help of a small torch. I then wash the eye very gently with cooled, boiled water to flush out any dust or debris.

There are various over the counter eye ointments and drops which can help to soothe irritation, Golden Eye ointment being one of the best known. This ointment is an antiseptic and excellent for minor irritations, though if symptoms don't improve after a few days you should seek veterinary advice.

Fucithalmic Ointment is a prescription only antibiotic ointment for eyes which

Close up of professionally sutured eye ball after a thorn had been removed. The eye went on to make a full recovery. Photo: Roly Boughton.

has an immediate soothing effect. Vets and human doctors prescribe its use for many eye injuries and conditions such as conjunctivitis; I can testify to its efficiency as I've used it on my own eyes on more than one occasion. Needless to say, you shouldn't attempt any home treatment for undiagnosed problems which could be exacerbated by incorrect care.

Always put eye drops or ointment into the eye with the utmost care. Don't touch the eye ball with the dropper and drop the ointment into the top corner of the eye (nearest the ear) so that any foreign objects or dust will be flushed towards the draining corner of the eye and out through the tear ducts or via that cunningly designed lip at the front corner of the eye.

Nature is pretty good in most of her designs and all but the most man made of dogs possess eyes which are not only well protected by bone and surrounding tissue, but drain correctly from the lower corner.

The above treatment is usually fine for minor injuries, but if you suspect anything nasty is happening within the eye like clouding, bleeding within the eye ball or loss of shape to the orb, then get the

The tiny white speck in this dog's eye is an old scar from a thorn scratch which needed no veterinary attention to heal successfully.

*Eyes are at risk when working in cover.
Photo: Robert Wilkins.*

dog to the vet immediately. DIY is never recommended for something as delicate as the eye.

Blocked tear ducts
Tear ducts do sometimes become blocked, though this is a rarity in lurchers and sighthounds. Constant tearing from an eye, where the liquid runs down the dog's face needs veterinary intervention and the vet will do a test with an interesting 'glow in the dark' liquid, which, if the tear ducts are not blocked, will show at the nostrils soon after being introduced into the eye itself.

Dry eyes
Once again, not usually a problem with running dogs, though if the dog is working in very dry and dusty conditions it pays to watch out for signs of soreness in the eye.

I always flush out my dogs' eyes with cooled boiled water when they've been working either during the summer through long grass when the air is full of pollen and dust, or in old grain stores or dusty barns.

I know running dogs aren't supposed to be earth dogs, but if you have one that attempts to follow their quarry to ground (some gutsy Whippets and terrier crosses do attempt this) you should clean the eyes thoroughly afterwards, just as you would a terrier's.

For this I use a clean plastic syringe and a bowl of cooled boiled water, nothing more. Drip lukewarm (less likely to cause a jerk of the head away from your hand than cold) water carefully into the top corner of the eye and you'll see dark 'worms' of moistened dust gathering at the bottom corner of the eye. This sort of dust gathers under the lids and can be really irritating. Sharp particles of sand can scratch the surface of the eye ball if you don't remove them by gently flushing them out. Wipe the muddy worms away gently with a damp tissue as they form at the eye's corner.

Keep going until the water runs clear from the eye, and don't forget to very gently lift up the upper and lower lids as well to make sure there is no dirt still lodged well back beneath the lids.

NOTE: Never attempt any DIY surgery on an eye and never touch the eye ball itself or introduce anything other than water or proprietary eye drops into the eye.

Using a plastic syringe to wash out the eye.

Point of interest

I have seen two coursing dogs which had each lost an eye, one as a youngster and the other at about four years of age, both ran well and caught their hares, having learned to compensate for the loss of one eye. Whilst two eyes are better than one, a running dog can still function with only one eye.

EARS

Most running dogs have flopped ears, as opposed to pricked up ears, and whilst flopped ears are of more man-made construction (wild canines always have pricked ears) sighthound types don't normally suffer from the type of problems we associate with the very heavily hair-clogged ears we might see on Spaniels. Ears should be inspected daily to make sure the inner ear is clean with no discharge (see Chapter on Parasites), also checking for thorns embedded in the pinna (ear flap).

Foreign bodies in ears

The most common problem I've encountered in my dogs' ears is when a grass seed lodges deep in the ear canal. Early signs to look out for are a tilted head carriage, with the dog carrying the affected ear at a lower angle to the unaffected side or incessant scratching at the ear area. Dogs often shake their heads excessively in an attempt to dislodge the offending seed as well, so pay attention to any of these signs.

You can try pouring a teaspoonful of warm olive oil into the ear as this might help to dislodge and float out loose debris or seeds which haven't implanted themselves in the ear tissue. Another old fashioned remedy is bicarbonate of soda which foams up when dissolved in warm water. Pour

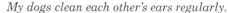

My dogs clean each other's ears regularly.

the foaming liquid into the ear. If you suspect damage to the ear drum itself DO NOT put anything into the ear at all, see a vet immediately. DO NOT ATTEMPT TO USE TWEEZERS OR ANY OTHER IMPLEMENT INSIDE YOUR DOG'S EAR. This is a vet job only as vets possess the correct type of tools for this very delicate and awkward job. The ear canal is deep and convoluted, very sensitive and easily damaged.

Some foreign bodies within the ear may dislodge themselves but grass seeds are so designed that they cannot go backwards, for they carry many tiny hooked barbs which enable them to push into the ground in order to germinate. It's a great design from the grass's point of view, but not so good when it enters the wrong environment.

Get the dog to the vet who may have to sedate the animal in order to extricate the grass seed. Don't ever risk letting nature take its course if you suspect a grass seed in an ear, or there is a real possibility of serious infection.

Torn ears

This injury is covered in the chapter on Skin Wounds on page 108.

Aural Haemotoma

The pinna (ear flap) may also be damaged as a result of hard impact, excessive head shaking (see Foreign Bodies in Ears above), or occasionally as a result of infection.

Mild cases may resolve themselves if the dog is kept quiet but severe cases may give rise to infection and need professional treatment. Signs to look out for are a swelling of and heat in the ear flap.

Parasites

Ear mites can also cause a problem and this is dealt with in the chapter on Parasites.

Dirty ears

Healthy dogs with normally constructed ears don't usually suffer from excessive wax or dirt in their ears. However, some dogs can suffer from yeast infections which respond well to a dilute solution of cider vinegar and water. Don't use brown vinegar though you can use white wine vinegar instead of cider vinegar. Dilute 5ml (a teaspoon) of vinegar in 200ml (half a pint) of warm water and syringe into the ear canal: massage into the base of the ear then stand well back whilst the dog shakes its head! Best to do this outside.

NOTE: Yeast infections often respond well to a cereal-free diet with plenty of green vegetables added. Spinach, steamed nettles, parsley and watercress are particularly good for cleansing the system of toxins which provide ideal growth conditions for yeast infections.

NOSES

The nose of the running dog is unlikely to sustain serious injury unless the dog collides with something at speed, but in the event of severe damage to the leather of the nose it is inadvisable to attempt home suturing or stapling to this part of the dog as the skin is so tough that complete sedation or a general anaesthetic will be required.

Grass seed inhalation can occur in running dogs which gallop through hay fields during the summer months, and whilst sneezing can sometimes expel the offending item, some grass seeds can track deep into the sinuses. Continued and severe sneezing should not be ignored and professional treatment is recommended.

THROATS

Coursing dogs can suffer from sore throats when running for extended periods of time. The effort involved whilst running with an

Above: Catching the air scent of game. Below: Nose work whilst ferreting.

open panting mouth can dry out the lining of the throat, and it is not uncommon for slightly unfit dogs to cough up some frothy phlegm after a hard run. At one time this was considered to be quite normal, but in reality post coursing coughing is an indication that the dog wasn't fit enough for the work involved.

However, dogs which run over cultivated land, either when dry and dusty, or muddy and wet, can inhale dust or particles of mud thrown up by the feet of their quarry. Normally this shouldn't pose a problem, but if the dog is either unfit or below par in terms of general health, this can lead to complications such as pneumonia or other bronchial infections.

NOTE: Severe coughing which lasts for days after a hard course could mean damage to lungs or diaphragm in which case the dog should be checked over by a vet. Many dogs have been 'blown' (irreparable damage to lungs or diaphragm) through overwork whilst unfit. I can't stress enough the importance of proper fitness training for any dog which is required to run hard after quarry which has both stamina and speed.

ANOTHER NOTE: Coursing a dog in warm weather will also increase the chance of lung and diaphragm damage because more stress is placed on the dog's body as it struggles to cope with intense physical strain as well as the weather conditions (see also section on hyperthermia in *Stuff That Can Kill Your Dog* on page 185).

CHAPTER SEVEN

Teeth

I remember judging a lurcher show many years ago out in the fens of Cambridgeshire. One superb animal caught my eye from the moment it entered the ring. This dog moved like a dream, almost floating over the grass with the pent up power of a cheetah.

When I came to look at the dog, which was panting slightly in the summer sun, I knew before I had lifted her lips what I would find and my fears were realised when the foulest of odours nigh on exterminated my olfactory senses for the day as I took a closer look at her mouth.

Not only was every tooth in this dog's head coated in thick yellow plaque, the gums themselves were swollen and crimson red, a sure sign of gum disease. Being such a young animal this lurcher's general health was still good, but over the next few years that appalling lack of care and good management could start to reap some pretty tragic rewards.

For example, how many people know that severe tooth neglect can actually affect the internal organs, causing disease and infection which can in turn shorten the dog's life considerably!

A thin red line at the edge of the gums is often the start of gingivitis (gum disease), and this is a reversible condition, whereas left untreated it can lead to periodontitis, which is a disease that involves loss of bone surrounding the roots of the teeth. It is the bacterial activity in periodontitis that can affect internal organs and cause serious illness.

The lack of visible evidence of this disease leads the dog owner to believe that all is well with their pooch's teeth where beneath the surface all may be very far from well. Periodontitis can only be seen on an x-ray of the jaw.

The term 'doggy breath', the acceptance that all dogs have foul smelling breath, shows just how widespread these problems have been throughout the history of the domestic canine.

Strange isn't it, just how much we tend to ignore both our own oral hygiene as well as that of our dogs! So many people are

The large molars are used for crushing bone and tearing meat from carcases; not an omnivore's teeth.

The healthy dog which has not been deformed by show fashion can grind up lamb ribs with ease.

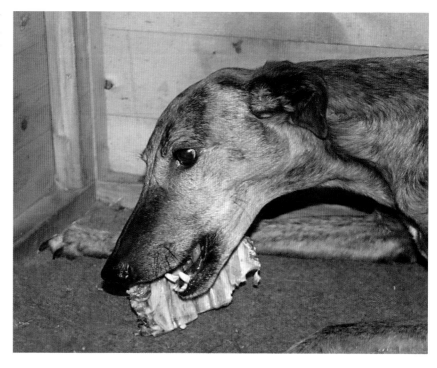

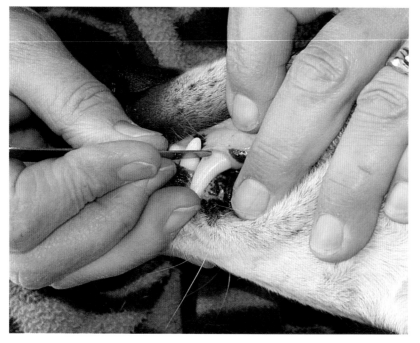

Using a small blunt knife to clean the canines always scraping away from the gums with controlled precision.

afraid of visiting the dentist that I wonder if this refusal to address the problem in themselves is something that also extends to their dogs.

Teeth are such an important part of a dog's anatomy, and yet so many people, even today, just don't seem to realise that unhealthy teeth can often mean an unhealthy animal. Committed raw feeders will know all this, and they won't be amongst those whose regular trips to the vet for costly descaling procedures are just one more side effect of feeding soft food. Dry biscuit feeders may notice a slight improvement when comparing the amount of plaque on a dog's teeth, but biscuit takes very little crunching and doesn't really clean the teeth like a chicken carcase or a rack of lamb ribs.

I've taken in rescue dogs whose teeth were so covered in plaque that you could barely see any enamel at all, yet within a month of crunching on chicken carcases, whole rabbit (including fur and skin) and breast of lamb those previously unhealthy and unsightly gnashers had been magically transformed into the gleaming white ivories we expect to see in a healthy young dog.

However, I have noticed that the canine teeth of all dogs, no matter how they are fed, do tend to build up a thin line of plaque along the gum line. This is because dogs only use their canine teeth to bite into their prey when killing, thereafter having little use as food processors, whereas the molars stay clean because they are used for chewing meat from bone, and for grinding up bones as well.

I find that this plaque can easily be picked off with a fingernail if done regularly. Put your fingernail on the tooth right up against the gum line, and pull downwards along the tooth. Providing you don't have brittle or weak nails you should be able to

Even carcase fed dogs can develop a thin line of plaque along the gum line.

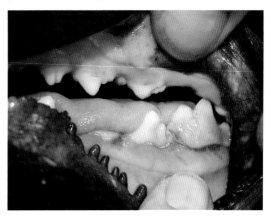
Plaque build up on lower molars. This dog is missing its upper molars due to an accident whilst very young and is consequently unable to chew on this side of his jaw.

scratch off the plaque with a forceful tweak, and as long as your dog is used to having its mouth examined it won't object to this in the slightest.

Premolars sometimes suffer from a slight build up of plaque too, but plenty of scratchy carcases such as chicken or young rabbit will help to keep this to a minimum.

NOTE: Foul smelling breath may also have other causes such as digestive or throat disease, but I've also noticed that if my dogs have contracted tape worm from scavenging rabbit carcases whilst out on exercise, their breath smells really bad until I've wormed them.

Very occasionally a dog may get a bit of bone stuck between its molars, and the resultant drooling and pawing at the side of its mouth will alert you to this very quickly, though I have seen some dogs which haven't reacted much at all if this happens.

It pays to check your dog's mouth on a regular basis, no matter what you feed your animals: once again, a problem nipped in the bud is seldom a problem for very long.

WORKING ACCIDENTS

Time and age will take their toll on even the best kept teeth, and dogs can suffer tooth decay as well. Dogs that come into contact with hard biting quarry can also suffer from broken teeth, and whilst I've only owned a few running dogs which have suffered from broken teeth, my terriers have managed quite well with missing or broken teeth over the years.

The front incisors sometimes become broken off or ripped right out in the hard striking dog which is run over stony ground, and whilst the canines are not often pulled out, they too can be broken off especially in the dog which tackles biting quarry.

You need to monitor broken teeth to make sure that they are not decaying or causing the dog any pain, and if an animal is reluctant to chew its food properly suspect a problem and get it checked out.

Worst case scenario in broken teeth is eventual decay and/or abscesses below the gum line around the root of the tooth. These will need to be attended to by a vet under anaesthetic. If your dog is suffering from several loose teeth which have not been caused by an impact to the jaw, then get the animal's general health checked out by a vet.

One lurcher I owned came back from a course on a hare which she caught in a hedge bottom, but it wasn't until a few moments later that I realised she had a hole in the side of her 'cheek'. I guessed that she must have struck something hard in the hedge bottom, either a sharp rock or piece of metal, or even one of those iron hard broken hawthorn stumps, precisely at the same time as striking her hare. The largest molar had been sheered off just above the gum line. This happened many years ago when I was younger and more ignorant than I am now and nowadays I'd have broken teeth or roots removed by a vet. As it was, the dog seemed fine, she ate normally and didn't appear to be suffering in any way ... or did she?

The fact that this lurcher had a very strange temperament in the first place made it difficult to ascertain any changes in mood or behaviour which might have been attributed to root pain. Of course I later learned that decaying roots can cause an animal a lot of pain, but as I've mentioned elsewhere, internal and ongoing pain is often very well hidden by dogs. Showing pain is a sign of weakness in a pack member and many dogs are reluctant to 'admit' their pain for fear of being picked on by the rest of the pack.

Molar roots in dogs are three pronged and almost impossible to dislodge through impact, so the tooth is more likely to sheer off in such cases. I have only seen one case where the roots were broken as a result of hitting a hard object and this wasn't initially apparent. In fact, it wasn't until the dog was anaesthetised for a completely different injury that the broken tooth was noticed by the nurse who was intubating the dog prior to surgery. The tooth was still in place but hanging on by one root only. The vet removed tooth and roots at the same time as carrying out the other procedure, which was to remove part of the dog's tail which had been broken. The dog carried on catching rabbits into old age and eating well despite the missing tooth.

Trauma to the gums can expose the root of the tooth on occasion, but unless this is very severe, leading to loosening of the affected tooth, leave well alone. Wounds to gums heal very quickly due to the antiseptic qualities of dog saliva. Did you know that on laboratory tests carried out in order to compare the number of bacteria present in both the human mouth and the dog mouth, the dog saliva came back having grown fewer bacteria on test dishes than that of the human? Dog saliva also contains an enzyme called lysozyme which attacks the cell walls of bacteria; this is another good reason to allow your dog to lick its own wounds as the lysozyme helps to remove bacterial infection in wounds.

TIP: Whilst young dogs get their adult teeth around the five to six month mark, the roots of the large teeth don't actually finish growing and embedding themselves deep in the jaw bone until the dog is between 10 and 12 months of age. It is a mistake to ask a young dog to do any work which might loosen those roots before they have finally set themselves into the bone. This secondary 'teething stage', when the roots are bedding into the jaw, is usually responsible for a further outbreak of chewing inappropriate items just when you thought it was safe to leave your best boots at ground level!

OLD DOG TEETH

No matter how well you feed and care for your dogs teeth can become worn and damaged with age and use. Old dogs sometimes produce less saliva as well, and this can lead to a build up of plaque when there is not enough saliva to 'wash' the mouth properly.

Monitor the mouths of old dogs regularly and don't forget to check the back molars for signs of damage. Watch how the dog eats, looking out for signs that the dog is reluctant to chew on one side of its mouth or the other. Inspect the inside of your dog's mouth if it has difficulty chewing at any stage of its life, but particularly when the animal is of advancing years.

I've had old dogs who just didn't want to chew hard bones when their teeth seemed just fine. Feed old dogs what they want, within reason. Cooked soft food won't shorten the life of an already ageing dog and I like to feed the old things what they can manage easily because eating is probably one of the few pleasures they have left at this stage of their lives.

CHAPTER EIGHT

Nutrition

There is so much information available both from books and on the internet nowadays on how to feed dogs that the mind boggles - a definite case of information overload! It should be easy to find the ideal diet for our running dogs, but all too often we can be blinded (and sometimes confused) by the science that the 'experts' throw at us. Yes, it is useful to understand how the canine body works, what types of food it can process and the best diet for the work we want the animal to do but you shouldn't need a degree in biology to feed a dog!

However, a little understanding goes a long way and although much has already been written on the subject, here are my thoughts on feeding dogs, especially athletic dogs. A lurcher or sighthound is no different to any other type of canine in that the digestive system of all dogs remains the same regardless of the size of the animal. But there are one or two differences in

Dogs that work in cold conditions need plenty of fat in their diet. Photo Von.
Photo opposite: A mixed bag of game all of which can provide excellent food for dogs.

what and how we should feed according to the precise breeding of the running dog, and the work it is asked to do.

Anyone who is dedicated to keeping their dog as healthy as possible will have experimented with different types of feeding regimes, so no matter where you source your information, only personal experience coupled with a reasonable level of understanding of the canine body will tell you what is right for your dog.

Everything I write is based on my own experiences over the past 30 years (and more!) and I hope that these experiences will help readers to add just a little more knowledge to their dog maintenance skills. I don't have a degree in canine nutrition, I'm very far from being a scientist but I have learned what works and what doesn't work when it comes to feeding my animals, and I like to think that I get the best from my dogs in the field. So here, in slightly more than a nutshell, is how I go about feeding my trusty workmates.

Back in the mists of time, I fed my dogs with what is sometimes cynically referred to as 'rabbit food': a muesli type mixture of flaked maize, crushed oats, split peas and fish meal, this last ingredient a most necessary addition to what would otherwise be a very low protein mixture.

These days most people know that the dog is in fact a carnivore and not a rabbit at all, though some 'experts' claim that the dog is an omnivore. Bears are omnivores, but they can digest grass, leaves and so on, something that dogs find almost impossible to do unless said vegetation has been cooked or pureed to break down the cell structure. Bears can survive on grass (just) even though they do better if they can get their teeth into meat and other forms of quality protein every so often. A dog wouldn't be able to survive on grass alone, so in my opinion a dog is not an omnivore.

However, Andy, my partner, fed his first lurcher on a proprietary brand of this type, occasionally adding a bit of tripe for good measure and not only did this lurcher run alongside his bicycle on the way to their lamping and ferreting grounds, often for several miles, she also worked her socks off during the course of her work, and trotted home again beside the bike. As Andy was young and had plenty of spare time and energy at the time he owned this lurcher she saw a lot of work, far more than many dogs, lamping several times a week as well as coursing and ferreting at weekends. Though never an out and out hare dog she did put up a decent show at the long ears.

This lurcher lived to a ripe old age, was never sick and nor did she suffer from any ailments apart from the odd working injury. Mmmm! I wonder how she would have fared on a raw diet or one of the modern 'high powered' super protein complete foods!

John Bromily, the successful coursing greyhound trainer, once told me that "a good dog will run well on fish and chips!" I took his opinion to mean that performance is innate within the dog and depends little on how that animal is fed, and whilst I have to agree with him to a certain extent, I know that any diet lacking in essential nutrients will, in the long term, have a detrimental effect on the body. We only have to look at humans who develop all sorts of behavioural as well as physical problems if they continually eat the 'wrong' sort of food: sugary, starchy products with little protein or fresh vitamins and minerals.

I've experimented with all sorts of feeding regimes and finally come to the conclusion that although a diet of raw meat, whole carcases, bones and mashed up veggies is best, (and cheapest) along with whatever form of carbohydrate your dog can tolerate, (more on carbs later) most can survive on an enormous variety of foodstuffs providing that they receive adequate amounts of the essentials such as fat and protein, no matter where this is sourced.

Nevertheless, even whilst feeding my long suffering hounds on a largely cereal based diet, I always felt that dogs, being primarily carnivores, should eat meat, and as I was fortunate enough to know someone who had access to a slaughter house, I also fed fresh, raw tripe plus odds and ends such as ox tongue and heart. My dogs were healthy, worked well and all was fine. Then kibble, nuts, biscuits or whatever you want to call it, and generally known as 'complete food' came on to the market! How easy was this! You simply took a scoop of the little brown (though sometimes alarmingly Day-Glo coloured) nuts from the bag, put it in a bowl and fed the dog! OK, so if you added meat the dogs seemed to get diarrhoea, and if you fed just the slightest bit more than the minimum necessary, they also got diarrhoea. With some of the cheaper complete foods came disgusting rancid wind, foetid breath and whether you spent a fortune or a pittance on this modern diet all dogs thus fed developed an overwhelming thirst in comparison to the amount they would drink had they been given raw meat

Hardly surprising really as the stomach needs a considerable amount of liquid to turn identifiable food into the soupy matter (chyme) that travels through the small intestine. The small intestine is where most of the nutrients in food are absorbed, with excess liquid being extracted via the walls of the large intestine and excreted from the body via the kidneys and bladder as urine. If insufficient liquid is present in the stomach during the digestion process not only does the whole body struggle to absorb nutrients, but the risk of kidney damage may also occur. Whatever you feed your dog make sure that clean water is always available, and doubly so if you are feeding a dry food.

Coats could suffer too if you bought one of those £5 per bag unlabelled complete foods, the smell of which sometimes reminded me of badly run chip shops; when the dog itself starts smelling of rancid chip fat you just know there has to be a problem! Faeces were sometimes green and slimy with a really disgusting odour, or covered in mucous, which is one of the body's ways of getting rid of toxins. Mucous-covered motions may also be a symptom of Colitis and similar conditions, such as malabsorption. If you are concerned, then seek a vet's advice. It is normal for the digestive tract to produce a certain amount of mucous as this helps food slide easily through the intestines, but an over-production of mucous often occurs if the wrong type of nutrient is ingested or is so rotten that the body needs to expel it before it can do any damage.

The digestive tract of a carnivore is much shorter than that of a grass- or vegetable-eating animal because meat is easier to process than vegetable matter containing cellulose. This is also helpful to the carnivore which scavenges rotting carcases and other unpleasant, bacteria-laden items as the bacteria don't usually remain in the dog's system for long enough to multiply in numbers sufficient to cause serious illness.

Mucous covered faeces which smell bad should tell you that what you are feeding your dog is not right for the dog's body, though this can also be caused by a heavy worm burden or other digestive ailment. I know that dog faeces aren't the most

Note the large molars which are designed to grind bone from carcases.

pleasant smelling at the best of times, but when what your dog produces from its rear end makes you want to retch, there just has to be something amiss.

With the arrival of the so called premium foods came the rock solid certainty, backed up of course by the claims of canine nutritionists, (I wonder how these creatures evolved!) that here were diets which would banish all ills, making your dog fitter, healthier and happier than ever before.

As humans from a technologically rapidly evolving society, we are taught from an early age to believe in science (well, my generation was brain-washed in this way at any rate)! I think that today's youngsters tend to ask more questions and believe far less of what they read than people of my age did when we were young. Today's younger generation have been taught to be highly sceptical of anything that smacks of advertising, including hyped-up and extraordinary claims regarding health or nutrition. As people began to learn of the negative results which can result from eating over-processed foods containing all manner of additives, colourings and preservatives, so did we begin to look at

how we fed our dogs and this gave rise to the increasingly popular trend of 'back to nature' feeding, in other words, raw meat and bones.

We are told never to add any meat to complete foods or we risk upsetting the balance so carefully devised by the scientists, so how then is it that these 'complete' kibbles consist of a mixture of both meat and cereals which we are also told should not be fed at the same meal due to their different digestion times? Answer: we are told that cooking homogenises (I hate that word and everything it implies!) the raw ingredients of a complete food, which is cooked at a very high temperature killing many vitamins and trace elements necessary to good health; these have to be put back into the mix after cooking, before the resulting sludge is extruded and baked (more heat treatment) into nuggets or nuts. Colours and preservatives are also added to make the product more appealing to the human eye and to prevent it from deteriorating over the many months that the final product may sit on some pet store's shelves.

Homogenised or not, added vitamins or not, I personally wouldn't want to eat anything which had been so heavily processed that I couldn't identify the original ingredients, and I don't like the idea of giving my dog such mysteriously concocted food either.

We also hear horror stories of unspeakable additions to such commercially manufactured dog foods: animal carcases in a state of advanced decomposition and cereals which have been condemned for human use due to inadequate storage conditions, no doubt lifting with various bacteria and other noxious life forms not fit for a Komodo dragon, never mind a dog!

The manufacturers' (not all of them, I'll admit) answer to such concerns is that

Boned out chicken carcases and wings are suitable for adult dog and pups over four months of age.

everything is heat treated to such a degree that any nasties are obliterated. What they don't tell us is that along with the nasties, most other nutrients are similarly obliterated, and it is now known that by over heating any type of food you are altering the chemical make up of most foods. *When you consider that at least 50% of the Vitamin C contained in spinach is destroyed by cooking, it gives you some idea as to the fragility of many vitamins and minerals which are found in the raw ingredients of most foodstuffs. Actually Vitamin C is a bad example to use when we're talking of feeding dogs, as canines synthesise their own Vitamin C within their bodies, like most other mammals. In fact, humans, apes, bats and guinea pigs are the only species which need a regular intake of this vitamin, being unable to synthesize it themselves in the liver. There is however, some evidence to suggest that Vitamin C supplements can aid in recovery from very strenuous exercise such as coursing, helping to prevent a build up of lactic acid. See chapter on exercise and conditioning.*

All animals evolved to eat raw food, be they herbivore or carnivore, and when you consider that only a fraction of time (a few thousand years) has passed since we began to cook our food, our digestive systems and those of our dogs, are still willing and able to deal with raw, untreated ingredients. If humans are perfectly capable of digesting raw meat, which of course we are, though most people prefer to cook their meat for reasons of hygiene as well as taste, then it is obvious that dogs are just as capable, more so.

You could argue that giving a dog raw minced vegetables is unnatural, but how is it that if one of my greedy lurchers steals half a cabbage from the chopping board and

You need an industrial mincer to process whole carcases.

then devours the lot (chewed, not minced, pureed or cooked) I don't then have to spend time the following day scraping green liquid faeces from the concrete of the back yard? Similarly, I have dogs which scoff celery, apple peelings, blackberries by the bowlful, picked themselves from the briars when ripe, and they don't excrete foul smelling diarrhoea as a result, even though the blackish coloured result might be full of seeds, just like the fox scats we find in the autumn when that harvest is at its best.

However, if I feed a bowlful of complete food and give more than the bare minimum to each dog, they do cow pats all over the yard, and those cow pats smell none too good at all.

The cheaper 'complete' foods are cereal-based because cereals are less expensive to produce than meat, and as all dog food manufacturers are in business to make money it stands to reason that they make up the bulk of their foods from the cheapest ingredients they can find. A dog's short carnivore digestive system is not really designed to cope with masses of starchy cereal matter however, and when that matter contains things like sugar beet pulp and soya one has to ask oneself if it can really be healthy to keep shoving such foodstuffs down a carnivore's throat! There is a big difference between non starchy vegetables such as leafy greens and carbohydrate laden cereals such as wheat, root vegetables and the like.

'You are what you eat' is a favourite saying of human nutritionists, and we all know that by continually stuffing ourselves with too much of the wrong kind of food we risk serious illness, not immediately, but in the long-term when our poor, beleaguered bodies finally throw in the towel and develop all sorts of ailments as a result of either an unbalanced or downright dangerous diet.

Think peptic ulcers, heart and bowel disease, not to mention a host of less sinister symptoms such as fatigue, aching joints, headaches: the list goes on. It is recognised nowadays that many 'modern' ailments suffered from in western society are a direct result of ingesting the wrong type of food over a long period of time. Why should dogs be any different? Ok, I know, we can all cite an example of a dog which has lived its entire life on a rubbish diet, and is still going strong aged 17 years, just as some people can smoke 80 cigarettes a day and still live until they are 90!

Neither am I trying to condemn the use of all manufactured food outright, and indeed I still use the odd bag of responsibly sourced kibble when I have run out of rabbits or forgotten to order my meat and tripe supply on time. Instant, processed junk food won't kill you unless you eat nothing else, and maybe not even then. Although I think of complete dog food in just the same way - an easy meal if nothing else is available at the time - I do tend to underfeed this stuff as my dogs aren't used to it. It doesn't hurt them to go a little short for one night.

However, intolerance to cereals, particularly wheat, is one of the most common afflictions to beset the modern dog, and I've a lurcher sitting right next to me as I write who, for the first five years of her life, ate and thrived on anything going, but became intolerant to certain foods in her sixth year. A little over a year ago she started to scratch incessantly, literally making her skin raw as she did so. To cut a very long story short, and after months of trying to get to the root of the problem, it turned out that she had become intolerant to cereals, ALL cereals except rice, which is now the only form of grain that she can tolerate. Incidentally, it is the gluten contained in many cereals which is often responsible for many allergic reactions or intolerances in dogs. Rice contains no gluten.

So don't think that because your dog does just fine on a certain food for months, or even years, that the food you are giving that dog is OK. Problems can take literally years to build up, and intolerances to certain food stuffs are the very devil to isolate and correctly diagnose. I've been there and experienced the helplessness of the owner who is at their wit's end when trying to get to the bottom of a skin problem. It's horrible to see a dog scratching itself raw when you are seemingly powerless to help. If ever I am faced with an itching problem in a dog I look at diet, once I've ruled out the obvious suspects such as fleas and mites. Incidentally, I gave this lurcher a cereal feed a few weeks ago just to confirm my suspicions, and within hours she was scratching herself silly again, though thankfully this only lasted for a couple of days. A dramatic and almost instant confirmation of my diagnosis!

I like to be able to see what goes into my food and I do the same for my dogs at least 90% of the time so let's move on to how to feed a natural diet, something I can get really enthusiastic about!

There are two schools of thought on raw feeding. The first tells us that we should give our dogs a mixture of vegetables, fruit and meat, and some carbohydrate, and to this end there are now several suppliers of 'natural' food on the market. The second school tells us that we should only offer our dogs meat on the bone, that vegetables are unnecessary and that any form of carbohydrate even more unnecessary to canine well-being. It can all become very confusing to the novice raw feeder!

When I first started feeding my dogs only natural, fresh food I spent hours painstakingly mincing and pureeing fruit and vegetables, then mixing the resulting slop with minced meat and tripe. I added brown bread or boiled brown rice and the dogs loved this mix, wolfing it down with unsurpassed glee. I also added bones in the form of lamb breast, chicken carcases and pork ribs and my dogs were soon in tip top condition, with gleaming coats, lots of energy and (very important if you keep dogs in large numbers) they were producing a minimum of waste.

The reduction in stool size is probably the most startling evidence of this change in diet. People who always fed complete food got used to shovelling up mounds of what appeared to be double the volume of the food originally ingested. How could this be so?

There are two reasons for such an explosion of waste from a dog's rear end: the first is down to insoluble fibre, present in large amounts in all vegetable matter and a glance at a cow pat tells you that even a cow produces a lot of waste matter, despite the fact that it possesses a long and complicated digestive system to cope with the stuff. Dogs have a much shorter digestive tract which is even more unequal to the task of processing vegetable matter and cereals are of course, vegetable matter. The second reason is one of my own deduction: I believe that when an animal which has not been designed to process dry biscuit (is any animal designed to do this?) is also forced to take in a great quantity of water to deal with that food, its system is put under stress in order to cope with such an unnatural workload.

If the body finds it hard to cope with an unsuitable food, it tries to expel it, either through vomiting, or by passing it as quickly as possible through the entire digestive system. My theory is backed up by the fact that I feed dogs at more or less the same time every evening, (it varies a bit but is usually within a two-hour time frame) but the time that food spends in their gut depends on the nature of that food. Cereal feeds must be expelled far sooner as not only is their volume greater, but I believe that the large quantity of insoluble vegetable fibre found in cereals irritates the canine gut which attempts to pass this matter through as fast as possible. Normally my dogs defecate whilst out on exercise which is usually after midday and can be any time up to late evening especially during the summer months. They are fed at roughly the same time every evening after exercise, but if fed on dry food I notice that they need to relieve themselves far sooner, and large stools begin to appear in the garden and yard well before their normal exercise time.

This contradicts what the scientists tell us: that cereals need to spend more time in the gut to be properly digested. I therefore concluded, in my highly unscientific way, that as my dogs were excreting cereal-based foods more quickly than meaty meals, they had to be: a) getting less goodness from these meals, and b) passing those cereals through their systems much faster because their bodies weren't 'happy' with this food.

My theories are at odds with what science tells us, that cereals take longer to digest than meat, but these are the only conclusions I can come to that make any sense. I am constantly on the look out for any new research on dogs in general, and particularly on feeding, but I've been unable to find anything which supports my theory, so you can either dismiss my findings as the ranting of a raw food fanatic or try a few little experiments yourself.

When you have a lot of dogs to feed, care for and clean up after, you tend to take more than a passing interest in the waste they produce. The quantity, smell and amount of that waste can tell you much about the internal health of a dog as well. The faeces of a healthy canine should be well formed, very firm and have little odour. They should NOT be soft or smell like a cross between a sewage farm and a cattle shed. If you compare the volume of the faeces a dog typically produces over any one day, it should be considerably less than the amount of food that the dog ingested

the previous day. If your dog excretes anywhere near the amount that it ate the previous meal, then it should be obvious that much of the content is not being used by the canine body.

Meat, fish, bone and fur, which to us may appear as highly indigestible, actually spend less time in a dog's digestive system than the grass eaten by a cow would in the bovine body. The specially designed digestive capabilities of carnivores enable bone, fur and skin to be broken down and assimilated by the gut in a surprisingly short time.

If I feed a whole, gutted rabbit to one of my lurchers, fur and all, the size of the stools produced the following day is nowhere near in bulk the size of that meal ingested. And best of all, when I pick up the faeces they smell relatively innocuous.

Still with me? Back to my history of dog feeding methods: I eventually got fed up with spending hours every week preparing my natural dog meals, and as the dogs themselves continued to look great, no matter how much or little veg I fed, my zealous attitude towards a perfectly balanced meal began to fall by the wayside.

For a start my dogs now receive far less in the way of vegetable matter than they did a few years ago, though I do still use the mincer for rabbit carcases, and whilst mincing skinned and gutted rabbits I generally shove a few carrots, celery sticks and leaves of spinach beet or spring greens through at the same time. Apples, pears, bananas, cauliflower, courgettes (I've never been really sure as to the nutritional benefit of courgettes which are mostly water, but they do contain vitamins and minerals) green and runner beans all get the same treatment if I happen to have a surplus at the time. Why do I not feed rabbit on the bone? One reason is that minced rabbit takes up a lot less room in the freezer than whole carcases, and as we are obliged to freeze rabbit for three weeks (some sources say four weeks though I've never had a problem freezing for three) in order to kill off any tapeworm eggs space can sometimes be at a premium.

Another reason is that rabbit alone would be very deficient in fat content for hard working dogs, and because our lamb or beef fat supply comes to us sporadically, mincing it up with the rabbit when we have a glut ensures that the properly balanced mix is all ready for consumption once thawed.

Balance! Now there's another problem often agonized over by novice raw feeders, myself included when I took the first tentative step away from manufactured dog food. I wonder if many people pay as much attention to their own diet as they do to their dogs, for as long as we eat more or less what we should, we thrive. (I'm not talking about those people who abuse their bodies non stop on a diet of junk food and sugar laden carbohydrates!)

We don't fall ill if we don't eat a nutritionally balanced diet at every meal, and neither will our dogs. If you feed your dog chicken carcases one day, then balance it out with a red meat meal the next. If breast of lamb is on the menu one night, then a meal of tripe and rabbit will do fine the next. Another thing: a dog's digestive system is designed to process lumps of meat and bone, not mush, and it has been stated that by feeding minced meat all the time you are encouraging the dog's gut to pass this type of food through the system too quickly thereby losing some essential nutrients. I do agree to a certain extent, but when you are feeding raw meat and bone this theory seems to fly out of the window, just so long as your minced food

Tripe, lamb ribs, chicken carcases, beef trimmings - the basis for raw feeding.

isn't beaten to a puree resembling runny mashed potatoes.

Feed a mixture of both lumps and mince and your dog's gut will sort things out quite happily. Believe me, mine do, though they can appear to feel cheated if they only get the minced mixture which is hoovered up in a matter of seconds. Neither do they excrete slurry if they have to eat nothing but their minced diet for a few days.

Dogs need to chew bones for the same psychological reasons that we need to chew on meat, toast, biscuits or a crunchy apple: we'd be just as bored and lacking if we only drank thick soup in order to survive. Chewing on bones and carcases also cleans

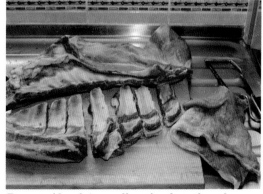

Breast of lamb is excellent for dogs though nowadays quite expensive.

the teeth wonderfully and exercises the jaw muscles as well as preparing the food for the main part of the digestive process which happens once the food is swallowed.

OTHER GOOD FOODS

Eggs are a number one source of protein, though of course wild canines would only find these during spring and early summer, and I usually feed my own dogs a gigantic omelette once a week when my hens have over produced and this is mixed in with whatever else is on offer on that particular day.

The reason I cook the eggs is because the white of the egg contains an enzyme called avidin, which stops biotin from being absorbed by the canine body. This can lead to skin and coat problems if too much avidin is taken in by the dog. Cooking the white of an egg binds the avidin and stops it doing this and whilst the occasional raw egg won't cause any ill effects, my dogs do get quite a lot of eggs because we keep our own hens, so I cook them to get around that problem.

Fish is also a great source of protein, though only coastal dwellers are likely to have access to fresh fish on a regular basis. Oily fish such as mackerel, sardine and sprats are excellent and if you get a glut of these in the spring, freeze them down into bags to add to the feed over the coming winter months.

My dogs loved raw eels when Andy caught these black river 'snakes' on a regular basis, and they seem to love mackerel and trout heads almost as much. Obviously I don't give young puppies such sharp and hard to eat items, and older dogs too can have difficulty in digesting fish heads.

I guess I'd caution anyone against feeding whole raw fish larger than a sardine if their dog hasn't got the digestive capability of a crocodile. I've had delicate little lurchers who were unable to cope with certain types of bones, and others which appear to be able to digest pretty much anything which comes from an animal. Always introduce new foods slowly in small amounts to gauge how your dog treats the food, and how its body reacts to that food. If you can't get hold of fresh fish, which you can feed in its entirety as long as it is raw, tinned fish is a good alternative. Pilchards in tomato sauce are probably the cheapest tinned product available at the time of writing, and tomatoes contain vitamin C and potassium which is a chemical needed to help metabolise proteins and carbohydrates.

SUPPLEMENTS

Quality is the key to supplements. Unscrupulous companies may sell cheap but cheap is not always best so look carefully into how the product is sourced and processed.

Dorwest Herbs, who produce supplements and veterinary medicines for animals in the UK, state the following: *"... We are the only company that has total control on all the processes involved in formulation, manufacturing, testing, packaging, storage and distribution of veterinary herbal products in the UK. Quality and microbiological checks, using scientific testing methods, are made on all raw materials before they are used to ensure that they meet the requirements of the British, Herbal or the European Pharmacopoeias, and to confirm that there is no pollution or contamination. To make sure the products maintain their strength and effectiveness throughout their shelf life, we undertake stability testing to ensure that no deterioration takes place and that every tablet retains its effectiveness throughout its shelf life."*

I add a gloop of cod liver oil two or three times per week. Buy this from a horse feed store and it comes in a lot cheaper than if you buy a similar product from a chemist, health food shop or pet food suppliers, and of course it keeps for ages so makes economic sense as well.

I also like to add a multi vitamin and mineral supplement once or twice a week. I don't know if my dogs really need this but it makes me feel happier especially during the winter when I tend to feed less fresh veg and fruit due to cost and lack of availability. The fact that nearly all my dogs graze more fervently on vegetation when out on exercise if they're not getting their daily veg ration prompts me to feed supplements more in the winter than in the summer.

I don't intend to go into the role of every vitamin and mineral in this book as there is plenty of information to be found on this subject already, and a good balanced diet using fresh, preferably organically produced meat and veg should provide most dogs with all the nutrients they need.

Kelp Seaweed is worth a mention as it is the stuff that SA37 based their man-made version on. It contains all 37 minerals and trace elements and is very commonly used to increase mineral content. Many complete food manufacturers use it for that reason.

Dorwest Herbs make a variety of veterinary medicines and supplements based on herbs and green vegetables, Keeper's Mix and Easy Green being the two I have used. If you are unable to source fresh herbs and greens on a regular basis then I'd definitely recommend adding a spoonful of either or both of these to your dog's meal.

If you mix either of these powdered supplements with water they look surprisingly like runny cow dung, (though without the same smell!) which probably explains why many dogs love to slurp from a nice fresh cow pat if they come across one whilst out in the fields. Partially digested vegetation is something that the canine body CAN make use of. Minced or pureed vegetables are all very well, but I'm sure that when a dog guzzles freshly produced maneure it is also benefiting from a horde of amino acids and enzymes present in the cow's digestive system, ready prepared for the canine gut to make full use of. Whilst this habit might not fill me with dog-loving joy, I try to ignore their ecstasy and remember to keep my face away from theirs until the green tongues and lips no longer smell of dung.

OTHER SUPPLEMENTS FOR PERFORMANCE

There are numerous supplements on the market specifically aimed at the racing Greyhound market, and I don't propose to go into them here. Call me old fashioned if you like, but even my very hard working coursing dogs ran perfectly well and, barring injury, stayed healthy and sound into old age eating nothing but naturally occurring foods.

You can pump your dog full of a variety of amino acid compounds and vitamins, but if you are feeding the animal a diet that is based on raw meat, whole carcases etc, I haven't found the need to supplement to this extent. After all, you aren't trying to create the canine equivalent of a body builder, simply an animal which can perform to the best of its potential in the field.

Incidentally, when I speak of racing dogs in this book, I'm referring to the lurchers and sighthounds that enjoy racing at country fairs or those events up and down the country organised by fellow enthusiasts. These events are a far cry from business-based Greyhound trainers whose very livelihood depends on winning by often a few hundredths of a second. Supplementing for specific conditions or ailments is a subject too vast to include in this book, and whilst I am aware of and do use certain supplements to enhance general health, particularly in the much older dog, I'd recommend delving into this subject in depth if you need to.

Think VARIETY when feeding your dog. A richly varied diet is the best way to ensure that your dog is getting all the nutrients it needs for the work that most owners wish to do with their animals. I look at each and every dog before I feed it, feeling its ribs (I should be able to feel, NOT see the ribs excepting the last three nearest the rear end of the dog) and I also take into account the work each dog is doing at the time, as well as the work it will do over the next week. I also like to just see the pin bones, though this does depend on the type of dog; Salukis and their crosses naturally carry very little fat and are naturally more 'bony' than a Collie cross, for example. The amount of subcutaneous fat carried by a healthy running dog depends much on its breeding and type.

If I know that we're likely to be out lamping the following night then I'll add extra fat (easily converted into energy) to the dog's meal, and after that night's work I'll make sure to increase protein content when the dog has a 'top up' meal the following morning. I only feed half the normal amount that night once we return home if the dog has worked very hard, feeding the rest in the morning when the dog has fully rested. The after hard work meal is of the easily digested variety, more meat than bone.

I sometimes add a handful of the muesli type dog food (cheap and cheerful with no additives therein: (yes, I know, 'rabbit food') with whatever meat I feed as this is vegetable fibre and essential roughage which prevents constipation, something that can occur if you feed too much bone. Some dogs need only a couple of teaspoons of vegetable roughage, others might need more and by observing the consistency of your dog's faeces you will come to know exactly how much of this fibre your dog requires.

However, some dogs are intolerant to many types of cereal and for those who have never suffered from an allergic reaction to certain foods it is interesting to know that animals aren't necessarily born with an allergy or intolerance to a certain foodstuff. Such a problem is all the more difficult to diagnose if the dog has been happily eating say, wheat-based foods for several years prior to showing any signs of allergy.

However, by eating something that is interfering with, or preventing, the proper absorption of a vital vitamin or mineral, sooner or later the body will start to react to that deficiency or excess. If the 'wrong' type of food is ingested over a long period of time the immune system will be weakened as it struggles to cope with that food, and it is thus less able to defend the body against harmful bacteria, invading viruses and even the effects of parasites.

It is well known that some dogs are intolerant to wheat-based products, though with others the root cause of an allergic reaction may be more difficult to trace. I even had a lurcher who couldn't tolerate raw chicken, initially vomiting it straight back after eating, then refusing to eat it altogether. She was fine with cooked chicken and also had no reaction to any other type of raw meat.

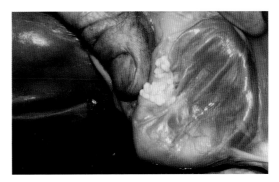

Above: Originally filled with fluid, this tapeworm cyst on a rabbit's hind leg will be rendered harmless once frozen for three weeks. Photo: Donovan Glyn.

Left: Large tapeworm cyst on rabbit's leg clearly visible even before skinning. Photo: Donovan Glyn.

Below: We leave skin and fur on feet and heads when preparing rabbits.

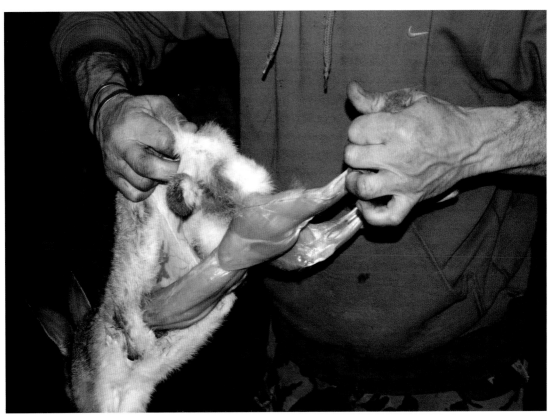

Intolerances to certain foods can take many forms, including behavioural problems, such as hyper activity (often linked to artificial colourants and preservatives in processed food) or sluggishness, though skin irritation and diarrhoea are two of the most common symptoms of allergic reaction. A friend of mine had always fed a well-known brand of complete dry food, but on getting to know me changed to an all natural diet. Two of his dogs, a terrier and a spaniel, displayed symptoms of lethargy and lack of confidence, but within weeks of changing their food to raw meat and bones, both dogs' characters changed dramatically. As one of the dogs was an elderly spaniel, her transformation was all the more startling. She gained a new lease of life and became far more outgoing than previously, voluntarily coming out of her kennel and into the house to socialise with her owner's family, something she would never have done in the past.

The somewhat timid terrier, once fearful of noise, people and travelling, changed into a confident and lively animal, which no longer had to be 'captured' before being put into the vehicle in order to get out into the field. OK, so this terrier never actually made the grade in working terms, but her quality of life and general demeanour improved to the extent that her owner was then able to find her a home where her happy nature would be appreciated without having to prove herself in the field.

Imagine suffering from a slight hangover all the time, that feeling of headachy sickness and lack of energy. Well, this is precisely the effect that some food intolerances will have on the body of an animal, an effect which will be mirrored in the animal's behaviour. Many people still manage to lead relatively normal lives even when suffering from an undiagnosed allergy, though their energy levels and quality of life are less than good. Dogs are no different, and if your dog seems miserable, lethargic or just not quite 'right' then I'd look first and foremost at diet, once serious illness has been ruled out.

Of course it can take weeks for the 'bad' elements in a diet to be eliminated from an animal's body and indeed, if intestinal damage has been caused by intolerance to certain foods, don't expect miracles to happen overnight. The body usually needs to be free from whatever has been irritating its system for at least a month, sometimes much longer, for some owners to see a real change in their dog.

Pulses, such as lentils and dried peas, are not generally considered to be good for a dog as their systems don't digest these very well. Similarly, certain root vegetables such as parsnips, sugar beet and turnips may irritate the gut, and even when pulped, pass through the intestinal tract virtually unaltered.

In my experience their only use is to add fibre to the dog's diet, fibre which I prefer to give in the form of carrots (these appear to be very well tolerated by dogs) leafy green vegetables, rice, or brown bread if tolerated. Fur is also excellent roughage, providing the animal it came from forms part of your dog's diet. I don't recommend going out and gathering sheep wool as a dietary addition, besides which, if you do feed rabbit on the bone, it is wise to freeze the carcase fur and all to kill external as well as internal parasites. I've found that feeding my dogs about half the skin and fur from a rabbit carcase per dog helps to wrap up any sharp undigested bits of bone or teeth to produce a smooth, uniform stool.

THE GREAT CARBOHYDRATE DEBATE

We, as dog owners, want to keep our charges in healthy condition, thereby allowing them to fulfil whatever role they may have to play in our lives, and whilst a dog is basically a carnivore, the fact that they have evolved alongside us humans for thousands of years does mean that they can cope with a far wider range of food stuffs than some of their wild counterparts. So, do dogs really need carbohydrates in their diets? And can they make use of carbohydrates in the way that more omnivorous animals do? First, the term carbohydrate can be misleading as there are two forms of carbohydrates: complex and simple. Simple carbs are basically sugar (glucose) and are able to be absorbed directly into the system through the walls of the intestine. They provide instant energy. Complex carbs (starch) are found in cereals, and they need to be broken down during the digestive process before they can be turned into energy. Dogs don't actually NEED simple carbs (glucose) any more than humans in order to maintain a healthy life. But they can process both forms of carbohydrate even though they prefer to derive their energy mainly from fat, unlike humans who obtain energy from the carbs found in cereals much more efficiently.

However, in answer to the second question, dogs can 'learn' to use carbohydrates in a similar way to us, but their systems need to become accustomed to that type of food over a period of time. The custom of 'carb loading', whereby a human athlete pumps itself full of carbohydrates before a competition in order to 'store up' energy, doesn't work on dogs, although some coursing people like to feed their animals pasta meals before an event. The dog would perform just as well without this 'carb loading' if it has been properly conditioned, (got physically fit enough for the work involved). A dog converts carbohydrates into fat, not instant energy, which is one of the reasons so many pet dogs nowadays suffer from obesity. They are simply getting a diet that is far too high in carbohydrates for their levels of activity.

However, research done on racing sled dogs shows that feeding an easily assimilated form of carbohydrate such as glucose (simple carb) immediately after a race, will restore the glycogen (energy) levels to normal better than if the animal had not been given this boost. In other words, giving glucose after a race or course can help the dog's body to regain energy. I don't give sugar water, sweet tea or any other home made drink containing sweeteners of any kind, but I use a racing Greyhound formula called Recharge, which does contain glucose, but also contains mineral salts. Recharge is especially formulated for racing greyhounds whose requirements differ tremendously to those of horses or humans. As dogs are unable to sweat through the pores of their skin they don't need rehydrating in quite the same way as horses or humans, and Recharge is tailored specifically to target the minerals lost by the dog during hard, prolonged exercise or in extreme hot weather.

Some people believe that if dogs receive adequate amounts of fat in their diet they shouldn't need to consume any carbohydrate at all. One only has to consider the Inuit dogs which traditionally thrived on meat and fat and nothing else, or packs of Foxhounds which ate nothing but fallen livestock to understand that this is true. BUT, an interesting point to consider is that different breeds or types of dogs the world over have evolved to cope with vastly differing foods, and whilst some dogs tolerate a high proportion of grain in their diet, others suffer from chronic diarrhoea or nutritional deficiency when fed a similar food. This 'intolerance' may have been inherited via the genes of animals which hadn't evolved to cope with such foods. This is not just my theory but one that is gaining ground in different studies of dogs the world over.

Just as humans from Asia have evolved over the millennia to thrive on a diet which is high in rice, so may have their dogs, and although the modern lurcher, and even many 'pure' sighthounds may be a composite of many different breeds, I find it interesting to note that canines from around the world appear to do very well on diets that are extremely varied.

If I feed a diet low in carbohydrate to my Saluki bred dogs, they lose condition fairly quickly. If I continue to deny them a decent carbohydrate intake in the form of cereals they will eventually suffer from muscle wastage as their bodies start to use muscle tissue in order to release energy. In my experience this type of dog needs a higher intake of carbohydrate to function and remain well than some other types such as Collies.

If I feed any form of carbs to my little fat Collie bred lurcher she lays down even more fat, storing that extra energy supply in case of hard times to come. She's the original farmyard dog who would have looked good on a meagre diet of scraps and bones! Or I need to run her for 20 miles a day beside my bike to use everything she eats! Needless to say she gets a fair amount of minced veg with her meat, and less fat than some of my more sighthoundy dogs.

Most grains in their natural form are highly indigestible to nearly all dogs, passing through the gut virtually unchanged. Cereals such as wheat and rice need to be cooked before the canine digestive system can make use of them. Without getting too scientific about things, the dog's pancreas (the organ responsible for producing digestive enzymes) must work overtime when faced with a diet loaded with carbohydrates, and dogs which are continually fed a diet composed largely of cereals which are converted into glucose and stored as body fat, are at a far greater risk of diseases such as diabetes and pancreatitis.

I remember seeing a fascinating video of desert Salukis at work coursing hare and fox in their native North Africa, but one salient point in the accompanying commentary amazed me and it was that these dogs were seldom fed anything but pitta bread and dates! In a highly religious Islamic culture where most dogs are considered the lowest of the low, it would be unthinkable for the humans to eat the hares caught by their dogs if the carcase had been broken open, so even the offal was denied those dogs.

It was up to the youngest man to run like the wind to relieve the dogs of their catch before they had a chance to taint the flesh, and the hare was also gutted on the spot and the entrails buried immediately. The dogs were chivvied away by the other members of the hunting party before they could render the carcase unusable by humans.

None of the dogs that appeared in this film appeared to be underweight or lacking in energy, which implies that their diet, one that we wouldn't dream of inflicting on our Western dogs, appeared to sustain them sufficiently for their work. There was no mention of how long these dogs lived for, nor what diseases or ailments they suffered, but both adults and puppies featured in the film all appeared to be healthy and well fleshed out. One can discuss the merits and failings of a dog's dietary needs ad infinitum, <u>but it is only by living with and working with our own dogs that we can learn what suits our own particular hounds best.</u> Each dog is different and we need to be sensitive to our dogs' overall condition in order to give them what will best suit their dietary requirements.

FEEDING THE VERY YOUNG

Puppies at weaning age and those which have not yet attained their adult teeth should not be fed small pieces of bone as their digestive systems are still immature, lacking the strength to break down chunks of bone. By all means feed tiny weanlings on whole rabbits: an ideal food where the meat can be sucked and gnawed from the bone by little teeth. Large items such as breast of lamb and even meaty leg bones may also safely be left in the bed of a litter of puppies. They will spend hours chewing the meat and tissue from those large bones with no risk of swallowing small pieces as their teeth and jaws are not strong enough to break them off. Just make sure that there are no shards or splinters of bone attached from the original butchering process which could be torn off and swallowed.

I feed chicken wings from about the age of eight weeks, and whilst such a wing may, on occasion be swallowed whole by a greedy pup, the bones of commercially bred chickens are very soft indeed as these birds have been bred to mature at a very young age. The wing bones in particular have not attained a density which could cause a problem to any but the most delicate of toy breeds or those dogs with problem digestive systems.

You *can* smash up wings on a wooden chopping block with an axe or hammer for very tiny pups such as Whippets and their hybrids. This, in part, copies what happens when the mother chews, swallows and regurgitates the food for her offspring. Healthy sighthound and lurcher pups of eight weeks upwards have never, in my experience, come to any harm by swallowing whole chicken wings though occasionally a whole wing might be vomited back up only to be chewed more thoroughly before being ingested once more.

Dogs are very good at vomiting up food that needs a bit more 'processing' and I never worry about this.

If you mince either chicken or rabbit carcases for your dogs, avoid feeding such whole carcase mince to puppies under the age of six weeks. I'm sure many people do feed such mince to younger pups without a problem, but I prefer to err on the side of caution and offer really young pups food which they can digest very easily.

Most puppies of six weeks and under will still be topping up with their dam's dwindling milk supply so you don't need to worry about calcium deficiencies just yet. If for some reason the dam is unable or unwilling to suckle her pups after three weeks of age then I would make sure that the litter receives a secondary source of calcium in the form of a proprietary milk for puppies until they reach an age where they could digest bone themselves.

Neither do I add vegetable matter at the start of weaning, (I generally offer well minced rabbit, chicken and beef from the age of three weeks) though by six weeks I'm adding small amounts of pureed raw carrots, greens and cooked rice to the meat. Just like some children, puppies can be finicky about eating their veg, so I bide my time and try them with a little every so often, leaving it out for a few days if they refuse to eat it, and testing them again the next week. I've never had an adult dog refuse to eat minced vegetables though I

Monitor the older dog carefully, checking teeth, gums and faeces to ensure that the animal isn't struggling to cope with bones.

do find that all but the greediest of puppies don't really like celery at an early age.

Once a pup has reached the age of about five to six months and has all its adult teeth I feel happy to offer whole carcases again, though care should be taken if you are feeding several pups together as greed and competition may force some to swallow lumps of bone without properly grinding that bone into pieces small enough to digest. My vet tells me that she has never encountered problems of bones impacting in the gut, though she has had to surgically retrieve all sorts of foreign objects such as stones, toys and the like from the intestines of her patients. Personally, I have found that if any of my dogs, old or young, ingests something of animal origin which it finds indigestible, they vomit this item back up, sometimes as much as 24 hours after it had been swallowed. Dogs vomit freely for a variety of reasons, and unless we are talking about an animal with real health problems, this is a natural process which shouldn't give any cause for alarm to the owner. Repeated vomiting is cause for concern, however, and needs medical attention.

FEEDING THE OLD DOG
I have noticed that in very old age some of my dogs have become intolerant to raw meat and bones. Intolerant is not quite the right word as the only ill effects they suffer are terrible wind and foul breath but that's reason enough for me to give them cooked meat, telling me that their whole system isn't as robust as it once was. The digestive system and its ability to function well deteriorates over the years along with

the rest of the animal, and I figure that if my dogs have attained a ripe old age they deserve a contented retirement in front of the fire after a lifetime's hard work. Feeding them cooked meat just makes them easier to live with though I've found that raw minced beef is much better tolerated than raw rabbit or chicken.

Contrary to some people's beliefs, old dogs do need a high protein diet because their systems function less efficiently than when they were younger. Giving an old dog top quality animal protein in a form that is easily digestible such as meat and animal fat allows the nutrients to be more easily assimilated by the canine digestive system than the proteins found in cereals. Protein is needed not just for growth but is used to maintain good health and a strong immune system, a weakening of which is seen in older animals which are not fed appropriately to their needs.

I generally give old dogs more meat in proportion to the amount of bone they consume and if they are prone to putting on weight, I lower the fat content a little. What I don't do is increase their cereal intake as this puts a greater load of work on the digestive system. Old dogs which are reluctant to eat much at all should be checked over by a vet for any underlying health problems.

FREQUENTLY ASKED QUESTIONS

Can I feed my dog solely on one food, such as whole rabbits or chickens?

I would never feed dogs on just one type of food as in each type of meat there are bound to be some deficiencies of certain vitamins or minerals. You can argue that a wild dog would only have access to whole carcases, but it is well known that wild dogs, wolves etc, also 'graze' on certain types of vegetation, herbivore droppings and fruit when in season when they feel the need to, something that is often denied the domestic dog.

Foxes are normally considered to be out and out carnivores, but how often do we see fox scat comprised of blackberries, snail shells and all sorts of vegetable remnants. I don't for one moment believe that foxes eat this sort of thing through starvation, as my dogs pick their own blackberries off the bramble, selecting the ripe black ones over the unripe berries. My dogs also carefully choose a variety of different grasses and plants to nibble when out on exercise, though I have noticed that they do this more readily if I haven't given them enough minced veggies with their dinners (a reminder to me to increase their veg and fruit rations!).

Variety isn't just the spice of life when it comes to complete nutrition, it is essential to overall health, and to restrict a dog to just one sort of food will lead to deficiencies. Another point to note is that wild rabbit contains very little fat, and whilst the natural fat content of a wild rabbit may sustain a fox or wild dog which hunts only to satisfy its hunger, our domesticated lurchers and sighthounds generally need a greater amount of fat in their diet if they are to work hard over the course of a long and tiring season. Fat provides energy, and when we ask our dogs to run again and again in order to satisfy our human need to catch game or win races we need to add extra energy giving food if our dogs aren't to lose condition.

A very lightly worked dog, or one that is less active, will need less energy food than a young, highly active animal. Neutered dogs also need fewer calories to maintain good condition. There are also those canny beasts which seem to

Hare is excellent food for dogs. Photo: Mike Bridle.

survive on next to nothing! Some lurchers containing a fair bit of Collie blood would put on weight if they so much as looked at a lump of fat, no matter how much hard work they are doing. Collies, both Border and Beardie, evolved to survive on the most meagre of diets, kitchen scraps and whatever they could scrounge on their owners' farms, often supplementing their diets with lamb afterbirths and even fallen stock. Sprinting dogs need larger quantities of fat and more protein if they are to maintain weight throughout a hard working winter and very fast Whippet or Greyhound type dogs will burn energy like no tomorrow, their anaerobic style of running using far more energy than the Collie or Saluki type.

Can I feed my dog raw bones? I always thought that raw bones were dangerous for dogs!

Bones should be an important part of a dog's diet, but the type of bone you feed your dog is equally important. I feed whole young rabbit and chicken carcases as these bones are small and easily digested by dogs, but I don't feed leg bones of larger animals such as sheep, deer, cows or horses.

Large adult animal leg bones are very dense and hard and whilst a dog is attempting to get at the marrow inside the bone it may either break its teeth in doing so, or the greedy type might swallow sharp shards of these bones if the dog manages to crack them apart. However, most domestic meat producing animals are slaughtered before they are mature and chicken leg bones are quite acceptable to dogs of a tough constitution.

Huge beef knuckle or shin bones can be useful to keep a sensible dog occupied in a kennel, but if you find that your dog is grinding away at these very hard bones for hours only allow access for an hour or so or they risk wearing the dog's teeth down which could expose the nerve, resulting in pain and infection. Once again, much depends on your dog's temperament and type as to how it 'attacks' its food, and although too much bone content in a diet can result in constipation and straining to pass hard, white powdery faeces, a certain amount of bone is essential to health. The accepted bone to meat ration in a raw food diet is approximately 60% meat to 40% bone, but this can vary from individual to individual and you need to monitor what comes out of your dog's rear end in order to adjust accordingly.

Dog faeces should be smooth, firm but not crumbly. If they hit the ground and bounce like marbles, or explode into a white crumbly powder then you are feeding too much bone. Similarly, if the dog strains to pass faeces, or yelps in pain when doing so then you need to immediately reduce the bone content in the diet, upping the meat intake until you reach the point where the faeces are the correct consistency. Sounds like a recipe doesn't it, with the dog's digestive system being the oven through which the raw ingredients pass to produce the end result! Seriously though, by watching what your dog passes you will be able to get a very good idea as to how to balance your feeding.

The other thing that bears mentioning whilst we're on the subject of feeding is the smelly subject of anal glands. All dogs have two anal glands, one on each side of their anus, situated just inside the anal opening. These glands are what give each dog their individual identifying scent, which is why all dogs sniff each other's rear ends when meeting. A tiny amount of the secretion produced in the glands is excreted each time the dog produces faeces, thereby leaving that individual's scent on its stools. However, if the stools are not firm enough in consistency to squeeze this secretion from the glands, they can become over full, painful and in extreme cases infected which can result in an anal abscess.

Typical signs of over full anal glands are bottom scooting, where the dog drags its back end along the floor, and you'll often notice an oily, fishy odour from the dog's rear end. Bad cases can irritate the dog so much that it can bite at the area around its anus and above the root of the tail, often growling and worrying at the area. My own line of rough coated lurchers tended to suffer from impacted anal glands when I fed them cooked food, be it kibble/biscuit or cooked stews with no bone content. Within weeks of converting to a raw, whole carcase diet all symptoms ceased, and since then not one dog has ever shown a re-occurrence of anal gland impaction. Yet one more reason to feed as nature intended!

Very dark stools are normal if you are feeding a lot of venison or hare, and paler stools are normal if you feed mostly chicken or rabbit. If you don't feed venison or hare be sure to get some beef into your dogs at least twice a week, as there are nutrients in red meat that you don't find in white meat, such as iron and the B vitamins. These are also found in heart and liver.

I do feed sheep, small deer and pork rib bones to adult dogs and pups once their teeth have firmly set in to their jaws (this happens between 10 to 12 months of age) and I have never had a problem with these.

WARNING: If you have more than one dog it's as well to separate the dogs before you feed bones because competition between animals may force some to chew too fast or not enough. Lumps of bones swallowed may make for difficult digestion or be vomited some time later if the fragments have proved too large to digest. Some dogs will lie quite happily side by side chewing bones, but I prefer to err on the side of caution and shut most of my dogs in separate kennels when feeding bones. Only the high ranking and confident bitches are fed together, secure in their place in the pack and the knowledge that no other dog will attempt to steal bones from under their noses.

Very occasionally a dog will manage to get a piece of bone stuck between its molars (the chewing teeth at the back of the jaw), so be alert to signs of distress, excessive drooling or pawing at the side of the mouth. Most such pieces of bone can be prised out with your fingers, but be careful when doing so! Accustom your dog to having its mouth inspected on a regular basis and it will allow you to extricate bits of bone without a problem. Fragments of bone that are stuck fast may need veterinary intervention but I've always been able to prise loose any bits of stuck bone.

Why are my dog's faeces black, soft and loose when feeding meat?

Feeding too much offal (liver, kidney, heart) can result in faeces which are black and loose. Offal is very rich and should only be fed in small amounts. Think whole carcase when you feed offal. Liver, heart and kidneys should only be fed in the amounts they would appear in a natural diet. Suppose you feed a whole rabbit to a dog, then most of the food will be muscle meat, a smaller proportion will be bone, and only a tiny amount will consist of the liver and heart. These are the proportions in which you should feed offal, so that a meal of let's say, half a chicken carcase and some minced veg and rice, will contain about a dessert spoonful of liver or kidney.

NOTE: *black, tarry faeces can also be symptomatic of bleeding from the stomach lining. Adjust the diet accordingly before panicking and if there is no improvement see a vet. The exception is in a bitch which has just given birth and eaten the placentas. This is quite normal and the colour and consistency of her faeces should return to normal once she has expelled the results of eating those placentas.*

Why can one of my dogs tolerate eggs but they give the other dog severe wind?

Dogs are just like humans and what can be good for one individual can be quite the opposite for another. Dogs can suffer from allergies to certain foods just like humans. If something has an adverse effect on your dog ... don't feed it that food!

What veg and fruit should I feed my dog?

I feed carrots, celery, spinach and spinach beet, some greens such as cabbage and broccoli, cauliflower, Brussels sprouts, apples, pears, capsicums (green, yellow and red sweet peppers), small amounts of garlic, tomatoes, runner and French beans, green peas, (fresh, not the dried variety), courgettes and steamed nettles.

There are many more vegetables and fruit you can feed your dog, but the ones I have mentioned are easily obtainable and cheap, especially if you grow them yourself. I don't tend to give my dogs much fruit, though occasionally an apple or two finds its way into the mix. You don't need to go to extremes when adding veg and fruit to your dog's diet and mine get what is easily available at the time.

The main foods to avoid altogether are: onions, grapes and raisins, chocolate, avocado and nuts which my dogs have never been able to digest anyway. I know that you are supposed to be able to grind down nuts to a powder for dogs but I've never seen the point of spending time mashing up nuts in order to supply dogs with something of such small nutritional value, especially as nuts wouldn't really constitute more than about a zillionth of a wild dog's diet.

I can't get enough meat to just feed my dog on raw food: can I mix raw and complete biscuit together?

It is generally understood that different types of food require different lengths of time in the gut. By mixing both together you may reduce the amount of nutrients absorbed by the gut: cereal needs to spend longer in the dog's digestive system than meat, so by feeding both together the cereal part of the meal is hurried along with the meat part, or could it be the other way round? Could this be the reason for loose stools when dogs are fed in this way? Some dogs process all types of food so well that they never produce loose stools no matter what combination of food types you feed at any one time: I love this sort of dog!

If you are going to feed a mixture of complete and raw you would be better to do so at different meals though once again I'm contradicting myself a little as I do mix cooked rice and raw meat together and don't have a problem. To be honest, I think that we make this raw feeding thing vastly too complicated in our desire to do things right by our hounds, so as long as the dog is healthy, happy and not dispensing sloppy herbivore-type waste from its rear end then we should be content.

I really don't want to go through the hassle of raw feeding. What complete foods can you recommend?

If you are going to take the easier route and stick to a dry, complete kibble/biscuit, and you have money to burn then check the ingredients listed on the side of the bag very carefully before you buy. I would avoid any food where the list of ingredients starts with cereals of whatever kind, as these will then be the main component in the mix. I would also avoid any food containing a long list of preservatives, colouring or artificial additives. By doing this I would pay a lot more for the dog food than if it were a cereal based product, but at least I would know that I would be less likely to be clearing up pools of pooh after my dogs, and I wouldn't be worrying about the long-term effects of feeding junk food to my animals. Just remember that dry food of any sort is not a natural diet in any way, and dogs eating dry biscuit will need to drink at least twice, or three times more than they would if they were eating moist, raw food.

How much food should I give my dog? He is always looking for more and would eat ten times the amount I feed him if l left the food down.

Dogs have evolved to be able to eat an enormous amount of food at a sitting. Just look at the African Wild Dogs or Wolves, which can ingest kilos of meat from a kill within a few moments, then retire somewhere safe in order to digest at their leisure, sometimes regurgitating what they have scoffed in haste to eat quietly in peace away from competitors or other predators.

Many domestic dogs have retained the same psychological need to gulp down their food as fast as they can. My own dogs would eat two or three times more than I give them, but this doesn't mean that I'm starving them: far from it! The fact that they don't need any more than I have given them just doesn't compute in the canine mind!

I have also noticed that if minced meat or carcases might have constituted the main part of their meal, it is eaten fast, and lacks the satisfaction factor that a tougher bone such as a pork rib or piece of lamb breast offers.

It's almost as if a dog needs to work for its food to feel truly satisfied, something that kibble fed dogs just don't have the opportunity to do. Some dogs are just inordinately greedy and I can tell tales of a lurcher who broke into the fridge and devoured 7 kilos of semi-frozen horse meat. She lay around for the rest of the day like a bloated python which has swallowed a whole pig, and then had the cheek to want some supper!

Needless to say she didn't get any. Or the nine month old pup who found a heap of rabbit skins and heads one afternoon before they had been properly disposed of and ate until he physically couldn't move, but then demanded and ate his supper the same evening with no ill effects whatsoever! (I hadn't noticed his rather rotund appearance until it was too late: well, he was very rough coated, which hid the hippo-like proportions of his stomach!) The next day he did indeed pass more waste, but with no signs of diarrhoea. He simply produced a number of large, grey, fox-like scats, testimony to the fact that a healthy dog can process bones, fur and even teeth and nails, and in unusual quantities, with no problem at all.

My friend's Spaniel once ate a complete muntjak skin with no side effects, not something I'd recommend feeding to a dog, but once again, this skin was processed internally with no problem, though his faeces did contain volumes of undigested deer hair for the next few days. The hair of larger herbivores such as deer, cattle etc is too coarse for most dogs to digest, though I'd guess that it cleans the digestive tract out pretty thoroughly.

I think that you and all these raw food fanatics make far too much fuss over feeding an animal which is only going to live for a few years anyway! So what if the dog gets cancer at eight years old, it's past its best by then!

Someone actually said this to me, and for once I was momentarily lost for words, but as I looked at this person who obviously took no more care of their own health than their dog's, I realised that you can't win 'em all, sad to say. Feeding my dogs what is best for them is reward in itself for me, and when I see how quickly their injuries heal, how much longer they remain active than so and so's cheap kibble fed dog down the road, how few parasites they attract, how much better their coats and breath smell, how the anal gland problems some used to suffer from disappeared almost overnight, how strong their claws are ... I could go on, but you get the picture.

DANGER OF BLOAT

The danger for a dog which binges on dry biscuit is quite real however, as dry food expands in the stomach causing impaction, possible kidney damage and even bloat (gastric torsion). *(Dogs can get bloat even on raw food and it is often the narrower, deeper chested type of sighthound which is most likely to be affected. Several small meals per day and withholding of water for an hour after feeding is recommended for such dogs.)*

I know of people who leave bowls full of dry biscuit down all the time for their dogs, allowing the dog to snack when it wants. This might be permissible for very sedentary dogs which are of a temperament to self-regulate their intake, but it is neither sensible nor safe to feed an active dog in this way, one which exercises or works hard when the gut is continually semi-full and striving to digest food.

Dogs weren't designed to graze like herbivores throughout the day or night,

152

and if owners want to work, race or gallop their dogs just for fun we need to make sure that the animal isn't allowed, or asked, to perform on a full, or semi-full stomach. Dogs at risk of bloat can be fed smaller more frequent meals to avoid filling the stomach once a day, and you should avoid any form of hard exercise such as running, chasing, jumping or swimming for at least 8 hours, preferably 12 hours, after a large meal. Even a trotting-only bike ride should be done on an empty stomach. The general rule must always be: feed after work or exercise, not before.

NOTE: *Don't feed a dog whilst it is still panting or hot after exercise or work. I like my dogs to rest for about an hour before I feed them after they have been exercised, though if they have been exercised in the morning and their main meal isn't until evening I only give a small amount of food and then only to young, very active or underweight animals. If a dog has worked hard all night on the lamp, or been out coursing all day then I only feed half the normal amount on our return home: the balance of that meal will be fed the following evening in the case of the lamping dog, or on the following morning in the case of the daytime dog.*

How much should a dog eat every day?

How much does a dog need to eat each day? As much or as little as it takes to keep the dog in good health for the life it leads. I don't weigh my dogs except for worming purposes. I look at them and feel them; my eyes and hands tell me how much the dog needs to be fed. Be prepared to adjust the amount of food you feed to your dogs depending on the work done, time of year,

and temperature etc. As a general rule of thumb I like to be able to see the last three ribs on my smooth coated lurchers (you need to be hands-on for rough coated dogs), feel but not see the pin bones, and in all but the very old or pregnant, there should be no flab in the undercarriage area. The exception to this last is the post season female who may be carrying fat around her mammary glands.

The 'bottom' line of a running dog is as important as its top line and if the abdomen appears convex rather than concave then that dog is over weight. However, older or unfit lurchers and sighthounds do show more sag in the stomach area as old or unfit muscles allow the abdominal contents to drop earthwards more than in young or fit animals, something also to be noted in females that have born very large litters. You shouldn't be able to feel 'blubber' under the skin, even in older dogs. No lurcher or sighthound should be covered in a thick layer of subcutaneous fat!

Is it OK to feed cooked vegetables to my dog?

Cooking destroys many fragile nutrients in food. Feed raw if possible, though very lightly steamed vegetables are better than those which have been boiled in water into which the nutrients are leached during cooking. Some people like to feed their dogs tinned tomatoes in order to help stave off lactic acid build up during hard work, but be aware that, as I've already mentioned, the vitamin C which helps to prevent lactic acid build up, will have been in part destroyed by the heating process prior to canning.

The following is intended as a ROUGH GUIDE ONLY. As I've already said, I don't weigh my dogs regularly and I certainly don't weigh their food … ever! I have only included weights in an attempt to give the novice raw feeder a rough idea as to what the amounts might look like in a dog bowl.

A TYPICAL DAY'S FOOD FOR AN ADULT RUNNING DOG WEIGHING 25 KILOS

Approx 250gram minced beef (my mix contains heart muscle as well as outer body muscle) mixed with between two and four heaped tablespoons full of minced veg and or fruit, 1 small cup of soaked muesli type dog food or cooked whole grain rice. ½ a boned out chicken carcase, two chicken wings or half a dozen ribs from a breast of lamb, usually already stripped of most of its meat by our thrifty butcher.

OR:

400gram minced whole rabbit (minus the guts of course but including skin and fur on feet and legs). 100grams of lamb or beef fat minced in with the rabbit. Vegetables and rice or muesli as shown in the first example also minced in with the meat and fat.

OR:

200gram of fresh tripe chunks, preferably unwashed, four tinned pilchards in tomato sauce or tin of sardines in oil (low salt option, though nowadays I've noticed that most tinned fish has a much lower salt content than it did a few years ago). Two slices of wholemeal bread, preferably as unprocessed as possible. Add veg if you want. Two lamb ribs or chicken wings.

OR:

Four cooked eggs (up to you how you cook them!), small cup of cooked wholegrain rice plus the minced veg, breast of lamb chunk approximately six ribs wide. Make sure there's enough fat left on it.

I would never feed any one of these 'recipes' to the exclusion of any of the others. I probably feed a combination of these over the course of a week, though I don't worry if the dogs don't get any one of these ingredients every single week. The above are amounts for a running dog that is not in heavy work, one that is getting about an hour's exercise per day which involves free running as well as lead work.

Cereals can be increased or decreased depending on the consistency of the dog's stools, and amounts can be adjusted up or down depending upon the dog's metabolism. Some dogs naturally need a lot more fuel than others. Nervy, highly strung and very active dogs may need half as much again as the amounts indicated. Increasing the fat content of any dog's diet will offer it immediately 'useable' energy.

HARD WORKING DOGS

Very hard working dogs such as lamping or coursing dogs or those engaged in high energy competitions such as racing will need considerably greater amounts of food than those listed. Once again, much depends on the type of animal and the type of work it is doing. Remember to increase the fat content in your dog's food if it is working hard on a regular basis, and as I've already stated, Saluki type dogs tend to do better if their carbohydrate intake is increased. Sprinters such as Whippets and Greyhounds do need carbohydrates but normally in a slightly lower proportion than the desert type dogs.

I have no intention of addressing the requirements of the racing Greyhound as people far more knowledgeable than I have already spent years researching and fine tuning the diet and care of these highly conditioned animals where milliseconds are the difference between winning and losing a race. If you feed carbohydrates then feed them on a daily basis rather than 'carb loading' just before an event. If you offer a well balanced diet throughout the dog's life it will be better able to make use of the nutrients in the food and it will perform better overall than if it is deficient in any one nutrient.

WHEN AND HOW TO FEED

I feed normal healthy adult dogs once each day during the evening, after exercise. I like to feed once the day is done so that the dogs know they won't be going out again and will relax quietly through the night, thus able to digest their meal without wondering if they might be walked or worked. Dogs which find it hard to maintain weight are fed a small breakfast in addition to their evening meal and this will consist of high fat, high protein plus an easily digested form of carbohydrate. A couple of large scrambled eggs on well buttered toast are an ideal breakfast for this sort of dog, or you could put a tin of sardines in oil over the toast instead of eggs.

Puppies of less than 12 months of age also have breakfast, similar to the one I feed to skinny dogs, but I also include a couple of chicken wings or lamb ribs as well for the satisfaction content. Bone will make a dog feel fuller for longer, hence the satisfaction.

IN CONCLUSION

I've now been feeding my dogs in this way for over 15 years and without exception they are thriving, far too well in some cases! Some may need more than the amounts stated, others much less: dogs vary in their calorific needs as much as people. My 28 inch Saluki lurcher gets almost twice as much as the amounts I have indicated, and the little fat Collie thing gets about half the recommended amount.

If you are the type of person who worries over every last detail of what you should feed your dog then by all means go out and buy a bag of complete 'wonderful dog' food, and leave it to the 'experts' to decide what your faithful mutt should eat. To be perfectly honest, there are some very good, responsibly sourced complete dog foods on the market, but don't expect to pay less than £40 per 15 kilo bag. Complete foods costing less than that amount may well use waste from the human food industry which by their very definition (waste) need extensive processing in order to render them fit for canine consumption.

Check ingredients on the side of the bag very carefully and avoid cereal-based products or products containing less than 10% fat unless you are using very small amounts solely for the purpose of adding vegetable fibre to your meat meals. The cheaper complete foods will also contain vegetable oil in place of animal fat, which whilst better than no fat at all, is of less benefit to the canine body as a source of energy. It's up to you what you feed your dogs, but I've seen too many benefits from raw feeding to ever go back to just opening a bag of kibble. After all, I've managed to sustain myself for over half a century quite well enough on a varied diet made from identifiable ingredients. Just keep thinking VARIETY when you raw feed.

CHAPTER NINE

Bitches and their seasons

Here's a whole chapter on the female of the canine species, her seasons (heats) and the effects of the hormone changes that accompany the female reproductive cycle.

You might wonder why I've devoted so much space to something that is, after all, a perfectly normal and natural part of the female canine and shouldn't really entail much understanding, but when we're talking about the effects of hormones on the female body, dogs can be subject to all sorts of surprising changes, both physically and mentally. Any man who has ever lived with a woman will understand that hormones can cause all sorts of seemingly implausible behaviour in the female of the species, though women will of course understand the whole roller-coaster hormonal cycle with no problem at all, even though the human reproductive cycle is very different to that of the canine.

When a bitch comes into season her body is already starting to prepare itself for the eventuality of having puppies.

You may have noticed on the run-up to her season that she is more enthusiastic, hunting harder and can sometimes become uncharacteristically disobedient, or she can be moody and quiet, preferring to spend long moments sniffing at interesting smells in the grass, normally where other dogs, both male and female, have peed. She may also begin to pee little and often to advertise the fact that she is shortly to come into season. These changes can be very noticeable, or you may see no difference at all: each animal is an individual.

However, it is a fact that most female racing Greyhounds will run at their best just before they come into season, something that, in the days before it was possible to suppress the reproductive cycle, trainers would hide from other people thereby allowing them to win good money on a bitch that at other times might not be quite so worthy of a bet.

If you keep both male and female dogs you may notice the males start to take an interest in the bitch several weeks before she actually starts her season. This is because the changing hormone levels can be picked up by male dogs from the smell of her urine, and she may also appear flirtatious, but only on her own terms, snapping any males off sharply if they dare to lay a paw across her shoulders. (This is the male dog's way of testing to see if she is receptive to his advances, something an inexperienced male may try to do to some females although they are not yet in oestrus; a tentative paw across the shoulders, which can be quickly removed if she turns to snap at him.)

Experienced males take no notice of these subtle changes on the run up to a season, but young and inexperienced dogs may seem a tad confused at the changing scent and may even attempt to mount the

Photo: Craig McCann.

suddenly very interesting female, which she won't allow them to do.

Bitches generally appear in tip top condition just before they come into season, and even in a relatively unfit animal, the muscles seem more toned up, the coat will shine and there may be a general air of brightness and a springy bounce to her step. Even elderly bitches, long past sensible breeding age, appear to be rejuvenated and often act half their age just before they come into season.

When she does eventually come into season (also known as breaking down in Greyhound circles) blood leaks from her vulva and whilst this may appear as just a small brownish discharge to begin with, especially in a pup that is having her first season it will soon become reddish in colour. Bleeding lasts, on average about three weeks, though the colour of the discharge can vary during that period, and a first season can be very light, hardly noticeable, or it can be very heavy with prolonged bleeding.

The vulva of large breeds such as Deerhounds and their crosses may swell to more than double the normal size, whereas in Whippets, Greyhounds and their hybrids the swelling may be much less obvious.

Female running dog pups seldom come into season earlier than eight or nine months of age, though generalised doggy books will have you believe that all bitches experience their first season around six months of age. Don't be surprised if a female running dog takes much longer to mature sufficiently to come into season. My own line of lurchers usually have their first heats at between 12 and 15 months of age, and I had one bitch who was four years old before she came into season. Thereafter she cycled once a year in the manner of a wild canine. There was nothing wrong with her at all and she went on to have two healthy litters of pups, the first at six years of age, the second at eight, which is quite old for most bitches to bear pups successfully.

Young bitches can almost come into their first season, show blood for a couple of days then stop again and not have a proper season until a few months later, and this is quite normal in some sighthoundy dogs or those at the bottom of a strong female pack. It's almost as if they don't feel they have the right to become potential breeders when there are more dominant bitches around.

It is unlikely that a few days of discharging in this way will result in eggs

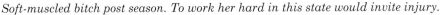

Soft-muscled bitch post season. To work her hard in this state would invite injury.

being shed from the ovaries, but it is better to separate males and females from the moment the bitch shows colour until it is quite obvious that the males are no longer interested in her, just to be on the safe side.

Some animals keep themselves so clean by licking their rear end that you may not even realise they are in season at all, so you need to watch them closely if you are not to miss the signs and there's been many an accidental mating take place when the owner has failed to spot that their bitch is on heat.

Some people say that as she nears the time when she is ready to be mated the discharge will change from red to lighter pink or even straw coloured, but I've found this not necessarily to be so. In many females the discharge does change colour whilst others seem to show the same red colour throughout their seasons.

As she approaches the optimum time for mating, her vulva will reach maximum size and the swelling will soften at the same time. The length of time a bitch will stand for a dog can vary from a few hours to over a week so you can't take any chances by letting males and females mix until the season is well and truly over.

Many people believe that the optimum time for mating is from about the tenth to the fourteenth day of her season. Whilst this is generally true, some females are ready to be mated as early as seven days, and others will only stand from day 20 onwards! Once a regular cycle has been established most canines are true to that cycle unless extreme lack of condition, injury or illness upset that regularity, but this is not set in stone and cycles can change without warning, emotional upheavals such as a change of home or companions being just two of the non physical causes of seasonal vagaries.

It is both unfair and annoying to both sexes to allow kenneled males and females to even see each other during the course of the heat and I have a special out of the way kennel for in-season bitches. Of course the males know that she is in there and in season, but they cannot actually see her nor get within 20 metres of her kennel which is separated by a solid six foot wooden fence.

House dogs unused to being kenneled can be safely crated in a separate room as long as you can keep doors shut between the dogs; this might seem unfair on the female, but as it's only for a few weeks each year, and as long as you give her regular toilet breaks and plenty of exercise (separately to the dog of course!) every day then I don't see this temporary incarceration as anything but a minor irritation to all parties concerned, both dogs and humans.

A good meaty bone or big rawhide chew will help to alleviate boredom for the crated dog, and I always like to cover the back, top and a bit of the sides of a crate with a blanket (except in very hot weather) as this makes the cage feel more like a snug den for dogs.

Out of sight out of mind this is not, but unless you can board either sex off your premises for the duration this is the best that I can manage. Many, not all, sighthound males have a markedly lower sex drive than some other breeds, and I've not had a problem with dogs attempting to chew their way through doors or walls.

Some degree of howling and marking (in the form of peeing on anything and everything) is to be expected from male dogs, one reason why it is often easier to kennel the males when there is a bitch in season nearby, but by and large I've found that once a young male has experienced the smells of such an event, and has not been allowed near that female, subsequent

Some lightly built bitches don't lay down fat though they still lose muscle strength after their seasons.

seasons provoke less and less response from such male dogs. This is not to say that they wouldn't attempt to mate a female if they could get their paws on her, but by and large, many sighthounds and their crosses are less maddened by those tantalising smells than some other types of dog. Dogs of terrier mentality can be a lot more determined to reach an in-season bitch.

It also helps if you have categorically established yourself as the pack leader, for in the wild, only the alpha male would be allowed access to a female in season. Underlings may go a lifetime without mating a female, so keep boundaries well defined and don't allow your own male dogs to rule the roost. If you are a woman owner exactly the same applies, as some wild canine societies are ruled by the females as well as the males: being the boss is the salient point, never mind your gender.

I always allow four weeks to pass from the onset of a season before I allow my females to mix with the male dogs again. Watch the bitch closely and monitor the state of her vulva: only when that has reduced in size to almost normal and there is no sign of blood should you consider the season finished. If your dogs live in the house together as a rule, then a good bath with a dog shampoo such as Dorwest Herb's mint shampoo enables you to remove any residual interesting smells and can help to restore the status quo within the pack.

Once a full season, or heat, has occurred, the female's nipples will appear more prominent: this is not to be confused with the nipples of a bitch that has suckled a litter. Before a first season the nipples on both sexes are almost the same in size: very small and barely noticeable, but once a bitch has had that first season they will be easy to see for the rest of her life, unless she has a very thick coat of course.

Her vulva will also have increased very slightly in size compared to the infantile state of the organ prior to the season, and in some individuals remains somewhat swollen for the duration of the ensuing pseudo pregnancy.

Whilst she is in season the bitch remains in good, fit condition, and there is no reason why you cannot work her (away from male dogs of course) but beware, for a dramatic change is about to follow once the actual heat has finished.

Every time the female canine comes into season her body undergoes some radical changes on the deepest level, preparing itself for a possible pregnancy and subsequent pups. It is generally accepted that even subordinate females in a wild pack will prepare their bodies for pups in the event that the alpha female, the only female to breed within that pack, dies either during labour or very shortly afterwards.

However, the changes that occur within either the truly pregnant female after she has been mated, or the pseudo pregnant female which has not been mated, are very similar, with the absence of developing puppies being the only difference between the two.

The hormone progesterone is responsible for these changes, of which there are many, but I'm going to concentrate on those which affect the working or racing ability of the lurcher of sighthound.

For about the first month of real or pseudo pregnancy you won't see much change in your dog; in fact in the working female you may even see an increased vigour and keenness in her work. I have my own theories on this one, which are as follows. Wild canines, especially those which lead more solitary lives with just one mate as companion, as opposed to those which have the back up of an entire pack to help kill prey, need to work hard during early pregnancy in order to eat as much as possible so that they can store a maximum amount of energy in the form of body fat. The reasons for this are twofold: developing pups need to grow within the mother's body, but just as importantly, the mother will be unable to hunt during the first two or three weeks following birth.

During this time she will use up that stored body fat both to supply milk to her offspring and keep herself going until such time as the pups are old enough to be left for a few hours while she hunts.

I remember one 'accident' which occurred with a lurcher of mine who put up, then ran and caught a hare when she was five weeks in whelp: not the ideal practice at all, but a wild dog would have had to do just that, and whilst I had no intention of allowing this course to take place, such accidents do happen if the dog is not on a lead, no matter how slight you think the chances are of seeing something like a hare in an area in which you have never seen one before! As this lurcher was very fit and not carrying excess body fat no harm came from her spree, and of course she was given the spoils for her supper: hare meat is super high protein, full of iron and B vitamins: just what a growing litter needs.

Anyway, let's return to the pseudo pregnant female, whose body is preparing for those non-existent pups. She has finished her season, and for the first month after that season she will continue to be in great condition, especially if she was hard and fit before hand.

Fertilized eggs don't attach themselves to the uterus wall until about 21 days after mating, and although the female which hasn't been mated will have shed all her eggs during her season, her body is still in the grip of the hormones which will dictate the physical changes during that post season period.

Opposite: Some people feel that the female of the species makes a keener hunter than the male. Photo: Craig McCann.

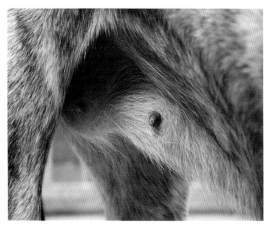

Bitch heavy in milk due to a phantom pregnancy.

About five to six weeks after the end of a bitch's season you may notice her muscles begin to soften. This may be visible to the naked eye or it might just be discernable when you run your hand over the large and powerful thigh muscles in a running dog.

She may also start to put on weight, soft fatty weight which seems to sit most over the ribs, loins and belly, which no matter how hard you diet the dog, just won't disappear. Some really fit and lean bitches never seem to put on this weight however, and once again, each individual is different, though I've never had a lurcher which didn't soften to some extent post season.

Towards the end of the phantom/ pseudo pregnancy her mammary glands may also become enlarged, even producing milk in some cases. There are also other changes which you cannot see, as fat is laid down around the internal organs, and the ligaments which bind the pelvic girdle in place will start to slacken and soften: this is necessary for the birthing process as a rigid pelvic girdle might not allow the passage of pups to the outside world.

External muscles will also soften dramatically, no matter how hard and fit you have attempted to keep your female athlete, and I believe that the phrase 'breaking down' when applied to the onset of heat in the bitch, originates from the fact that when the muscles lose their tone to a great extent the animal is incapable of winning a race.

Running or working such an animal hard during the flabby period can cause muscle rupture, damage to ligaments and even skeletal issues: after all, the skeleton is held together by ligaments and muscle, and if those all important bits are losing their tone the whole body comes under increased stress, which of course, heightens the risk of injury.

Taking all those changes into account it should be obvious that working a running dog hard when this unfit is a recipe for injury. We humans have developed in our hunting dogs a prey drive which is so far in excess of the drive in wild canines that our domestic hunters can and do damage themselves when worked unfit. Some dogs will literally run themselves to a standstill or even death when faced with a fleeing prey animal, something that no wolf would do. Better to go hungry and live to hunt another day than die in the attempt: an adage some owners would do well to remember when they slip their exhausted dog on just one more hare.

It is down to the owner of a hunting or racing dog to see when the animal is not fit enough to continue chasing, and to cease fast work until those few weeks have passed.

Most bitches lose their post season flab at around 10 weeks after their season has finished, but some take longer, much longer, and I've known some females remain soft and flabby for as long as 16 weeks after a season, a nightmare if this falls within the working time of year.

Some very fit working females may show little sign of a pseudo pregnancy, and Andy, my partner, works a lightly built lurcher who doesn't really seem to lose muscle tone in the way I see in my own line of lurchers. Neither does she experience great enlargement of the mammary glands, though if you feel along her underside you can detect a slight increase in what I call 'blubber', a layer of subcutaneous fat along the line of her teats.

However, whilst looking apparently normal, this particular lurcher does experience a dramatic drop in power, and this is very noticeable when she is running rabbits on the lamp.

Normally a dog which has a very high catch rate indeed, catching around 80% of all rabbits she runs, this rate drops off alarmingly and she would be lucky to catch one in five rabbits run. She just appears to be too slow, unable to turn properly and generally lacklustre in her approach to the job in hand. This state of affairs continues until the 'imaginary' puppies would be about three weeks old, and is entirely due to the hormones, of which progesterone is one of the major culprits, being produced in her body at this time.

Incidentally, progesterone was, in the past, used to stop the female cycle in racing Greyhounds, just as the human contraceptive pill simulates pregnancy in women, tricking their bodies into believing they are pregnant.

I used this once on a very fast lurcher, with disastrous results, and turned a superb and very fast animal into a bag of lard over night, with the result that one of the slowest lurchers I knew at the time ran straight past her on the run up to a hare at a doubled up coursing meeting! It took a full month free from the effects of Ovarid before this lurcher regained her speed and power.

I'll come back to how to postpone and stop seasons in a moment, but for now let's concentrate on that post season period. As I write, one of my best lamping lurchers is in the throes of this flabby, lack lustre period, and normally a really racy flying machine, Minky spends most of her time asleep, only really coming alive at the prospect of food.

Increased appetite is also common during the last few weeks of both real and imagined pregnancy, this trait coming to a head when the pups are born. Never a food thief by nature, Minky turns into a meat seeking missile, diving into other dogs' food bowls at feeding time and generally appearing desperate for any food to the extent that she drools (a very unlurcher-like trait) whenever we eat or prepare our own food.

During this phase of her phantom pregnancy she carries a fair amount of subcutaneous fat, her mammary glands are baggy and swollen and her whole air is one of a just whelped female desperate to feed her pups by guzzling down whatever she can.

My old lurcher Rattis, normally steady as a rock with our chickens, has been known to kill and eat the odd escapee in the blink of an eye when she is in the throes of a phantom pregnancy, and it's all down to those raging hormones!

I have also noticed that females which have had real litters in the past tend to suffer from the symptoms of the phantom pregnancy far more dramatically than those animals which have never born a litter, sometimes with symptoms which last until the invisible pups would be over six weeks of age!

The Azewakh, a North African sighthound of immense elegance and stature, was on the verge of extinction until the Western World got its hands on the breed. This was due in part to the fact that the indigenous people never bred from a female until she was eight years of age, believing that once having produced puppies, she would never be able to work again to her former standard, and whilst modern thinking has proved this to be definitely not the case, I can understand the reasoning of the Azewakh's indigenous owners for phantom pregnancies can take a very real toll on the overall health and condition of the older canine.

Age has a part to play in regaining fitness as well: if an older animal is allowed to become very unfit through lack of exercise, the aging muscles will take far longer to attain good hard condition than in a younger animal faced with the same scenario. Older muscles lose elasticity and the body in general slows down, which means cell regeneration happens less efficiently and quickly.

You cannot do anything to stop the rise and fall of hormones in the female without using artificial means to halt that process, and there are, nowadays, several means of temporarily suppressing seasons.

Durateston is one such artificially administered hormone often used to prevent racing greyhounds coming into season, but it should be used with great care, having initially been developed to increase the libido and raise sperm count in male animals at stud.

Durateston is testosterone, one of the most important male hormones, though it is also present in the female body in smaller quantities. Increasing the testosterone levels in the female exaggerates male characteristics which in turn prevent the ability of a female to come into season.

There is however, a risk of damage to the liver if this hormone is used over prolonged periods of time, or in the wrong dosage and whilst I found it to be effective and it did not reduce working ability and speed in the lurchers I used it on, I really don't like messing around with the female cycle unless absolutely necessary.

I've said it before and I make no apologies for repeating this statement: I don't like altering natural cycles, and if I were to suppress a bitch's season I would be very wary about doing so for more than a couple of months, say on the run up to a competition, or for the few months of hard work during the winter months in the case of a working running dog.

If I were to suppress a heat I would use Durateston, and then only at a dosage of 1ml per week no matter what the body weight of the female dog in question. When I first asked about using Durateston to suppress a heat my own vet prescribed the drug in a high dosage (apparently the dosage required to increase libido in the male dog) which damaged the bitch's liver almost instantly! Luckily the dog came back to full health within a matter of weeks, but it does show how dangerous it is to tamper with nature.

Some people who have routinely suppressed a bitch's season for several years have, when they eventually decided to breed from that bitch, found it impossible to get her in whelp … ever! Despite using proven stud dogs the bitches failed to conceive, yet one more reason I'd hesitate before suppressing a heat.

SOME POINTS OF INTEREST FOR OWNERS OF BITCHES

Something to note is that females in multi dog kennels often cycle together, BUT as nothing is ever that simple as getting all the seasons over and done with in one go, you'll probably find that the most dominant and senior females come into season first, with the subordinate and younger females following on, maybe two to three months later.

My own lurchers seem to cycle in pairs, with two coming into season within a couple of days of one another, which is great because I can then kennel those two together for the duration of their season, and allow them to indulge in all the flirting and mock mating they wish.

A word of warning though: only kennel two in-season bitches together if they know each other very well, are part of the same pack and are normally the best of buddies. Seasons can bring about behavioural changes and a status seeking subordinate may feel better able to challenge a more dominate bitch when they are in the grip of those hormones, leading to fighting and injury. Nature times the reproductive cycle of wild canines to coincide with mid winter, thereby allowing the young to be born during the spring when their prey is also breeding, an obvious advantage for wild predators whereby mothers and their pups can feast on the young of their natural prey: easy targets for hard working packs or solitary females.

Whilst this is the ideal solution for wild canines, for people who work their running dogs through the winter it couldn't come at a worse time. Although many domestic breeds of dog tend to cycle every six months, very fit and lean bitches may cease to cycle whilst in peak working condition. Minky invariably comes into

It is possible to keep spayed bitches trim and fit though attention must be paid to their diet and exercise regime. Natural feeding helps neutered dogs maintain a healthy weight. Photo: Von.

season in the autumn which means that she is at maximum blubbiness right at the time when I want to be working her hard. Light ferreting duties are all that Minky is fit for during her phantom pregnancies, and by the time her hormone levels have subsided to the anoestrus stage (mid way between seasons) our own hunting season is over and we're into spring once more.

Whilst you can't halt the natural process of post season flab, you can help keep things in check a little by the use of Raspberry Leaf tablets. These have long been known as an old wives' remedy as an aid to childbirth in women. Raspberry Leaf is said to keep the uterus well toned and tight, and should never be given to a female who is truly pregnant until the sixth week of pregnancy or they could cause a miscarriage.

However, by starting a course of Raspberry Leaf tablets on the very first day of a bitch's season, and continuing over the next three months, you can minimise the effects of a phantom, or pseudo pregnancy.

And they do work, though not on every female, but it is something that is worth trying if you don't want to go down the normal route of suppressing a season, and these tablets won't do any harm whatsoever.

Nothing will remove the hormones but I've definitely noticed a decrease in loss of muscle tone and subcutaneous fat in the lurchers I've thus treated, but only if I've remembered to start the treatment at the onset of a season. Start giving the tablets once the season has finished and you'll not see anywhere near the same effect.

Intervet UK, who make Durateston, state that when administered just as the bitch's season is ending, most of the physiological effects of the phantom pregnancy are considerably reduced. I've not yet tried this either, but may well do in the case of Minky if I want to get a full winter's work out of her before she gets too old!

What about spaying a female to permanently stop all these post season problems? Many female pet dogs are routinely spayed at an early age nowadays, though I'd always wait until a bitch has had her first season before removing such an important organ from the body. *'It has been observed that spaying can significantly increase the risk of urinary incontinence in bitches. Early neutering also increases risk of urethral sphincter incontinence in males.'* A.Aaron et al., Vet Rec. 139:542-6, 1996.

Puppyish behaviour and alteration to coat type and density are also well-known side effects of early spaying, although not so prevalent in bitches which have been allowed to reach full maturity and had at least one season before they were spayed.

Personally, I'm not in favour of spaying for the sake of it, but I fully appreciate that the many and worthy rescue shelters and charities which routinely spay and castrate all their dogs are bound to do so in an attempt to reduce the huge numbers of unwanted and abandoned dogs, of which more and more seem to be lurchers.

Yes I know that providing you keep the dog on a very strict diet to prevent weight gain the neutered animal should not put on weight, but I don't have my males or females neutered for the following reasons: first I don't like interfering with nature any more than I have to, and second, I want to be able to breed from a particularly good animal if I wish to do so, something that spaying would obviously preclude!

No sensible working dog owner would breed from an animal under the age of two, and even that is very young if the dog needs to be truly tested in the field over a number of seasons before the owner decides that a particular individual is worth breeding from. By the time a female is four years old she will probably have had at least three heats so the owner will have no doubt learned how best to cope with all that the female cycle entails, or at least, one would hope so!

The female cycle can be irritating to owners of working dogs, but I find it no more than a blip in the lives that my dogs lead, and fortunately I have enough dogs to fill in the gaps left by those suffering from phantom pregnancies when I want to work them.

There is also documented evidence (see *Journal of Reproduction and Fertility* ISSN 0449-3087) to suggest that neutered dogs and bitches are more likely to suffer from certain cancers, heart problems and loss of bone density than in animals which have not been surgically deprived of their hormones.

I am truly appalled at some of the information available over the internet on doggy sites, many of which imply that your female dog will fall foul of all sorts of horrific problems if she is not spayed; problems which can range from pyometras and mammary cancers to death caused by giving birth should the dog become pregnant accidently.

Some of this information is so biased and put out in such a way that the novice owner might well feel frightened or bullied into having their own bitch spayed unnecessarily.

Of course there can never be any risk of a female dog suffering from pyometra (a potentially life-threatening uterine infection) once the uterus has been removed, so in that respect spaying removes this particular risk. However, I have, in over 40 years of living with dogs, come into contact with only one case of pyometra in an unspayed female and this elderly, overweight and sedentary animal was not one of my own dogs.

Neither have I experienced mammary cancer in my dogs, despite keeping both breeding and non-breeding animals over many years. Yes, the risk is there, but unless I knew that a particular health risk was very high I wouldn't have any part of a dog removed just because that risk existed: should we all have our appendixes removed just in case we might one day suffer from appendicitis? I think not!

Finally, and then I'll get off my soap box, the risk of disease or infection in any dog will be greatly reduced if it leads a healthy, active life and is not allowed to become over weight.

I'm also of the opinion that by feeding a natural diet of raw food appropriate to the animal in question, we strengthen the immune system which helps it to fight off infection and disease.

FAIRLY MINIMAL FEMALE PROBLEMS!

The following problems are minimal if your life revolves totally around your dogs and you don't share your abode with other people who might not be quite so tolerant of all things canine; the trail of blood spots on furniture and carpets and sometimes a distinct musty odour whilst female dogs are in season might be more of an issue for those who are house proud or who would be considered 'normal'!

If you can't put up with the more basic aspects of the female heat then crating is an option, though this is unfair on the animal if you are out at work all day, especially as I've noticed that young females in season for the first time also have a genuine need to urinate more frequently, possibly because their bladder becomes irritated by the changes within that part of their bodies as the uterus finally matures to become an organ capable of reproduction.

Females in season also want to scent-mark frequently in the same manner as male dogs; they need to advertise their exciting appeal to any males in the hope of attracting a mate! Exercise and work during this period should always be undertaken well away from other male dogs, and whilst there are fewer roaming Romeos in today's strictly confined dog society, there is always that chance of an unexpected encounter.

Gone are the days when free-roaming male dogs marked and prowled their territories, always on the lookout for a potential in-season female, but most working and racing dog owners don't routinely castrate their charges so it does pay to be on the alert, especially if you live in an area well populated with such dogs.

And then there is The Howling! I was woken one morning very early by a full blooded 'howl on' from the whole pack, started (naturally enough) by an in-season lurcher who was determined to tell everyone that she was now ready to stand (be mated).

Banished to a crate in a side room, her body's demands needed voicing: hormones and instinct are a powerful force.

A female dog is, when the time is right, as desperate to be mated as the male dogs which want to mate with her, so extreme vigilance is necessary if you keep both males and females under the same roof and you are to avoid unplanned litters of pups.

You also need either no neighbours or very understanding neighbours if you keep several females, for even the quietest of lurchers and sighthounds can become pretty vocal when they really want something. As well as the physiological changes that can occur during a phantom pregnancy, a bitch may also go through behavioural changes which may range from an alteration in attitude so minor as to be unnoticeable right through to a full blown 'I'm having puppies' nesting, guarding monster of a wanabee mother.

So why does anyone keep female working lurchers and sighthounds? It would be so much easier just to keep males, wonderful, stable, non-temperamental males! No annoying rises and falls in hormone levels, no annoying drops in condition, and just as importantly, no maddening behavioural changes to make you tear your hair out when your seemingly keen and determined worker seems to lose all desire to catch or worse still, wants to eat what she has caught instead of retrieving it to you.

Just as some people get on better with male dogs, so do some click better with females. I keep both, and accept their differences, but if I was restricted to only keeping one dog I'd definitely keep a male as I'd not want to lose half the working season because of hormone fluctuations.

It is said that females are more loyal: I disagree. It is also said that a dog is permanently 'in season', being constantly on the look out for an opportunity to mate: I disagree there as well, and the dogs that I've owned have in general been easier to live with than the many females I've put up with over the years!

Of course a male will be quick to notice if there is an in-season female around, and he might also be a tad more assertive when meeting other male dogs. Once again, unless you have a truly alpha male, a natural pack leader, it is your ability to behave as the boss, a respected leader rather than a weak, ineffectual creature who cannot command his or her dogs attention which will make your male dog easy or difficult to

live with. Allow him to think that he runs the show and you'll have a problem; let him know that you are in charge and most little challenges will be just that: minor blips in an otherwise blissful relationship between you and your dog.

Below photo: Craig McCann.

CHAPTER TEN

Parasites: internal and external

All dogs can get parasites, both internal and external, though the working dog is likely to come into contact with a wider range than dogs which never venture into the countryside.

I'm not going to go into a mind boggling scientific study of the little blighters which can cause our dogs so much damage, but preventing their existence inside and on the outside of our running machines is paramount if dogs are to remain healthy and perform at their best.

INTERNAL PARASITES: WORMS
We are talking about worms of course, and whilst there are many different types of worms which can invade a dog's body, the most commonly seen in the UK are Roundworm *toxicara canis* and tapeworm, of which there are 12 types, the most common being *dipyldium caninum*.

However, there are others which include Heartworm, Lungworm, Hookworm and Whipworm and as global traffic increases and global warming (well, they tell us it's a fact so I'm going to have to go with that for now!) heats up the British Isles, it is likely that more and more cases of foreign parasites will be seen in the UK.

Whilst the roundworm can seriously damage puppies it seldom affects adult dogs. Puppies need to be wormed at three weekly intervals if the roundworm life cycle is to be halted. Roundworms spend their entire life cycle within the dog and are not hard to get rid of, but I've found that the best way is to use a multiwormer at three, six, nine and 12 weeks of age.

You can buy specific puppy wormers which include liquids and paste (a messy business with any dog let alone a puppy) but I've found it a lot easier just to cut a tablet of *Drontal Plus* into as many pieces as is necessary for a litter of pups. *Drontal Plus* are not a coated tablet (covered with a hard shell) so cut down easily with a sharp knife on a chopping board.

Whilst *Milbemax* make a tablet specifically for puppies and dogs less than five kilos in weight, I prefer to use a proprietary puppy wormer for very small pups. *Milbemax* operates over a large weight range which means that young pups are getting a higher and therefore potentially undesirable dose of the active ingredient.

I have found *Drontal* to be very well tolerated in all dogs, unlike *Lopatol* which I haven't used in years: this used to make some of my dogs vomit. Drontal also do a liquid puppy wormer which is excellent by all accounts though I prefer to use tablets.

All you have to do is open the pup's mouth and push the morsel of tablet to the back of the throat with your finger. Make sure you don't have long sharp fingernails which may scratch the puppy's throat. Once a tablet reaches the back of the throat a swallow reflex kicks in and the pup is obliged to swallow.

Older dogs can become a little canny when being wormed, partially regurgitating tablets and secreting them in the corners of the mouth, then waiting until your back is turned before spitting them out! I've found that pushing a tablet into a noggin of butter or margarine helps tablets to slide down the throat very easily, though I haven't found this necessary with little pups.

Modern multiwormers such as *Drontal Plus* and *Milbemax* are very effective at killing most types of worms though it should be noted that *Drontal Plus* doesn't kill lungworm which is reported to be on the increase in this country. Lungworm is contracted when a dog eats a slug or snail infected with this parasite.

Milbemax does kill lungworm, but only if you follow the correct protocol, which may mean several doses over a number of weeks. Your vet will advise you on the correct protocol.

Symptoms of lungworm infestation may include coughing, lethargy, fitting, loss of appetite, vomiting or diarrhoea. I know that any one of these symptoms may also be caused by other problems, but a dog suffering from any of the above for more than 24 hours should be taken to the vet for proper diagnosis.

Most people who work their dogs will carry out a routine worming programme every three months. Some people worm every six months, which is what I do, and I've not yet had cause to worm more frequently apart from when my dogs have guzzled the remains of a rabbit they found whilst on exercise.

Panacur is another wormer which is favoured by many working dog people though once again, a single dose is not enough to kill worms. *Panacur* is specifically designed to kill roundworms, but puppies MUST be treated for three consecutive days, which is why I prefer to give a single dose of a multiwormer: it makes my life a lot simpler as well as being, in my opinion, more effective.

NOTE: *Milbemax* should only be used within the recommended dosage for Collie type dogs and other herding breeds. Apparently there is less margin for error in these dogs. I'd advise anyone with a heavily Collie blooded dog to talk to their vet before using *Milbemax*, just to be on the safe side.

Panacur can also be used to treat other types of worm but it is ESSENTIAL to follow the manufacturer's directions. For example, in the treatment of lungworm, a daily dose for seven consecutive days is needed, and further treatments may be required in the case of heavy infestation.

Panacur may kill some types of tapeworm and then only after prolonged treatment: far better to use a multiwormer in my opinion.

There are also 'spot on' products available which claim to treat both internal and external parasites. I feel dubious about putting something on to my dogs which is so strong that it eliminates ALL parasites at one go. There are enough nasty chemicals in our lives without adding to them in this way. This is only my opinion, but I've never found it necessary to treat my dogs in this way.

SOURCES OF TAPEWORM INFESTATION

Dogs can contract tapeworms from many sources, though feeding sheep's paunch or raw, fresh (not previously frozen for three weeks) is the quickest way to do so, in my experience. *See chapter on Nutrition*

Some dogs can carry quite a heavy tapeworm burden without showing any loss of condition, whilst others react quite severely to the presence of worms in their body. A staring coat and foul breath always alerted me to a tapeworm problem in one lurcher I owned long before she began to excrete the segments. Other dogs have shown no signs of ill health at all despite the obvious presence of these worms.

EXTERNAL PARASITES

Fleas, mites and lice are the main culprits.

Fleas

The most common fleas to be found on dogs are cat fleas. I've rarely seen dog fleas on my animals and then only after going to a dog show or country fair. Fleas are species specific but can survive on the blood of other types of animal for a time.

If you have a flea infestation it is very important that you treat the dog's environment as well as the dog. This is because fleas don't actually breed on the dog, but usually hop off into the surroundings (your house or kennel) in order to lay their eggs. Eggs which are laid on the host animal normally fall off before hatching into larva, which are gravity led down into warm dark places such as dog bedding and carpets.

The eggs hatch out into larvae which feed on organic debris in their environment; this can include shed skin cells, faecal matter, dead insects etc. When they have eaten enough they pupate, and eventually hatch into adult fleas. When sufficient food is available the whole life cycle may take as little as two weeks, though both larva and adults can survive for many months, lying dormant in cold conditions.

I haven't needed to treat my dogs for fleas for many years, but I do spray the kennels and house very thoroughly twice a year. There are several good household sprays available which kill both flea larvae and pupae as well as adult fleas. You need to pay particular attention to the cracks behind skirting boards, edges of carpets

Incessant scratching may mean a flea or mite problem.

where the vacuum cleaner doesn't reach, and any dog bedding. Kennels should be treated after removing bedding and vacuuming thoroughly, making sure to use a dust nozzle attachment to get right into the corners.

If you vacuum very regularly and you have no hard-to-access areas then spraying the house and kennels might be unnecessary.

If I do notice a dog scratching (especially round the base of its tail and around its ears) I use a flea comb to winkle out the parasite. It is easy to test a dog for fleas with such a comb: comb through the hair thoroughly then tap out the comb on to a white piece of paper. Tiny black sand like grains on the paper, which become red when moistened, are flea dirt (faeces made up of dried blood).

Even if you haven't found a flea, the presence of flea dirt should alert you to a possible infestation.

I have in the past used *Frontline* spray when I have found fleas on my dogs, and although the instructions tell you to spray the dog all over, I have found this to be unnecessary. Spray a strip along the top of the dog from behind its ears to the root of its tail, and under the dog from between its hind legs along the belly, chest and up to the throat. As fleas move around all over the dog's body rather than remaining in one place spraying in this way eliminates all fleas without soaking the whole dog. This saves a lot of spray when you have multiple dogs.

Natural flea control

If you'd rather not spray chemicals around your home or on to your dogs then an old fashioned method of flea control is Diatomaceous Earth. This is a fine powder made from the fossilized remains of microscopic shells, and it is the razor sharp edges of these shells which lacerate the flea's outer body, thereby allowing the flea's body fluids to leak out: result being dehydration and DEATH! (chuckles gleefully).

Diatomaceous Earth is completely harmless to mammals and birds and I've also used it to combat harvest mite on dog's feet and in my chickens, and their house for red mite and northern fowl mite ... with great success. You can sprinkle it in your kennels, around the hen house and on to carpets (though of course frequent vacuuming won't leave it in situ for long) as well as directly on to a dog. Make sure that it penetrates beneath the top layer of fur: I comb it through thick-coated dogs but don't rub it hard into the skin.

Diatomaceous earth doesn't work on burrowing mites such as sarcoptes or demodex as these live beneath the skin's surface.

Because there is no chemical content in diatomaceous earth parasites can't build up immunity to it as they might do to chemical sprays. Diatomaceous earth also kills dust mites and other insects including flies, though they have to land on the powder first.

WARNING: Don't use it near beneficial creatures such as bees: we need to help what few bees we have left so don't be tempted to sprinkle it over your aphid-ridden roses!

TIP: Some dogs attract fleas like magnets, whilst others are seldom bothered by them. The saliva of fleas can cause a severe skin reaction in some animals which can lead to scratching and skin infections. Always check out an incessantly scratching dog so you can nip any problems in the bud.

Also, be aware that fleas and worms go hand in hand. The dog which ingests a flea whilst grooming itelf may also ingest tapeworm eggs at the same time - fleas may carry tapeworm eggs.

Lice

Lice are quite different to fleas in that they never need to leave their host in order to reproduce. Their entire life cycle is spent on the dog, and they don't hop either! In fact they are quite slow moving and this should mean that they are easy to treat, which they are as long as you do this properly. Simply combing through the fur won't take-off all the eggs (nits) which are attached to individual hairs as you would in humans with nits: there is simply too much fur on a dog to carry out this procedure effectively. Lice are less easily contracted than fleas because their speed of movement and life cycle restricts them to one host, but they can crawl on to other dogs when there is close contact between animals.

You can buy shampoos for louse treatment but *Frontline Spot On and Spray* kill lice though you need to cover the whole dog with the spray in order to kill the eggs. Buy a recommended louse treatment and follow the instructions to the letter.

Ticks

Ticks are slow crawling critters which attach themselves to their hosts by means of their mouthparts, anchoring themselves firmly into the skin of the unfortunate animal. Whilst most dogs don't appear to notice that they are carrying a tick or two, be aware that some ticks can transmit serious diseases such as Lymes disease. Ticks carrying Lymes disease are more common in parts of the country where deer and sheep are found.

Ticks can be removed by using a specially made hook, though I've always zapped them with a spray of Frontline, which kills them quite quickly. If you pull a tick off your dog with your fingers you may well leave the mouthparts embedded in the skin. The healthy body normally seals this 'foreign body' off by forming a little scab which comes away once dried up, though some dogs (possibly those with a less than effective immune system) do suffer a reaction to the tick's initial bite and subsequent injection of saliva.

Mites

There are many types of mite, which are microscopic creatures living either on the skin surface or burrowing beneath it.

Sarcoptic mites

These cause what is known as mange and are one of the most damaging mites. Severe infestation can lead to extensive hair loss as a result of persistent scratching and nibbling at the affected areas of the body. A secondary skin infection can also be caused on areas where the skin has been broken by scratching.

Treatment can be prolonged, usually consisting of several baths in medicated

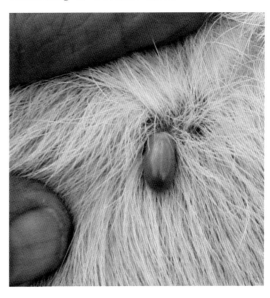

Fully engorged tick the size of a small pea.

177

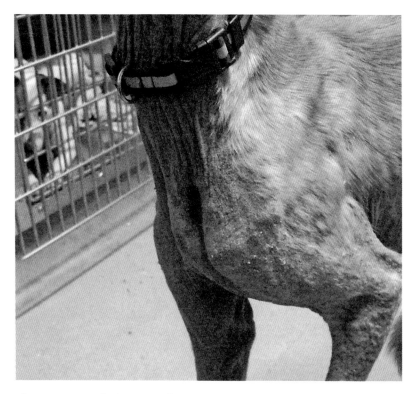

An appalling neglected case of demodectic mange seen in a rescued lurcher. Photo: Sam Coleman.

shampoos or lotions. There are certain products available which although licensed for dogs can be dangerous to certain breeds. For example, *Ivermectin* should not be used on Collie types and used with caution on other herding breeds.

Sarcoptic mange is endemic in foxes in some areas of the UK, and dogs which come into contact with foxes are obviously at risk of contracting the mite.

Isolate any dog you suspect of being infested with sarcoptic mites and get it to the vet immediately for confirmation and treatment. A deep skin scrape is normally done to test for mites in the dog though they are not easy to find even under a microscope as they live and feed deep under the skin.

Sarcoptic mange is contagious, and although close physical contact with an infected animal is the most likely cause of infection, the mite can survive in the environment for several days,

particularly in moist conditions. There is an American product called *NuStock* which is a sulphur-based cream said to be very effective at controlling mange mites. I have not had occasion to use it in cases of sarcoptic mange but have used it to treat mild forms of Demodectic mange with great success.

It is a messy treatment, though relatively cheap when compared to a modern topical parasiticide obtainable only by vet prescription which will do the job just as well with less mess.

Demodex mites
Demodex mites seldom cause as much problem as sarcoptic mites and are usually only transmitted from a mother to her puppies, the pups becoming infected due to their immature immune systems. Some sources state that all adult dogs carry a certain number of demodex mites, though

178

a strong immune system will prevent these causing a problem.

Adult dogs with weakened immune systems may show signs of demodex mange. Demodex mite damage is most usually seen on the feet and around the face on young puppies, showing up as bare patches of skin. It doesn't normally seem to be as irritating to the dog as sarcoptic mange.

In all my years of breeding lurchers and terriers I have yet to see a case of demodectic mange, and this bears out what I have read concerning demodex mites … that it is only likely to occur in mothers and puppies with weakened immune systems.

Pregnancy is a stressful time for the bitch's body, and if she is infested with a large number of these mites a 'flare up' of the condition is possible. She then transfers the mites to her pups when they are born.

Healthy, properly fed and contented bitches show no signs of demodex because their immune systems are strong enough to keep infestation at bay. A bitch puppy which has suffered from demodectic mange when young should not be bred from as she will be likely to pass it on to her own puppies.

Ear mites

The ear of a dog is a great place for harbouring mites and fungal infections: warm, moist and protected, especially in the case of flop-eared dogs, in other words, most types of running dog.

Symptoms include a brownish discharge which is the faecal matter from the mites. Severe infestation causes scratching and if left untreated can cause real damage to the ear canal. A rather sickly, musty smell from the ear is usually associated with the presence of ear mites.

Ear mites can be easily treated with *Canaural* ear drops, though many people swear by the more old fashioned *Thornit Ear Powder*. I've only ever used *Canaural* and with great success. I've never had ear mite problems in dogs of my own breeding, which once again bears testimony to the fact that a strong immune system and natural feeding will keep most parasites at bay. Ear mites can also be successfully treated by some of the newer topical flea treatments.

Harvest mites

These can be a nightmare in warm, moist conditions and unlike other forms of mites, it is the larvae of the harvest mite which causes intense itching in dogs. They are visible to the naked eye and can be seen as tiny orange dots in the fur, usually around the face, ears and feet where they lodge after a dog has pushed its way through infested grass or crops.

Some people don't like to use straw as bedding for this reason, though I've found that spraying fresh straw with an insecticidal spray against fleas helps.

Harvest mite can be easily treated with a direct application of *Frontline Spray*, though some sources say that the *Spot On* version is not effective against this parasite.

Thornit Ear Powder can also be used against harvest mites: rub the powder into the fur on the affected areas. *Thornit Ear Powder* contains zinc oxide which helps to soothe irritation as well.

Walking dandruff or cheyletiella

Cheyletiella mites to give them their correct name are in themselves less damaging than Sarcoptic or Demodex, and are known as walking dandruff because they resemble tiny moving specks of scurf. Of course in any but a black smooth coated dog they are impossible to see.

Easily transmitted from one warm furry animal to another they are apparently endemic in wild rabbits (something I only recently found out) and although many dogs will be carrying these critters with no ill effects whatsoever the dog that has a weakened immune system may begin to react to their presence by scratching itself. Whilst the mites themselves do little damage it is the scratching which can lead to reddening and soreness of the skin which opens it up to infection.

Frontline Spray is effective on these surface dwelling mites though more than one treatment may be necessary to eradicate them fully.

NOTE: A dog's immune system may be weakened by stress just as much as by illness which is why so many animals which go through rescue shelters suffer from seemingly mysterious ailments. Stress can cause prolonged digestive problems just as much as skin problems.

HOT SPOTS

Hot spots are a term used for intensely irritating patches on a dog's body. Their exact cause is unknown but they are usually a result of a bacterial infection in the skin, sometimes due to an infected flea bite, or if a dog has scratched at the spot where a mosquito or horsefly has bitten. Dogs with weakened immune systems are more likely to suffer from bacterial infections of any sort, so once again, good diet is essential in order to keep the whole animal as healthy and disease resistant as possible.

BALDING THIGH SYNDROME

There are many theories as to what causes hair loss on the outer thighs of some Greyhound and their hybrids. Thyroid problems are one thought but extensive tests done on Greyhounds have proved this to be incorrect.

One of my lurchers used to have bald thighs until ... wait for it ... she stopped eating any form of cereals. Having had bald thighs all her life the fur magically reappeared after six months free of cereals. I'm not setting this in stone, but it is worth changing your dog's diet if it has this problem though remember that a long standing condition may take many months to right itself.

Adding Kelp Seaweed to the diet may also help as it contains all the known minerals necessary for good health. A zinc deficiency can cause certain skin conditions such as dryness, scurf and intermittent itching.

SOME NATURAL DETERRENTS AGAINST PARASITES

There are many plants and herbs which can help to deter parasites in and on dogs. I can't say for certain that all of them work as well as modern chemicals, but I have found that a daily dose of garlic in whatever form you prefer to use does seem to help keep the digestive tract free from worms to some extent.

A clove of fresh garlic in the food every day is the most natural way to give garlic to dogs, though some sources say that it may have a similar effect as onions. I don't feed onions but I do feed garlic and have never had a problem. However, I find it easier to give garlic in tablet form and I use Dorwest Herbs' Garlic and Fenugreek tablets which help to stimulate the immune system in general as well as being recommended as a treatment against arthritis.

Lavender oil is said to be a good deterrent against fleas, though, like all essential oils, it is very strong in its undiluted state and shouldn't be applied directly to the dog's skin. It is recommended to dilute this oil in a carrier oil such as sweet almond oil before combing through the hair, particularly in the areas where fleas like to settle: base of tail and behind the ears.

Never use essential oils near or on a dog's face as they are very strong, even diluted I'd avoid areas round nose, eyes and mouth, though the smell is both calming and relaxing to dogs and humans alike.

As I have masses of lavender and rosemary growing in my garden I sometimes sprinkle fresh and slightly crushed branches of these herbs into the straw in my kennels. The dogs don't seem to mind and the herbs help straw stay smelling sweet for longer as well as keeping mosquitoes and flies at bay.

Strewing herbs were used in ancient times to sweeten homes, but when you consider that both humans and dogs probably relieved themselves in the darker corners of castles, homes and the like, the smell must have been nigh on intolerable. Suffice to say all creatures had much stronger immune systems in those days!

I'd recommend Jackie Drakeford and Mark Elliott's books: *Essential Care for Dogs* and *Essential Care in the Field* if you are interested in natural remedies and treatments for dogs.

Photo: Steve Taylor.

CHAPTER ELEVEN

Stuff that can kill your dog

There are far too many infectious diseases to go into in this book, which, after all, is not a book on diseases. However, the working running dog is more likely to come into contact with certain diseases and dangers than dogs which seldom venture into the countryside.

It goes without saying that all puppies and dogs, whether they live in the town or country, should be vaccinated against the three main killer diseases: Parvo Virus, Distemper and Leptospirosis, otherwise known as Weil's Disease. It used to be customary to vaccinate a dog every year for its entire life, but some vets are now of the opinion that annual boosters are probably not necessary for Parvo and Distemper.

If I really don't want to give a dog annual boosters for the rest of its life, then doing the first puppy vaccinations and just the one booster at about 14 months of age is an acceptable option. But in the case of dogs which come into contact with rats or those which work in rat infested places, it is important to know that the Leptospirosis vaccine gives only temporary cover against this dreadful disease.

The Leptospirosis vaccine should be done on an annual basis, and in some cases only gives protection for six months. I know of a dog which was up to date with all its vaccines and still managed to contract Leptospirosis from which it died. No death from disease is pleasant but death from Leptospirosis can be prolonged and agonising as the liver breaks down, literally poisoning the body slowly over several days.

It is also true that not all vaccines will 'take' once injected into a dog, and for those owners whose dogs come into contact with rats, water in which rats have urinated or indeed, food which has been soiled by rats, it might well be advisable to get blood tests done a couple of weeks after the vaccination. These will tell the owner if their dog has acquired immunity against this disease.

Annual blood tests are available which will determine your dog's immunity against the diseases already mentioned.

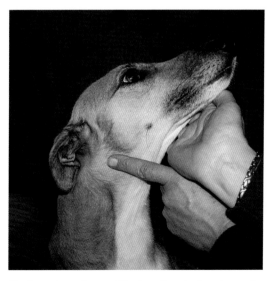

Feeling the submandibular glands for signs of enlargement which is an indication of infection.

By running a blood test you can then make an informed decision as to whether it will be sensible to boost your dog's immunity by vaccination.

Adult dogs which are out and about in society, meeting other dogs and animals, will have stronger immune systems than those which spend their lives locked away in pristine kennels. Whilst I might not boost my adult dogs I would never forego those first puppy vaccinations, which for the sake of even today's high vaccine prices, is far, far better than losing a pup to a preventable disease.

NOTE: Never ignore any signs of illness. These may vary from lethargy (an unwillingness to run or work), loss of appetite to fever, prolonged vomiting or diarrhoea or both. Whilst dogs can pick up 'bugs' just as we can, we need to monitor a dog very carefully if it shows signs of being ill in any way and get it to the vet if symptoms worsen.

It is not uncommon for a dog to be slightly under the weather for a day or so as its body fights off some unknown bug, but unless you are very experienced it is easy to miss the signs of serious illness in the early stages.

Any illness which causes the dog to vomit more than a couple of times merits veterinary attention immediately, for dehydration caused by prolonged vomiting can lead to death, especially in the very young and old.

KENNEL COUGH

Kennel cough is the term given to a highly contagious illness which can be contracted either as an airborne virus, or bacterially, and it affects the upper respiratory system. It is passed from dog to dog very easily by coughing or sneezing and is just as virulent as human flu.

Whilst the illness itself is not usually life-threatening, it can develop into pneumonia if the dog is subjected to stress (eg hard running) or is in poor health generally. Large animal rescue shelters and big kennels are a haven for illnesses such as Kennel Cough for the inmates of such places are understandably stressed by being there in the first place. Stress affects the immune system which leaves the animal prone to infection of all kinds.

Kennel Cough is usually characterised by a rasping, hacking cough which often sounds as if the dog has something stuck in its throat and is trying to clear it. The dog may also have a runny nose and eyes. Its submandibular glands will be swollen and it will generally appear unwell.

It is essential to keep affected dogs well away from others, and in a warm, well ventilated area.

KENNEL COUGH IS VERY CONTAGIOUS! DO NOT TAKE THE DOG OUT IN PUBLIC BECAUSE EACH COUGH WILL RELEASE MILLIONS OF VIRAL SPORES INTO THE AIR. THESE CAN TRAVEL CONSIDERABLE DISTANCES BEFORE BEING BREATHED IN BY THEIR NEXT VICTIM.

Most cases of Kennel Cough will resolve themselves with little or no treatment and antibiotics are only given if a secondary infection (pneumonia) develops. You can ease sort throats with spoonfuls of honey (preferably Manuka honey) and a child's cough linctus may help to calm incessant coughing, particularly if the cough is non-productive (ie dry).

Feed only soft foods which will not irritate the membranes of the throat, and keep the dog warm and quiet. I once rescued a lurcher who was very ill with

Kennel Cough for a fortnight, and all he could manage was pureed meat broth. He found it painful to swallow and had little appetite for food. I added tinned cat food to his meat broth to encourage him to eat and managed to keep him in reasonable condition whilst his body gradually fought off the illness. He made a full recovery, but it took at least three months before I could safely let him run. This type of case is not unusual in stressed rescued lurchers.

You can vaccinate against Kennel Cough (a nasal spray) but like all viruses, this illness is constantly evolving and vaccination is not always successful. Boarding kennels routinely demand an up to date vaccination for this as well as the other infectious diseases already mentioned.

VERY IMPORTANT

You absolutely must not run the dog for at least two weeks (I'd normally give a dog at least a month) after it has finished coughing. I have known lurchers to suffer from permanent lung damage as a result of being worked too soon after having contracted Kennel Cough. Inflammation of the lung tissue can develop after days of incessant coughing, and whilst this normally resolves itself given enough time, running or working the dog whilst the lungs are still in a damaged or delicate state can lead to permanent scarring and a subsequent loss of performance.

NOTE: Antibiotics do not kill viral infections, only those of a bacterial nature. In severe cases of Kennel Cough the vet may prescribe antibiotics as a precautionary measure, but don't expect your vet to do this unless the dog is at risk from secondary infection or is already suffering from it.

DANGERS IN THE FIELD AND LIFE-THREATENING EMERGENCIES

Whilst we're on the subject of disease, I've included a list of dangers which running dogs are likely to encounter when out in the field. Much of the land over which we work our dogs is farm land, and as such may harbour poisons and chemicals which, if ingested by dogs, is liable to kill them.

Of course we can't guard against everything which is likely to damage our animals, but a little common sense will go a long way in avoiding unnecessary injury or even death.

Although this book is essentially a guide to the maintenance of running dogs I thought it a good idea to include a run down of the emergency situations you are most likely to come across whilst exercising, working or racing the running dog.

HYPOTHERMIA
AND HYPERTHERMIA

Hypothermia must not be confused with HYPERTHERMIA. Hypothermia is cold induced whilst Hyperthermia is heat induced.

Both conditions can lead to death, though heatstroke, the name commonly given to hyperthermia, can kill a dog within minutes if the animal cannot be cooled down quickly enough.

Whilst the obvious cause of hyperthermia is known to everyone, that of leaving dogs in cars on sunny days, it is important to realise that even a winter's day can be deadly to the dog shut in a closed vehicle.

Sighthounds and lurchers are particularly prone to hyperthermia in this situation as they dehydrate very rapidly. This is because they have relatively little body fat with which to rehydrate themselves. Fat contains a lot of water which is why a camel's hump is able to

Almost a case of hyperthermia. Note the deep red tongue which has expanded to allow increased cooling.

sustain it for a considerable length of time when no water is available.

Fat literally saved a mongrel Collie's life in one case when the dog was left in a closed car for several hours. Sadly, the two lurchers which were also in the car died from dehydration and hyperthermia whereas the fatter dog was able to maintain its hold on life by drawing on the fluid contained in its fat reserves.

Exercising or working the running dog during warm weather can also lead to hyperthermia (see chapter on Conditioning), as can an unexpected chase on game in the summer months.

SYMPTOMS OF HYPERTHERMIA

Very fast, shallow panting is one of the first signs of hyperthermia, as are a bright red tongue, pale gums, sticky thick saliva (as the dog dehydrates), unsteadiness when walking, and ultimately collapse and death.

TREATMENT

DO NOT immerse a severely hyperthermic dog in a cold bath or river but DO get the dog into the shade as fast as possible and cool it down with whatever means you have available.

Whilst total immersion in very cold water is dangerous, placing the dog in a water trough or the shallows of a lake or river is fine. Cool the underside of the dog and make sure that you support the victim until it has recovered sufficiently before allowing it to drink.

Similarly, do not run a cold hose over the back of a dog which has collapsed in the heat as this has been known to cause cramping of the muscles if they are very hot. Instead, place damp cool towels against the rib cage, between the hind legs where the major blood vessels run close to the skin' surface, and under the chest.

Sponge cool, not ice cold, water between the hind legs, and on top of the dog's head. The aim is to cool the over heated blood slowly so that the cooled blood is carried to the internal organs to reduce body temperature in a controlled manner. Cooling hot internal organs too fast can result in organ failure.

Severe hyperthermia can result in organ failure and death as the dog literally cooks in its overheated body and even moderate hyperthermia may render the dog unfit for work in the future because of damage to internal organs.

Anything more than mild hyperthermia from which the dog recovers within a short space of time should be treated by a vet as there may be organ damage.

Racing dogs are at particular risk from hyperthermia as most racing competitions are held outside at game fairs and shows during the summer. Make sure that racing dogs are caught up and placed in the shade away from the events between races, even if the sun doesn't appear to be over hot. Excitement also plays a part in the dehydration process which of course

Dogs need access to shade when necessary.

increases the risk of hyperthermia. Dogs lose both heat and moisture by panting so you should keep them as calm and cool as possible when they're not actually running.

If you are out in the field working your dog during warm weather (never a good idea in the first place as you can't always control the amount of running they do) you should make sure that any work is undertaken within easy reach of water in which your dog can immerse itself completely to cool-down at frequent intervals.

Some dogs, regardless of their breeding, seem to suffer more during hot weather than others. Get to know your dog's heat tolerance and don't take any chances if you have a dog that simply can't cope with any form of exercise in warm weather. Exercise dogs preferably very early in the morning or very late evening, though early evenings are deceptive as the heat which has built up in the ground during the long summer day is released when the air cools slightly making evening exercise more dangerous than cool early mornings. Old dogs may suffer more from the heat than younger animals as their

thermostatic abilities decline along with the rest of the body. Never leave any dog, but particularly old ones, in places where they cannot lie quietly in deep shade. At the time of writing my oldest lurcher, aged nearly 12 years, can just about cope with plodding down to the lake in hot weather, and the distance is only a few hundred metres. Once there she simply lies or stands in the water until it is time to come home. The young dogs swim and race about, generally tolerating the hot days much better, though I do have one lurcher which overheats very easily. Luckily she is of a sensible disposition and makes sure that she stays wet most of the time we are out on exercise during the summer.

If the dog is kenneled outside make sure that the interior of the kennel doesn't become a torturous hot box, and that there is an adequate air flow through the run and kennel. Good kennels have ventilation hatches placed high on the walls of the kennel which encourage the hot air to rise away from the dog's body and out of the kennel.

187

Old dogs find it harder to cope with hot weather than youngsters.

Make sure that the dog always has access to a shaded run, though as the sun moves across the sky during the course of the day you may need to place additional blinds in front of the bars or mesh. I've installed window blinds which are screwed to the run roof and these can be raised or lowered depending on the time of day and heat of the sun. The blinds can be removed completely once the hot weather has passed.

You can add electrolyte solution to drinking water during hot weather, and also to portable bottles for use in the field. Recharge is the best electrolyte solution available (see page 22) and should be a permanent resident in your medicine cupboard. Electrolyte solutions rehydrate dogs far better than plain water, though adding sulphur blocks to drinking water may also help to enable dogs to withstand hot conditions better.

Sulphur is a very important component of every cell in all living things and helps the body to make more efficient use of oxygen. Dogs use more oxygen when panting, excited, during hot weather and when physically active.

HYPOTHERMIA

Hypothermia is the exact opposite of hyperthermia, and is the technical term for body temperature which falls below the normal.

Hypothermia is unlikely to occur in most working running dogs in the UK unless they are being used as water retrievers during the winter. Wildfowlers' Labradors have evolved to have thick layers of subcutaneous fat, something you shouldn't see in a sighthound type, but running dogs which work cover on shoots over a long wet day are at risk from becoming uncontrollably cold.

True hypothermia (as opposed to being just a bit cold and miserable) is just as dangerous as hyperthermia, but is more insidious in its onset and less easily recognised by the owner.

Violent shivering in a dog should never be ignored, especially if the dog is wet. Whilst even quite smooth coated dogs can cope with dry cold conditions providing they are active, wet dogs can quickly become very chilled.

During recent fox control on a shoot, we started the day in blizzard like conditions, a blizzard which soon turned to wet slush as the temperature was just above freezing. Whilst the terriers, with their thick greasy coats coped well despite being sodden all day long, my nine year old smooth coated lurcher grew colder and colder despite working hard all day.

No doubt her age didn't help her to maintain her core body temperature, but the constant falls of wet snow from burdened branches made sure that she stayed cold despite fairly constant action.

Although not technically hypothermic, she was shivering each time we stopped to discuss our next move, and once home, she remained colder to the touch than she should have done. I put a fleece coat on her, gave her a bowl of warm meat broth (easily digested) and she slept on her sofa for several hours, completely worn out with the day's battle against the elements, though she had recovered enough to guzzle down her normal meal later on that evening with no ill effects whatsoever.

The two young rough coated lurchers who had worked alongside her all day were none the worse for wear and felt warm to the touch at all times.

I've recounted these events just to show how different dogs react to the same conditions, and how important it is to take into consideration the age and type of dog when monitoring their welfare.

Slender Whippet and Saluki types can easily become hypothermic as they have less fat than Collie or terrier blooded lurchers, and it is very important to ensure that the working running dog is carrying enough weight if it has to hunt during cold, wet weather. Very lightly built or underweight dogs aren't carrying enough body fat and run the risk of becoming hypothermic if they are not receiving a diet adequate for the work that they do, particularly if that work is carried out in cold, wet conditions.

Dogs that work at night on the lamp in really cold wet weather are doubly at risk of becoming chilled, and any fall off in performance during the course of the night's work should be immediately assessed.

How many times have I heard people complain that their dog stopped catching during a night's work? What do some of these owners do? Instead of stopping to consider why the dog might have failed to catch, they continue running the dog, which because it has been bred to chase at all costs, keeps trying and trying, despite being in no condition to succeed. Of course

hypothermia isn't always the cause of such failure as injury, inadequate diet (low blood sugar levels: see chapter on feeding) can also play a part in below par performance, but do keep in mind the weather conditions as they can really affect a dog's performance.

I had a very 'delicately' made coursing bitch, who could tolerate warm weather coursing far better than most. Mostly Saluki in make up, she suffered badly during the occasional downpours on coursing days in the middle of winter, becoming so chilled that she physically couldn't run properly after a drenching. Muscles simply won't work properly if they are cold, and are also at increased risk of injury if the dog attempts to work hard.

This bitch had a very fine, smooth coat and virtually no body fat. Her muscles, lacking any protection from the onslaught of cold rain, stiffened and refused to operate as they should until she had warmed up again. This was not hypothermia, just cold, and a situation which was quickly remedied by putting a fleece coat on the dog and getting her into a warm vehicle.

SYMPTOMS

True hypothermia can be a killer. The first signs to look out for in a dog are severe shivering, a failure to pant, even after running and the dog whose ears and skin inside the hind legs feel cold to the touch, or whose gait becomes unsteady and uncoordinated. Uncontrollable and continuous shivering is the first sign of hypothermia but this mustn't be confused with the surges of shivers which are typical of Whippets and other highly strung types of running dog.

Whilst shivering increases the blood flow to the muscles, it draws heat away from the internal organs, which is why, when moderate to severe hypothermia kicks in, dogs no longer shiver. The body is, by this time, shutting down the extremities in an attempt to keep the all-important internal organs alive.

Once the dog's body temperature falls below normal (around 39°C) the dog is colder than it should be. Once that temperature falls below 37°C the dog becomes hypothermic and if not warmed up will ultimately die.

As I said before, hypothermia is unusual in running dogs in the UK, though puppies and old dogs are of course more at risk than healthy, fit adults. I've seen small pups become almost hypothermic on a summer's day if they've spent too long swimming in a lake, their continuous shivering a sign that I should have got them out of the water sooner. Small puppies chill very quickly as their body mass isn't great enough to protect their internal organs from cold, and they need to be dried off fast to prevent further chilling. Unlike human children who have no fur, the wet coat stops the sun's heat from warming up sodden pups for quite some time in thick coated types.

Running dogs which have fallen into icy water are the most likely hypothermia candidates in the UK, and their survival often depends on the length of time they have spent in the water and the first aid knowledge of their owners.

TREATMENT

Get a hypothermic dog out of the wind, water or cold immediately. Cold wind and wet combined are a deadly combination, and the wind chill factor will exacerbate chilling.

Wrap the dog in anything you have to hand (I carry a space blanket with me in my first aid kit when we're out working in the winter months) and I've taken off my own coat and wrapped it round a large lurcher in the past, though small dogs can be snuggled inside your coat against your body. Now is not the time to worry about a little mud and water ruining your clothes if your dog is at risk.

Once inside a vehicle or your home you must dry the dog thoroughly, though DO NOT put the dog next to a hot radiator or fire. Carry old towels in your vehicle at all times as you never know when you might need one. Warming a dog up too fast is just as dangerous as cooling a heatstroke victim too quickly, so don't be tempted to smother the dog in hot water bottles either.

Use your own or another dog's body heat to warm the patient up slowly, and absolutely DO NOT give hot food or drink to a dog suffering from hypothermia. Give small amounts of warm fluid only until the dog has recovered. By small, I mean a teaspoonful of fluid every 15 minutes, no more than that amount.

Extreme cases should be rushed to the vet immediately as organ damage may have occurred and even if the dog may appear close to death, remember the saying: the patient is only dead if he/she is warm and dead (extreme cold can shut down heart and respiration to virtually nothing, but if the patient has regained normal body temperature without regaining normal heart beat and respiration there really is no further hope left for a recovery). There are remarkable cases of dogs surviving from near death states of hypothermia, so take the dog to the vet even if it appears that all is lost.

PHYSICAL DANGERS IN THE FIELD

Physical dangers in the field range from shocks from electric fencing, collision with farm implements and risk of trampling or goring from farm or wild animals. Always try and reconnoitre your dog's working environment before actually working a place. This is not always possible, but if you take a few moments to suss out a field or area before you hunt, this can save your dog's life. We all know of the rusting harrow lying hidden beneath weeds or grass, or the coils of barbed wire long forgotten by the farmer, just waiting to ensnare the running dog. Dogs which run through woodland are equally at risk of impalement on branches, and open land dogs which run on arable flat land where there are no hedges, only drainage ditches, are at risk every time they attempt to jump the yawning chasms which open up underneath them without warning.

It pays to accustom young dogs early on in their lives to the dangers they are likely to face as adults, and I'll never forget taking a friend on some flat land for a day's coursing, not realising that his dog had never before seen a dyke (drainage ditch). As we slipped our dogs on a hare they powered away towards such a dyke: my dog leapt the dyke and my friend's dog disappeared from sight. When we arrived at the edge of the dyke the dog lay dead with a broken neck; a tragic end for a young and enthusiastic dog.

Likewise, dogs which need to work around barbed wire need to learn its potential to hurt long before they are able to run at sufficient speed to cause damage when they hit the stuff. Take young pups regularly through barbed wire fences so that they learn to negotiate the dangers in a non-hunting situation. A puppy of 16 weeks old is not too young to learn how to crawl through a barbed wire fence, and the odd minor scratch gained through such early lessons may save you many heartaches and vets' bills later on in life.

Life is dangerous for the working running dog, though racing dogs can also run the risk of injury during pile ups at the end of a lure course. Nowadays race organisers are usually pretty good at making the end of the race as safe as possible, though it pays to check out how the race will end and into what device the lure will disappear. Good race organisers make sure that the lure machine itself is situated well away from the covering (often a piece of canvas or carpet under which the lure is dragged) which hides the lure at the end of a race, though before this was commonplace I saw some horrendous crashes which resulted in injury when dogs piled into the machine itself.

WHEN ACCIDENTS HAPPEN

All but the luckiest dogs in the world, or those which never do anything at speed, will injure themselves at some time or another during their lives. Be prepared to deal with a dog which may behave completely out of character when it is shocked or injured.

Pain makes even the most laid back of dogs react in unusual ways, and if an accident has happened at speed the dog may well be not only hurt, but disorientated as well. Put yourself in its skin! One moment you are running flat out after something, the next you are lying on the ground in pain and possibly unable to move.

BARBED WIRE

The first thing to do when you get to your dog is to talk to it calmly. If the dog is hanging from a barbed wire fence you will need to hold the dog firmly to prevent it from damaging itself further in its struggles to escape the pain.

Whilst you are running towards your stricken dog take stock of the situation, start shedding your coat, or even your shirt if the accident has happened during hot weather. You may need something to: a) press against an open wound to stop bleeding; b) to cover the dog's head with to calm it down, or c) to wedge in its jaws if it is trying to bite everything and anything within range. If you are on your own and your dog is hanging (often from the skin on its belly or the skin inside its hind legs) from barbed wire you must first support the animal to stop further damage. Then you must attempt to untwist each tine from the skin, not easy at the best of times, and to which end I'd suggest always carrying some very strong wire cutters in your pocket if you habitually venture forth alone in barbed wire country. You might never need them, but if such an accident happens only once in your life time it will have been worth the many years you've carried such a tool. Cutting the wire on each side of the dog if you cannot untwist the tines might prove to be the simplest solution when alone.

ELECTRIC SHOCK

If your dog becomes enmeshed in electrified netting then the first thing you should to is to switch off the fence, if you can. Most electrified fencing is of the pulsed variety which means that the electric current is not continuous. This is nowhere near as dangerous as electrocution suffered from chewing mains wires, and whilst the shock from an electric livestock fence is nasty and may put some dogs off their work for a day or so, it isn't life-threatening. Single electrified wires usually elicit a yelp and a shocked retreat: dogs can't understand what has happened and I've known shocked dogs refuse to re-enter a field ever again as they (quite sensibly) associate the place with pain.

Electrified mesh is usually made of plastic with wires running through it and doesn't generally entangle a dog to any great extent though dogs running at night are more likely to become tangled up. Unless you have bare feet or a very weak heart you can stand on the mesh to hold it down whilst you extricate the dog. The shock isn't unbearably painful unless you have wet hands and even then isn't life-threatening and most dogs although understandably shocked (excuse the pun) are unharmed by such an experience, though they may appear fearful and confused by such an accident. *Rescue Remedy*, available in health food shops and chemists is great for minimising the effects of such shock and can be used as a restorative after any injury or accident.

SHOCK

A dog can go into a state of shock as a result of injury or blood loss and true shock is very dangerous. When a dog is in a state of shock the pulse is weak and difficult to find, the animal may feel cold to the touch, have very pale gums and tongue and in severe cases may lose consciousness. The state of shock can follow any severe injury, either immediately following the injury or sometimes not showing for several hours afterwards. This is a TRUE EMERGENCY and needs immediate veterinary attention.

On your way to the vet, keep the dog warm, lying down with its head slightly lower than the rest of its body if possible: this is so blood is encouraged to reach the brain. Do not try and revive the dog with brandy or any other alcohol as this will have a disastrous effect as blood flow will be increased to the limbs and away from the vital organs which may send the dog into deeper shock.

ANAPHYLACTIC SHOCK

Anaphylactic shock can be brought on by many things, though I've seen it most as a result of wasp stings or snake bites. When the dog disturbs an active wasps' nest the entire colony come out to attack the intruder, never mind that the dog was just walking across the nest site (wasps often nest in holes in the ground deep in brambles or other vegetation). A typical scenario is when you're out exercising your dog in late summer and it has chased a rabbit into a bramble. Dogs stung many times don't all suffer from anaphylactic shock, and just like people, some tolerate multiple stings without a serious reaction. However, others may go into shock after receiving just one sting.

The typical stance of a dog suffering from anaphylactic shock is quite unmistakable. The dog will stop running, and stand quite still. Its gaze will appear unfocussed and if it has been panting this will cease. In extreme cases the dog may lose consciousness and fall over. It's a scary moment for both owner and dog, and an emergency situation which usually means prompt veterinary attention.

Sometimes the dog isn't suffering from true anaphylactic shock, but simply in severe pain as the result of multiple stings. Wasp and bee stings really hurt but if your dog is unable to move and is showing any of the following symptoms don't waste time waiting to see if it recovers, but get it to the vet straight away. Symptoms of anaphylactic shock may include: weak though fast pulse rate, vomiting, diarrhoea, unconsciousness, pale gums, cold limbs.

Less severe cases respond well to an antihistamine tablet. I give a whole Piriton to a large running dog and half a tablet to a small Whippet sized dog. I've never had a really severe case of anaphylactic shock in my dogs and I've normally found that such treatment has had a miraculous effect on the dog within half an hour.

HIVES OR URTICARIA

The common term for a severe allergic reaction, also associated with insect stings, though also caused by contact with an irritant such as certain plant saps. I've only come across this once, and that was in one of my terriers, though small, thin skinned and smooth coated running dogs which bust through cover are also at risk. Once again, an antihistamine tablet will usually sort out the problem, though the dog may look depressed and in pain from multiple swellings all over its body. If an antihistamine tablet doesn't show any signs of working after 20 minutes then get to the vet fast.

DROWNING

You can give mouth to nose resuscitation to a dog which has been pulled out of water apparently unbreathing. Close your hand round the end of the dog's nose and blow air gently from your mouth into the nostrils.

Cardiac massage can also be used, and as with hypothermia, the patient isn't dead until it is warm and dead. Very cold water can have the effect of shutting down the bodily functions in a similar way, so don't give up too soon.

CARDIAC MASSAGE

Shock, traffic accidents, drowning or poisoning can all stop a dog from breathing or stop its heart. If this happens it is crucial to give cardiac massage immediately.

You **must not** give mouth to nose resuscitation unless the dog's heart is beating. Put your ear against the left side of the chest just behind the elbow to listen for a heart beat. If there is no heart beat you must administer cardiac massage until the heart starts beating again. It is pointless blowing air into an animal's lungs if the heart is not able to move that oxygen around the body. With the dog lying on its right hand side (if possible), place both hands, one on top of the other, at the base of the dog's ribcage, right over the heart just behind the dogs left elbow. Press hard moving your hands towards the head very slightly: this will help to push blood from the heart and towards the brain. Repeat this rhythmically six times at one second intervals.

Keep this up until the heart starts beating again. Once the heart has started beating you may give mouth to nose resuscitation.

If the dog has stopped breathing but its heart is still beating you obviously don't need to do the cardiac massage, but get on with mouth to nose resuscitation straight away. Make sure there are no obstructions in the dog's mouth, pull its tongue forward so it cannot block the airway. If there is damage to the nose the dog can still breathe through its mouth but only if the tongue is not blocking the airway.

Keep the neck as straight as you can, cup your hands round the dog's nose and breathe steadily into its nostrils for two to three seconds. You should see the chest rise. Pause for two seconds then repeat the process until the dog is breathing for itself again.

If the dog's heart stops beating whilst you are breathing into the dog, you must administer cardiac massage again. If the dog stops breathing whilst you are doing the cardiac massage, breathe into the dog's nostrils at a rate of one breath per minute until the heart starts once more. Then go back to mouth to nose resuscitation only.

Keep going for 10 minutes. If the dog is still not breathing or there is no heartbeat after this time then give up. Many years ago I saved a young lurcher who fell and winded herself on the coursing field. She turned a somersault in mid air landed heavily on deep plough and her heart stopped. Luckily I had only to massage her heart for less than a minute before it started beating again. The crazy thing was that I didn't really know what I was doing at the time, and all I did was to rub that area of her chest really hard for a moment or two. She then took a deep gasping breath and started to recover. This dog had only winded herself, but her heart had stopped from the shock of the fall.

I got home and I made sure that I learned how to resuscitate a dog properly, realising that this dog had been very lucky. Instinct prompted me to do what I did, but ignorance of the correct procedure wouldn't have saved a dog in a more serious condition. Learn the procedure and remember not to freeze with panic if it happens to your dog. Always take a couple of deep breaths before you do anything when confronted with an emergency situation.

NOTE: large, heavy and strong people should be very careful when attempting cardiac massage: it is easy to break ribs of both humans and dogs if you don't know exactly what you are doing. How about going on a first aid course for humans? The same principles apply to dogs. Even the recovery position is similar in that the dog should be laid on its side, not its back or front. Always place the dog on its right side unless any injury would make this more dangerous for the patient.

MORE LIFE-THREATENING SITUATIONS

Insect bites and stings aren't usually life-threatening, but dogs can suffer from anaphylactic shock just like humans. Even one sting can have a devastating effect on a susceptible animal. My terriers are usually the ones to receive wasp and bee stings after they've dived into cover after rabbits, though the bigger dogs can be just as much at risk if they run over a wasp nest in the ground.

If you see your dog emerge from bushes or cover swaying on its feet, then stand dead still with head lowered and eyes oddly unfocussed, you may suspect a sting reaction.

Bee and wasp stings can be really painful to both humans and dogs, and whilst some dogs may lick at the affected spot, be sure to look for the sting which may still be embedded in the skin.

Many people believe that only bees leave their stings in their victims, but I've pulled out just as many wasp stings with poison sac attached. It is important to do this for while the sac and sting remain in the dog the poison keeps pumping into the victim. Don't grasp the sac with your fingers or tweezers as you'll inject more venom into the dog. The best way to pull out the sting is to scrape it off with a finger nail: it can't hurt you as the sting is in the dog. Or put both thumbnails against the skin either side of the sac and prise it out with one quick flick.

Always carry antihistamine tablets or liquid in your first aid bag during the summer. The liquid is more bulky to carry but is absorbed through the stomach walls more quickly than the tablets. Use a child's dose for medium sized running dogs; dose up or down according to the size of the dog.

Severe anaphylactic shock can kill within moments if the airway swells up which is why you must get the dog to the vet immediately if you see a strong reaction to a sting.

I've had small dogs almost go into shock, collapsing on the ground barely conscious, but by the time I've carried them back to my vehicle they've recovered enough to

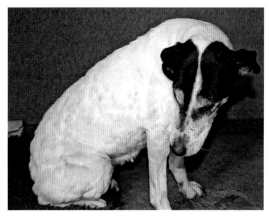

Severe hives in a terrier which was alleviated by antihistimine tablets.

want to jump into their boxes. Even if the dog seems to have recovered completely you should monitor it for several hours for anaphylaxis can blow up again like the aftershock of an earthquake.

The above photo shows a severe allergic reaction to a bee sting in a terrier (I've had to use the terrier to show this reaction as I've not come across this in my lurchers). The dog was very quiet, obviously in pain and didn't want to move at all. I gave her half a Piriton tablet and the bumps disappeared within 20 minutes. There were no ill effects afterwards and now make sure to keep her away from any cover during wasp season.

POISONING

The countryside can be a dangerous place, even though modern farming practices are a lot safer than they were mid twentieth century.

However, chemical spillages on farm tracks, run off from roads where a spillage might have occurred after an accident, as well as unscrupulous dumping of hazardous waste are all potentially dangerous to dogs.

Try not to let your dogs drink from puddles on farm tracks or from stagnant water in ditches and dykes, especially near roads. Keep garden pesticides, anti-freeze and all household cleaners well away from dogs and be extremely careful if you have put rat or mouse bait anywhere round your home or garden.

CHEMICAL POISONING

Unfortunately you are unlikely to know at the time just when your dog ingests some dangerous chemical but by keeping your dog out of water filled ditches near roads and motorways you are reducing the possibility of chemical poisoning which can result from run off from a spill or leakage on the road.

Landfill sites, whilst not legally allowed to take toxic waste, have been known to harbour various chemicals which unscrupulous people have dumped into skips and bins. Never allow a dog to run over an active landfill site, which quite apart from anything else, will be strewn with broken glass, tins and all manner of sharp objects.

CONTROLLED SUBSTANCES

I'm not talking drugs here, but the various poisons legitimately used in pest control. Whilst today's laws are very strict on the use of such poisons, dogs are still in danger of ingesting these products if they have not been properly sited in boxes and areas inaccessible to non target species.

Many of the rodent baits are slow acting and they kill by affecting the blood's clotting ability, and although you are unlikely to see your dog eating rat bait at the time, cuts and scratches which refuse to stop bleeding are a warning sign that something is wrong. I've known a lurcher eat enough rat bait to kill several dogs, though happily her owner realised only hours after the event what had happened and the dog is still alive. Had her owner not realised

that his lurcher had eaten rat bait and had she subsequently suffered a collision with another dog or an object she would have probably died of internal bleeding quite quickly. As it was, she was on medication for several months until blood tests showed that the poison had gone from her system. Anti-freeze is another far too common cause of poisoning because its sweet taste is appealing to many dogs, and can cause kidney failure and death.

SYMPTOMS OF POISONING

Symptoms of poisoning may include: vomiting, diarrhoea, nervousness, panting, uncoordinated movement, dilation of pupils, accelerated or unusually slow heart rate, and in extreme cases, convulsions or loss of consciousness.

Get the dog to the vet immediately you suspect a case of poisoning, if possible taking the cause of the problem with you, such as the mouse bait box or bottle which you think might be responsible.

Many poisons are acutely caustic, so it is not always a good idea to try and induce vomiting in a suspected poisoning case. Check with your vet if you know what poison your dog has ingested before attempting to induce vomiting.

Do NOT give salt water to induce vomiting because if the dog doesn't vomit as a result the excess salt in its system can be as dangerous as the poison itself. Bicarbonate of soda dissolved in water is a much safer way to induce vomiting, though check with your vet first.

Some poisons do not have an immediate effect, such as the anti-coagulant mouse baits but if the dog has ingested some of the often sweet tasting coloured blocks of such bait, it may have reduced clotting abilities.

I've known dogs to ingest mouse bait and show no signs of poisoning until they have injured themselves. A wound which refuses to clot is a sign that the dog may have eaten bait, though internal (and unseen) bleeding can also arise if the dog bruises itself as a result of a collision. Vitamin K injections are the only solution if the dog has eaten rodent bait, and sometimes many weeks of treatment are needed in order to save the dog's life.

Whilst many terriers and gundogs are of the type to snaffle up any tasty morsel they may find, most sighthounds and lurchers are a little more reserved in their tastes. Still, don't take chances and keep dogs away from likely baiting areas such as barns and animal sheds. Many farms are still littered with rodent bait despite modern health and safety laws, but if someone decides to DIY their rodent problem these laws are not always adhered to as they should be.

Landfill sites are another dangerous place for dogs, and whilst many are teeming with wildlife, they are also teeming with noxious bacteria which can kill a dog in double quick time. Landfill sites are full of household and other waste in an advanced state of decomposition. Even the areas surrounding such sites may be littered with remnants of rotten food, dropped from the skies by the ever present hordes of seagulls and crows which frequent these places.

Don't allow dogs to pick up old bones and food items if you exercise within a mile or so of a landfill site. One of my lurchers became very ill after eating a piece of rotting sausage which had been dropped by a bird near our landfill site. Only his incredibly tough constitution enabled him to survive the potentially lethal explosion of gastrointestinal bacteria.

The same dog also survived suspected chemical poisoning, producing fluorescent

Take care when working dogs near farms or landfill sites.

green diarrhoea for several days after drinking from a dyke near a road some time after the sausage incident. This was a situation out of my control as he had just finished a lengthy course and had dropped into the dyke for a drink.

We can't safeguard our dogs against everything, but we can be aware of dangers and learn how to react accordingly. If you and your dog are working or holidaying away from your home area it is a good idea to arm yourself with a list of local vets in case of emergency, including their out of hours telephone numbers. I've usually found that most emergencies seem to happen either over a weekend or at night!

CHAPTER TWELVE

Housing

I've included a chapter on housing the running dog in this book because the conditions in which an animal lives have a direct bearing on its overall health. Whilst most owners nowadays have a pretty firm grasp on kennel essentials I've come up with a few refinements to the average kennel over the years, ones which have proved of benefit to my dogs.

Running dogs generally have far thinner skin than breeds such as Labradors and terriers, and they feel the cold more as a consequence. They also lack a thick layer of subcutaneous fat, and the smooth coated types have thinner coats as well which mean that a good layer of bedding is also a necessity if unpleasant conditions such as sores on hocks and elbows are to be avoided.

A useful kennel which doubles as storage for hunting equipment. Photo: Barry Leavesley

Large bony dogs are also prone to a thickening of the skin on elbows and hocks which can also develop into bursas if the dog is forced to lie for long periods of time on a hard surface. Bursas are fluid-filled swellings with thickened skin which develop to protect the bone on hocks and elbows if there isn't enough bedding to cushion the weight of the animal.

We all know that a dog needs to be housed in a dry and draught-proof kennel, unless of course it lives with you in the house, though many older houses can be very draughty so make sure that the dog bed has high enough sides for the dog to be well below any under door air currents, unless your canine companions sleep on the sofa like mine do!

It is said that outside dogs are generally healthier than house dogs, and whilst I might agree if your house is centrally heated to tropical temperatures (which does neither human nor animal any good) I can see no real benefit in keeping a dog outdoors, though of course this is often the most practical arrangement if the house is full of young children from which the dogs need protection!

However, I like to live with my dogs: they are better socialised, more in tune with human behaviour and generally calmer because they are with me for most of the time. Some do spend nights or part of the day in kennels and runs, but for the most part mine are indoor dogs.

Permanently kenneled dogs can suffer from lack of stimulus if they spend most of their time alone with nothing to do, leading to over excitement and manic behaviour when they are initially freed from their kennels. Dogs which live alongside humans in the house are less likely to 'go nuts' when they see their owners, and injuries (see Tail Injuries) resulting from manic greeting

behaviour can be greatly reduced if the dog isn't isolated for the greater part of the day.

The fact that my dogs are always right in front of me (underfoot would be a truer statement!) also means that I am instantly aware if a particular animal is feeling under the weather which enables me to take immediate action if necessary.

Whether as working or companion dogs most are pack animals and prefer to live in groups, but of course this does depend on the individual breeding of the animal as well. Some working dogs have been developed for specific purposes, which may have introduced into the breed more of a go-it-alone attitude and less tolerance to the bumping and barging that is part of pack life. Terriers are a good example of this type and it follows that some running dogs containing terrier blood may not exactly suit the sometimes mayhem of a crowded house without becoming a little over stimulated by such an environment.

SECURITY AND COMFORT

In this supposedly civilised society it is a sad fact that more and more dogs are stolen, often from their own kennels, every year, and if you do need to house your dogs outdoors be prepared to put in a security system to rival that of the Bank of England.

I was told of one owner woken in the wee hours of the morning by a terrible din outside, and he found that thieves were in the process of breaking through the concrete block wall of his kennels. They would have already succeeded had he not had the forethought to reinforce the block walls with steel bars!

This is an extreme example of the lengths to which dog thieves are prepared to go, but does illustrate the point that security must be paramount when keeping dogs outdoors in the UK.

Whilst concrete, stone and steel offer the best possible protection against thieves I prefer a wooden construction for the kennel itself as this is warmer in cold weather.

If I kenneled my dogs outdoors on a permanent basis I would build a reinforced concrete run, complete with a roof laid on top of more bars welded to the upright sections. I would also use barred panels for the run walls as opposed to mesh which is all too easily cut through with wire cutters.

I would stand a wooden shed inside the run as opposed to a traditional style dog kennel which offers only the bare minimum when it comes to space.

The shed/kennel would be twice the length of the dog and the same width, about four foot by four foot for a Greyhound-sized dog. This gives the dog space to move about, stretch out on its side in summer and room to 'make its bed' in a corner during colder months.

The kennel would also be six foot high, for there is nothing worse than having to stoop or crouch in order to clean out the bedding, or attend to an injured dog.

Having plenty of head room also allows air to circulate freely in summer, and I'd also place a small hatch or window on one side, preferably the side which faces away from the prevailing wind. This can be kept closed in winter and left permanently open during the summer months.

There would also be a full sized door in one side of the kennel, and a dog hatch in another side. This hatch can be fitted with draught strips of clear plastic for dogs that don't chew, and these can be attached to a batten which can be removed altogether if necessary in warm weather. The full sized door gives you easy access when changing bedding or attending to an injured dog.

The only downside to a full height shed is that hot air rises which means that heat from the dog's body is likely to keep the dog cold at floor level. I fit an artificial ceiling in the shed during colder months. All you need to do is fix battens to the inside walls of the shed at the appropriate height which would be about a foot above the dog's head height when it is standing up.

Lay a ply wood 'ceiling' on the battens, and if you use straw for bedding, you can pile new and unused straw on top of the board for added insulation. I also store wood shavings or old blankets on top of the false ceiling.

When warmer weather comes along you simply lift off the boards in order to turn the shed back into a full height kennel thereby allowing air to circulate more freely and keep the temperature down.

I also screw a board about 16 inches in height along the door side of the shed, partly to keep in loose bedding which would spill out when you open the door, and partly to cut any draught which may seep in around the edges of the door.

As added insulation I have also put sheets of expanded polystyrene between the upright studs in the shed wall, then tacked a sheet of ply over this to create a very cosy kennel indeed.

You can of course go and buy any number of incredibly expensive purpose-built kennels and runs, and some are truly palatial works of art, but first and foremost you should consider the needs of the dog, rather than the beauty of the construction!

I've seen healthy and contented dogs in kennels and runs which looked shabby to say the least, made up of old pallets, sheets of exterior ply and bits of corrugated iron sheeting and left over wire. I've also seen miserable, cold animals in state of the art kennel blocks which had been designed to impress the human eye rather than catering for the comfort of the dog.

Roller blinds in place to shade kennels in summer.

You can buy supposedly thief proof integral runs and kennels made from powder coated metal, and whilst these have a life time guarantee (your life time that is!) I wouldn't like to house my dogs inside such kennels.

The heat and moisture which rise from a breathing dog can create condensation on the walls and ceiling of such kennels, which in turn means that the dog lives in damp and cold conditions throughout the winter months. Damp and cold can lead to arthritis, pneumonia and all sorts of other conditions which can affect the long term health of your hound.

Good quality wooden kennels will last you plenty long enough if properly treated with an animal friendly preservative on an annual basis and I've only recently ditched a shed that was probably almost as old as

I am! I can personally vouch for the fact that a wooden house is a lot warmer to live in than a brick or stone built abode, even though ours is a little draughty due to badly fitting windows!

SUNLIGHT

Dogs love to bask in the sun, and even on sunny winter days mine prefer to lie out in the yard or their runs, taking in the rays which generate Vitamin D production in the body (essential to bone growth and assimilation of Calcium in the body). Be sure to site your kennels and runs in a south facing direction if possible, so that dogs can benefit from the sun.

I put dog sized pieces of old carpet down on concrete yards and runs, though if you have a dog which is likely to urinate on them then a wooden, carpet covered bench may be fixed to the wall of the run. If you keep multiple dogs in the house it is likely that your furniture will become the dogs' beds, but for those more 'normal' people who keep just one or two dogs, make sure to situate their beds, boxes or mats in a draught-free and snug place: dogs need to feel secure in their own beds even if they spend much of their time lying across doorways or other main thoroughfares, apparently for the express reason that they enjoy being tripped over!

BEDDING

You can use straw, hay, shredded paper, blankets or Vetbed in your kennels. The one thing I would never use is wood shavings as they are not only very messy, but they don't allow a dog to make a nest in which to curl up when the weather is cold.

Yes, straw and hay can harbour fleas, ticks and mites, but as long as you treat the kennel regularly for such pests by using a proprietary spray such as Indorex or Acclaim 2000 you will be able to keep on top of potential infestations. Mites of whatever sort are more resistant and need dosing with something like FicamW which is only available to licensed pest controllers.

Make sure straw or hay are mould free and sweet smelling and be prepared to change this bedding weekly during the cold damp months because wet dogs will flatten and soil what they lie on very quickly.

Personally I like to use straw as it is relatively cheap, fluffs up well and doesn't flatten to quite the same extent as hay. It is also less likely to contain thistles and other irritating vegetation than hay. Straw does break up when scuffled up by a dog over a few days, and does produce a lot of dust, which in turn can attract mites and other dust loving insects. Be prepared to vacuum out the cracks between floor boards

if your kennel has them, as well as corners, each time you change the bedding. Damp or soiled straw can go into the chicken run if you keep chickens, or on to the compost heap, so it is a recyclable material as well.

Another bonus when using straw is that it helps to remove mud from dirty wet dogs very well. Wet dogs like to roll around in the straw to dry themselves, and mine only need an hour or so in a straw filled shed to emerge clean and dry, though rough haired dogs will need a comb through to remove particles of straw from their coats before they enter your house.

NOTE: Heavy coated dogs which frequently enter their kennels dripping wet will need their beds changing very frequently: maybe up to twice a week during prolonged spells of wet weather. This is because straw, once dampened, breaks down into small pieces very quickly and loses its insulating properties.

I've tried various types of shredded paper and decided against this in my kennels for not only is it very expensive, unless you have an enormous supply and your own shredding machine, but it also damps down very quickly and becomes a hard papier mache like covering once wet. Shredded paper needs replacing far too often during wet weather for my liking, but for dogs which are seldom wet or muddy it is a clean and hygienic option, providing you replace it as soon as it goes flat and dirty.

Blankets are OK as long as your dog never goes into its kennel whilst wet, for they too take in moisture and retain it for far too long to do a dog any good. They also lack 'nesting' potential unless you have a Whippet type burrowing dog which has the instinct to get right under the covers.

Vetbed, the synthetic fleece product, is far easier to wash and dry than wool

very easily and leave no lingering smell of urine which might encourage the dog to soil the same spot again. Use an antibacterial surface cleanser to wash the floor and avoid strong disinfectants.

Strong disinfectants should only be used if you rinse thoroughly with clean water after application, and the same applies to concrete runs as well. Some straw in the run, and change the bedding to something which doesn't remind the dog of its habit.

Some people lower the ceiling of the kennel to prevent the dog doing any more than lying down once it has crawled inside the kennel: dogs find it difficult to toilet when lying down, though I've seen several nervous females pee when lying down in unfamiliar situations as they didn't want anyone to know that they were urinating: this was, by the way, nothing to do with peeing themselves through sheer fear: they simply needed to go but didn't dare do it openly.

Personally I don't like the idea of forcing a dog to lie in a kennel in which it can't even stand up: a dog which is confined to a kennel and run for much of the time needs to be housed in conditions which are as comfortable and stress free as possible.

A cramped kennel could well be the cause of even more stress, and if the dog is fouling its bed for reasons other than physical illness then making that place even smaller and more uncomfortable will only exacerbate the problem.

What you can do is make the actual bed area within the shed/kennel as small as possible so if the dog is peeing in one corner of a large bed area, reduce the bed size and you may be able to break this habit, but do make sure that the dog has easy access to a material it wants to pee on and in such a place where it can relieve itself with ease.

If a dog persists in soiling its bed area no matter what you do then try keeping the dog in the house! Seriously, this worked for me with a very scatty Saluki type lurcher who had been initially reared in filthy conditions before she came to me. Unbelievably dirty in her kennel despite all my efforts, I finally brought this dog into the house at the age of 10 months, and she never once soiled or peed indoors: problem solved!

No normal, healthy, well balanced dog wants to lie in its own faeces or urine so any such problems are likely to be either a behavioural issue or one relating to weather conditions.

NOTE: some dogs may become incontinent through illness or disease,

so make sure that there is not a physical reason behind a dog fouling its bed before you address any behavioural issues.

Temporary incontinence is also sometimes seen, particularly in male dogs, after a very hard course or excessive exercise when the dog is not well enough conditioned for the job it has been asked to do. See chapter on exercise and conditioning.

Other causes of bed soiling can be caused by fear of neighbours if the kennel is situated near your garden or yard boundary. If your neighbours or their dogs are frightening your dog this may lead to problems of this kind. Similarly, nervous dogs which have been startled by hot air balloons or helicopters appearing directly above their runs may refuse to toilet outside.

A dog needs to feel confident in its own home, be that a human home or an outside kennel. Dogs which are worried or afraid of anything in their environment are likely to have behavioural problems and these may manifest as toileting issues.

Wherever you keep your dog, think safety, warmth and comfort, which in my opinion should never involve the animal being chained up. Not only can this be dangerous (dogs have choked to death when strangled by the tethering chain) but chaining also inhibits natural movement and can increase aggression. Dogs thus restrained are more likely to be aggressive as they cannot run if they feel threatened.

I have seen six month old pups chained to a kennel in the back yard, and the bald spots and sores on their legs where the chain has constantly rubbed the skin. Not to mention the fact that a young dog thus chained cannot move a decent distance from its kennel in order to toilet. Unless you are there to pick up faeces and swab down the surrounding area on a very regular basis the young dog will end up paddling around in its own mess, continually dragging the chain through the muck. UK laws surrounding the keeping of wild animals are far stricter than those which apply to domestic dogs, more's the pity, for man's supposed best friend is often treated to degrees of suffering which just shouldn't be allowed.

Keeping a dog calm and happy means that it will be healthier all round and better able to do the tasks you ask of it. Dogs don't ask for much in life, and a warm, safe place to rest should be the very least we offer them.

BOREDOM IN KENNELS

Boredom in kennels can manifest itself in a variety of ways, the two most common being barking or chewing. I do not believe that any dog should have to live in a small enclosed space 24/7 and whilst most people have to work, exercising the dog and giving it some quality time both before and after your absence goes a long way to alleviating such problems.

Routine is essential for kenneled dogs, especially those which are left for many hours whilst the owner is at work. Once a routine is established most dogs will settle down quietly providing that their needs have been attended to, but be aware that some dogs will refuse to soil in their runs, and this can be a cause of barking or howling.

TIPS FOR CONTENTED KENNELED DOGS

Exercise your dog before you go to work in the morning (or evening if you work nights) even if this is only a 10 minute dash round the block. If the dog has emptied its bladder and bowels it will rest more comfortably for the time it is kenneled.

Offer a small meal, a piece of breast of lamb or lamb ribs, or if you have a dog which won't grind away all day on a large bone to the destruction of its teeth, then a beef knuckle will provide jaw exercise and pleasure. Chewing is a psychologically calming activity for dogs.

Those indestructible rubber toys which you stuff with food are also great for filling time. In an age where zoo animals are routinely offered 'enrichment strategies' to make their lives more interesting it is appalling to think that intelligent creatures like dogs are still expected to sit quietly in kennels for many hours with nothing to do. Leave a radio playing softly in the background as this can help a dog to feel less alone.

If possible, kennel two dogs within sight of each other if they get on well. Kennel sharing is not recommended for dogs which spend many hours shut in the kennel, besides which, you wouldn't be able to leave them with food or bones, just in case this caused problems.

Even if you have never had a problem with allowing dogs to share kennels, and many people do kennel two dogs together, a kennel fight resulting in severe damage or the death of one of the dogs will make you change your ways forever.

Yes, I've kenneled mother and daughter together with no problems at all, and I've also kenneled dogs of the opposite sex with one another. Much depends on the individual temperaments of the dogs and whether or not they are of the 'snuggle up' type. Whippet types seem to love piling together in a heap even during warm weather, though I've noticed that my Saluki types are less willing to share bed space, grumbling and muttering to themselves if another dog climbs on to a sofa beside them.

place?

These and many other signs of simmering resentment and tension may go on for years without ever causing a full blown fight, a fight which may one day explode from nowhere. But there's always a cause for the explosion if and when it does occur: its just that you missed the first signs of dischord.

have to mean a walk, just some quality time where the dog can stretch its legs a bit, relieve itself and receive some human attention. If this isn't possible then make sure you attend to the dog the moment you get home.

I was brought up to see to the animals before I fed or watered myself and even as a child of 12 years of age I had to walk and

Hares and running dogs have much in common both being supreme athletes.
Photo: Craig McCann.

CHAPTER THIRTEEN

Mental health

What goes on inside a dog's head is as important as the physical aspect of the animal, indeed I would say that the mental aspect of a working running dog is even more important than its physical perfection, because the best physique in the world won't be of any use if the correct mental attitude is missing.

The following are some of my thoughts on running dogs, and whilst I know that all sighthound breeds are not the same, most are sensitive to a degree not usually seen in many other breeds. However, this sensitivity should not be confused with nervousness.

Many running dogs display symptoms of what some people would call 'nerves', they are highly alert and yes, they do appear to be more highly strung than the more pedestrian breeds such as Labradors. This is not necessarily a state of fearfulness, rather, the keyed up state of mind in which a very fit and healthy athlete operates at his or her best.

A 'switched on' running dog has the ability to react very fast physically, which is something that novice owners find out early on during a puppy's early months. A sad tale here, one which illustrates how the running dog pup, behaving completely within the normal behavioural parameters for a pup of this type, ran to its death on a country road when it saw its young owners some hundred metres on the far side of a country lane, opposite the drive of their house.

Quite naturally, the pup, which had apparently just escaped through an open door, ran to greet its children, down the drive and straight across the road, just as a speeding car came round the corner. The owners, distraught, told me that they hadn't realised how fast their three month old pup could move!

It isn't just the physical speed which surprises people, it is the very short reaction time between sight, thought and physical reaction: in this case to run towards the children. This pup was down the drive and under the wheels of a car when a Labrador pup of similar age would have still been thinking about trundling down the drive.

Sighthounds have evolved to be quick, both in the physical sense and mentally. They need to be mentally sharp in order to power their bodies into the pursuit of prey within milliseconds; any hesitation could mean failure to catch. Think of the running dog as it ambles down a hedgerow, seemingly relaxed to the point of somnambulism, but let a rabbit appear from the hedge and you'll see just how quickly such a dog becomes alert, with ears pricked and eyes focussed on the potential prey.

Inexperienced and young dogs then charge full bore at the rabbit which of course dives back into the hedge, leaving the would-be predator bouncing frustrated in the field. Old hands remain alert, scanning the field for further prey, and whilst the body might move slowly as the dog creeps along the hedgerow, its mind will be so highly focused that the dog may well not hear you call its name when its attention is thus engaged.

I would never compare this heightened state of alertness with nervousness: to me a nervous dog is one in a state of fear, though I've heard some old wives' tale regarding nervous running dogs.

I was once told that a 'nervous bitch makes a good hare dog', and I've had good reason to ponder this saying for I've owned two such 'nervy' and highly strung lurchers which were very good at the job. This isn't to say that a laid back dog can't catch a hare, far from it, but I do wonder if that exaggerated state of nervous tension isn't in some way linked with a very high prey drive. One of my best ever hare dogs was a wimpy, over-sensitive bitch who screamed if you touched her unexpectedly. In the field this over-sensitivity translated into

the ability to read the hare in a way which made her a very effective catch dog indeed. Her heightened senses and awareness allowed her to learn very fast when it came to understanding her prey. Ask her to perform 'obedience tricks' however, and you'd be whistling in the dark long after the dog had put two fingers up at you and disappeared over the horizon with more important matters to attend to!

It would be impossible to live permanently in such a state of heightened awareness, and once my dogs return home from work or even a good exercise session, they sleep deeply, sometimes for hours at a time. Deep sleep is necessary for both physical and mental health. At a cellular level, sleep allows the body to mend from injuries, grow whilst young, and very importantly, switches off the conscious brain to allow the animal to relax fully.

Dogs which have been mistreated, abandoned or have otherwise fallen foul of humans are often unable to relax fully. Even their sleep is broken by nightmares. I've seen rescued dogs dream terrible

Sighthounds are far more sensitive than the more pedestrian types of dog.

dreams from which they awake wide eyed and fearful, taking some moments to realise that they are no longer in a bad place.

Equally, I've seen dogs relive a particularly exciting hunt, and depending on what quarry has been involved, their yips, growls and twitchings tell me that they are reliving the chase. If a dog re-lives happy events in such a way it is obvious that it also re-lives bad experiences.

Running dogs, with their heightened sensitivity suffer terribly when abused or abandoned, and many dogs 'shut down' completely, withdrawing into themselves, becoming unable to respond to human kindness. It takes real dedication and understanding to rehabilitate these dogs, something which can take months if not years of patience and understanding on the part of the owner.

Unfortunately the running dog is all too often passed from one owner to another in this world of swap and change, and whilst some dogs appear to adapt to such changes with no apparent ill effects many do suffer on a deeper level which may ultimately manifest itself as physical illness. As I've said earlier in the book (see chapter on parasites) stress can depress the immune system, and a weakened immune system opens the door to all manner of diseases and illnesses. As an example, chronic diarrhoea or malabsorbtion (the inability to make proper use of food which often goes with chronic diarrhoea), sores that won't heal and all manner of skin problems.

Dogs containing Saluki blood are very much one owner or one family animals, and it is difficult to appreciate just how attached they become to their owners as they don't always show their feelings. It is possible that this trait is being 'bred out' of some coursing bred hybrids, because animals which refuse to accept a change

of ownership easily are obviously not easy to work in the field, being more likely to hit the far horizon rather than return to the new owner. Easily-handled dogs are far easier to buy and sell than animals which go off their food or won't come to call when finding themselves in a different environment.

The Saluki mentality is also responsible for its supposed intractability: only a fool would send a Saluki to someone else for training! It is the close and trusting bond between Saluki and owner which enables us to bend this most independent of dogs to our ways, something which a professional dog trainer could not hope to do during a few weeks of training a dog they didn't even know well. You just can't train a Saluki in the same way you could a Collie. Salukis weren't born into the service of man and one must at best, work alongside them and channel their skills into how we want them to hunt, for hunt they will, even the most show bred of specimens.

I firmly believe that there are people who can work with Salukis (and heavily Saluki-saturated dogs) and others who will never have the correct mental attitude for this type of dog. I'm not saying one is better than the other, but if a person wants an ultra obedient, stop on a whistle type of dog, there are easier types with which to work.

INTELLIGENCE
Intelligence has been defined as the ability to learn. Note: the ability to learn. This may be completely different from the desire to comply with commands issued by the owner. Unless you can adapt your own mindset to that of a Saluki type dog you might as well give up right away, for they don't accept formal or traditional training methods very well at all. The Saluki

brain seems first and foremost geared to the finding and catching of prey, and it is only later on in life that these dogs come to realise that you, the owner, might be in some way important to that finding of prey or that you might have other uses such as providing comfort and food.

My own experiences with this sort of dog have forced me to adapt my training methods enormously, and it is only once a pup has recognised me as part of its pack that I attempt any formal training, though I don't do much at all in this way. Providing the dog comes when it is called (most of the time!) and accepts handling whenever I want to handle it, I tend to allow such dogs do grow up unstressed by demands that just don't compute in their minds.

The Saluki is a good example of a dog which is highly intelligent when it comes to figuring out how to catch its prey, but the mindset needed to carry out formal obedience exercises such as 'sit', 'stay' and 'fetch the ball' is often lacking.

I know there are exceptions to every rule or generalisation, and I have, at the time of writing, a dog which is nearly all Saluki who loves playing fetch the ball, just so long as there are no rabbits to hunt in the vicinity.

Now take the Collie blooded dog, normally a type which gets really enthusiastic doing the most mundane 'obedience' exercises, though just as dedicated to hunting when given the opportunity.

On the face of it you'd say that Collies are streets ahead of Salukis in the intelligence stakes, but when I see my Saluki types hunting a field, using every patch of cover from which to sneak up on a sitting rabbit I see something very similar to the Collie stalk and freeze behaviour which is so inherent in herding breeds. The biggest and most important thing to consider when you choose a dog with which to share your life, is whether or not you can give the animal the life it needs, the stimulus it needs to be happy and fulfilled and the time some dogs need to mature into adults. Three years is not excessive in the case of Sighthounds.

When you consider that every breed of dog alive today (apart from the toy breeds which were designed purely as companions) had its origins as a worker of one sort or another, it is obvious that those origins play a large part in the mental make up of a dog. Cross a terrier with a Greyhound and you'll get a doer rather than a thinker, which isn't to say that the dog can't think, rather that the animal reacts so fast to stimulus that the thought process gets left behind at the starting post! Terrier crosses make superb hunting dogs, and they are mentally usually pretty tough and single-minded.

Because terriers have evolved to be forward going (this might be putting it mildly in most instances!) they are usually very easy to train and their attitude is anything but fearful in new situations. Funnily enough though, I've found my terriers and terrier crosses to be every bit as sensitive to human correction as a Saluki type, though physically the terrier types are far tougher and less likely to fold up on the floor when they injure themselves. This is because they have a much higher pain threshold, necessary given their vermin-killing role in life.

Then take the Whippet, just as forward going as a terrier, designed to pursue, single mindedly, without much thought to self preservation. It is easy to understand why these gutsy little dogs are at risk of injury each time they pursue their prey in the open field. Watching Whippets lure coursing at a country fair shows just how

214

single-minded they are, and although these dogs know full well that the lure is nothing but a bunch of rags, their mental blueprint has been so engineered by humans over many years' breeding, that a Whippet will run like a demon after anything that moves, unless trained very thoroughly not to.

Are Whippets intelligent? They're very far from stupid, though their drive and intensity when chasing might make them appear a few pence short of the proverbial shilling at times as they risk life and limb in their efforts to catch; never mind whether the prey is a real rabbit or a furry toy on the end of a lure. Whippets are usually easy to train and easy to live with at home, but real Jekyll and Hydes ... couch potatoes at home and exocet missiles in the field. Cracking little dogs with hearts of lions: I love them!

For my own use, however, I prefer the mindset of the lurcher to lurcher bred dog. Those who have seen my lurchers will know that the trait of steadiness comes high on my list of priorities.

Can you instil steadiness into a running dog? Yes, providing you take the dog out regularly into the field where there is no game to see with the eye, where the pupil must use its nose to find its quarry.

Most (though not all) flighty dogs do eventually learn to calm down and work sensibly IF THEY ARE GIVEN THE OPPORTUNITY TO DO THIS ON A REGULAR BASIS. However, there are certain genetically inherited traits which you'll never eradicate, regardless of the amount of time and training you put into a puppy. Far better to do your homework before buying a puppy rather than to find that those inherited traits just don't suit your particular mindset or temperament.

A thoughtful moment waiting to go out.

TEMPERAMENT

Temperament is inherited from parents, grandparents and right back through the long line of a dog's ancestors. I wouldn't like to breed from a truly nervy animal any more than I would breed from a dog which has shown itself to be lacking in the brains department. To be honest, a dog with very little brain just won't last long in the field.

I've known and owned some lurchers which were of the 'berserker' variety, prone, like the Viking warriors, to go insane during the heat of battle. I don't want this trait in a dog; the animal which loses its rag when engaging biting quarry is a time bomb at home, and I've seen such dogs explode inappropriately with tragic results. These dogs react to aggression and pain with a completely over the top defence system and have, to my mind, no place in the world of the worker.

The dog which remains calm and business like in all its work is one to be prized beyond measure, and this temperament usually brings with it a degree of self preservation, at the same time as retaining drive and commitment.

I believe that far too many dogs are being bred from without being thoroughly tested in the field. Whilst many owners might not wish to work their dogs, correctly bred working animals normally produce sensible offspring. These will usually adapt to a working environment far better than those which have been bred simply to look beautiful on the end of the lead.

I have nothing against dog shows, and I did at one time enjoy parading my (in my opinion) beautiful lurchers around a ring! It's nice to have people admiring your dog, but working ability, temperament and soundness should come first and foremost.

However, it would be a sad day indeed if our lurchers and sighthounds were to be relegated to mere show ponies. Happily, there are many people who are doing all they can to keep working ability alive in the running dog, and the lurcher seems to be more popular than ever today despite ever increasing legislation. Whether your dog is a full time hunting companion, a weekend helpmate when ferreting or a pet which enjoys the occasional chase on a bunny, we need, above all, to understand what makes running dogs tick.

GETTING THE BEST FROM YOUR RUNNING DOG

Dogs are generally simple creatures: give them adequate food, exercise and attention and they are happy. Deny them any of the above and they suffer, though nowadays in a society where too many people and their dogs don't get enough exercise it is the dog that is blamed for 'being bad' when through boredom or frustration it develops what we humans term as behavioural problems.

Dogs are still in that happy evolutionary state where physical exercise equals satisfaction. To them it's not a question of having to prise themselves up off the settee and force themselves to run about: like children, dogs really NEED to burn up energy, energy which if denied a useful outlet, may lead to aggression and destructive tendencies.

Many people have forgotten what real physical work entails, though they expect their dogs to adapt to a similar lifestyle, eating too much and not moving enough. Physical exercise not only tones the body but calms and focuses the mind and the old saying "a healthy mind in a healthy body" might just as well have been coined for dogs as humans.

Dogs are also social creatures. They delight in order, routine and a solid pack structure in which they know their place. 99% of dogs are happy to accept being part of a human pack just so long as they can follow a calm, assertive and fair leader. It is extremely rare to encounter the dog which just cannot fit into a pack of one sort or another, and such a creature is really an anomaly, a freak of nature which, were it a wild canine, would not survive very well at all.

It is unnatural to confine a dog on its own for the greater part of its life (see also chapter on housing). The stress and boredom suffered by such dogs is often translated into inappropriate (in our eyes) behaviour and if the owner isn't sufficiently clued up to recognise the warning signs there may be trouble abrewing. Pack leaders don't distance themselves from the rest of the pack: they are there with their subordinates night and day. When there's a squabble amongst the underlings they step in to sort out the problem. When the pack needs defending they are there, fulfilling the role of protector. They provide food, but most importantly they represent the security without which dogs may feel afraid, stressed and confused.

Whilst dogs are amazingly good at adapting to our human needs and ways, we should never forget the basic nature of DOG: one which craves and needs the security of our pack.

As an example, the dog which barks incessantly in its kennel, alone, bored and in desperate need of companionship. What do most owners do in such situations? They come storming out of the house and throw a bucket of water over the animal.

This might well have the desired effect on the dog, which eventually learns that barking means getting wet, shouted at or in the worst scenario, beaten.

Yet, such lessons do nothing to establish a good bond between owner and dog. Yes, the dog may well obey you through fear of punishment, but do you really want a dog which cringes each time you look at it or raise your hand? Fear is the mind-killer. A frightened dog is unable to learn, is unable to adapt to new stimuli and is, if pushed far enough, more likely to retaliate and bite.

I am very firm with my dogs, they respect me as their leader, but I also give them boundless affection. I attend not only to their physical needs but I make sure that their mental and emotional needs are met as well.

Some dog behaviour books tell you never to give in to your dog's demands for affection as this will make the dog think it is superior to you. Whilst I might agree if you have a dog which has mastery of the universe in mind, the more sensitive sighthound nature is quickly wounded when the owner ignores a gentle plea for affection.

When my own dogs want attention they stand a couple of feet away from me, eyes fixed on my face, gently wagging their tails. If I ignore them occasionally there will be

no harm done, but to ignore such tentative gestures for reassurance or affection on a permanent basis can lead to a break down in communication.

If I'm busy I may just give the dog a quick stroke on its head then tell it to go away firmly, but usually I make the time for a quick cuddle and a few kind words. Doing this won't make the average running dog get ideas above its station: it will merely reinforce the bond between you and your companions.

"Spoil the dog and ruin it as a worker", "You'll make the dog soft if you stroke it" are two examples of just how ignorant some people are when it comes to understanding their dogs.

My best vermin-killing lurcher spends her idle time curled up on the sofa; of an evening she likes to sleep with her head in my lap if I'm watching TV. No one told her that 'real' working dogs don't do that, and no one could ever make me believe that my dogs would work better if I left them alone in a kennel 24/7, denying them any show of affection.

A dog that feels safe and contented in its home is far more likely to give of its best in the field than one which is constantly deprived of its basic needs.

To feel really safe either at home or in the field, a dog needs to have total confidence in its owner, and people with temperament problems of their own might do well to address their own issues before directing the blame for wrongdoing on their dogs.

No one is perfect and we all make mistakes, but by adopting a mantle of calm leadership in all canine matters we can learn to control them with quiet words rather than screams and shouts. I know, for I've done my share of screaming and shouting over the years; I'm naturally an impatient sort of person and I've had to

Happy dog.

work long and hard to get a handle on my own nature.

The clever and authoritative leader uses presence not punches to get what he or she wants, and it is that presence, that state of calm power which will get your dog's respect far better than any amount of bullying and beating.

I might have gone on a bit on this subject, and I know that most people who are reading this book will agree with what I'm saying. However, if I can change the mindset of just one person who has previously treated their dogs in a cold and off hand manner, then I've succeeded in this part of my mission.

Very few dogs will be able to give of their best if they are constantly passed from one owner to another, and it's a sad fact that those people who do buy and sell dogs on a regular basis are exactly the type of owner most likely to neglect their dogs' most basic needs.

Love is a word which many men shy away from, for fear of appearing 'soft' or 'womanish'. Truly strong men aren't afraid to show that they love their dogs. It is great to be proud of your dog's achievements, though not if those achievements are merely an excuse to cover up your own inadequacies.

I have seen someone hit a dog when it returned from coursing a hare. The bitch had 'jacked' (given up the course whilst the hare was only 30 metres in front of her) but she was so unfit and fat that she'd have been hard pushed to catch a myxie rabbit. Nonetheless, her owner hit her when she returned to his side.

I can only assume that this individual felt ashamed that I'd witnessed his dog's failure, and that he hit her in some attempt to shift blame on to the dog. The failure was his, for neglecting to get the dog properly fit for the job in the first place. I've had lurchers who came back to me heads down, with the spark gone from their eyes when they had failed to catch a hare. I always commiserated with them, never told them off because I know that not all hares are catchable and that if the dog had tried its best it could do no more than that. The same dogs, when successful, came back to me as fast as their weary legs could manage, proudly carrying their prize, eyes shining and heads held high despite the weight of the hare in their jaws.

I always praise my dogs when they retrieve a catch, going overboard with delight and congratulations. Don't anyone tell me that a dog doesn't know when it's done well: they know because you have taught them what praise means. You'll have praised them as little pups when they came to your call, and they will have learned that it feels good to come to you.

Whilst dogs don't pat each other to bestow approval, they do rub heads and bodies against each other, and generally indulge in a physical and sometimes vocal moment of affection when they are happy or simply reinforcing a relationship bond.

Incidentally, dogs much prefer being stroked or rubbed than patted: a hard pat can even be interpreted as an act of aggression unless the dog has learned that this strange action is one of human affection.

Doing right (a dog has to learn what is right and wrong from our point of view and this can take time) makes a dog feel wanted, secure and part of the pack. Being a valued part of a strong pack means everything to a dog.

It doesn't take much on our part to make our dogs happy, just a few words and a caress, but it means the world to the dog which has just achieved its purpose. It is through the little things in life that we can measure our success as dog owners, and

whilst I'd never claim to be the greatest trainer in the world, my dogs all love retrieving their catch to me for they know that the praise which I give them is just one more measure of that acceptance and security they feel as part of my pack.

AND THOSE WHICH JUST AREN'T GOOD ENOUGH?

Not every dog will excel at what we humans want them to do. Whilst real prowess is something we should all aspire to, not everyone can be a winner. Are you someone who just can't take failure in a dog? Do you feel it reflects badly on you as a person? And just what do you do with a dog that hasn't made the grade?

I feel that one of the problems faced by running dogs nowadays is due to the competitive nature of their owners. Gone seem to be the days when a dog only had to please its owner. Nowadays so many dogs are held to be an indication of their owner's status amongst their peers.

How many people seriously need a dog to catch 40 rabbits in a night out lamping? How many people really need to win every race held at country fairs across the country? Of course we all like to win, for our dogs to be good at something, but would the sky really fall in if we didn't and it isn't?

When it comes to sporting competition the ugly side of human nature comes to the fore all too often, and dogs have been passed on for failing to allow their owner to bask in its glorious achievements. What was at one time a solitary endeavour, the running of a hare for the pot, a night on the lamp for pest control, has become for some people an excuse to get out in the fields mob handed and kill as many animals as possible, regardless of whether or not the owners really need that much game in their freezer.

I know that you can't change human nature, and we've all been young and done stupid things at some stage in our lives. One of the blessings of getting older (there have to be some doesn't there!) is that I no longer care if I have the best dog in the world or not. I don't care if my dog misses a few catches; the only thing that matters to me now is that I enjoy what we do together, my dogs and I.

Just occasionally you'll find yourself with a dog to which you really aren't suited. Some dogs prefer to be in a one owner one dog partnership, unable to give of their best when part of a big pack. Some dogs may need a very quiet and calm environment when your home might be the equivalent of a manic fair ground. Others may revel in being part of a noisy, bustling home, becoming bored and destructive if they don't have canine friends to play with.

When this has happened to me I've sometimes spent months trying to find the correct home for a dog, and sometimes I've succeeded and sometimes I haven't, later hearing that the dog that I so carefully and trustingly placed in a stranger's care has been moved on within a few months.

There is nothing we can do in such circumstances and the only regrets that I have in my life are that I have let such dogs down.

AND ON A HAPPIER NOTE

There is nothing more guaranteed to bring happiness and satisfaction than owning a dog with whom you have a truly great relationship. We can't all be superb trainers, we can't all spend the amount of time we'd like to with our dogs, and we certainly can't all achieve our dreams. But in a life where death is the only certainty, I urge you to spend a few moments each day just reflecting on what your dogs actually mean to you. Review your attitude towards them, ask yourself where you could do better in terms of building that relationship between you and your dogs. Reflect, for even a second or two, on your past mistakes and resolve to try harder in future.

This might sound like namby pamby shrink speak to some readers (psychologists call it cognitive behaviour therapy!) but by simply taking the time to assess your strengths and weaknesses as a human being and by being totally honest with yourself, you can improve the bond between you and your dog a lot, in some cases.

If we behave in the right way towards our dogs we are rewarded by unlimited devotion. If we behave badly towards them neither owner nor dog will feel truly happy. Patience and understanding is the key to successful dog ownership, none more so than in the working dog which has to do a damn sight more to fulfil our expectations that the dog which merely has to 'be'.

I have, at the time of writing, a lurcher called Starlight. She is now nine years old, carries a couple of niggling injuries which are exacerbated when she works in cold, damp conditions, but this dog owes me nothing at all. She started her working life in the coursing field and did very well, winning competitions during her first working season at less than two years of age. She went on to become my numero uno lamp dog, at the same time as wreaking havoc on the local fox population. She is the most complete all round hunter I've ever had, with a laid back temperament and the sharp inherent intelligence of the perfect predator. I shall never have another like her, and though she wasn't the very best retriever in the world she is the epitome of what defines the running dog.

Forgive me this indulgence as I write about Starlight. I wanted to dedicate this book to her, but I've dedicated it to all the dogs who have taught me so much over the years. We have to be in the right frame of mind in order to learn, just like our dogs, and I'm fully aware that when young, we humans just aren't very well programmed to learn the lessons we value as older adults.

All I can say is remember to value your dogs. There are very few dogs which are totally useless at all tasks. The working running dog shouldn't be consigned to the bin because it has failed at the one task you demand from it. Dogs which have failed at one discipline may well prove to be excellent at a different task. We're supposed to be the more intelligent of the two species, so use that intelligence to think laterally and find something different to do for the supposed failure. I've known failed coursing dogs become great ferreting partners; lurchers too slow to catch a cold become good picking-up dogs on shoots and otherwise timid creatures excel at ratting.

Most importantly, forget what other people think or say: your dog has only to please one person: you! Life shouldn't be a competition as to who has the best dog: if people spent less time worrying about the reported prowess of the dog next door, so to speak, they'd be a lot more contented with their own animals. End of.

Starlight.

Deerhound Greyhound. Photo: Steve Brown www.i2iphotoonline.co.uk

Index